Sourcebook for Earth Sciences and Astronomy

SOURCEBOOK for
EARTH SCIENCES and
ASTRONOMY

Russell O. Utgard

The Ohio State University

George T. Ladd

Boston College

Hans O. Andersen

Indiana University

The Macmillan Company, New York
Collier-Macmillan Limited, London

Acknowledgments

The authors express their gratitude and appreciation to the individuals, 'companies, publishers, suppliers, organizations, and institutions who made materials available for this sourcebook or who gave their permission to reprint material.

The introductory sections dealing with the descriptions of audiovisual materials were written by Dr. Fred John Pula, Director of University Audiovisual Services at Boston College. Dr. Pula is a recognized author in the field of audiovisual communication. His most recent publications include *Technology in Education: Challenge and Change* and *Media Processes in Education*. Both are published by Charles A. Jones Publishing Company, Inc.

Preface

The teacher represents a vital variable in the classroom. He can greatly facilitate and enhance the learning environment through the methodology and materials he utilizes. We are concerned with the latter here. Each teacher should seek to bring to the learning situation the full range of instructional materials that are most pertinent to the topic under consideration.

This book represents an attempt to supply the secondary (grades 7-12) teacher of earth science with a composite listing of a wide range of instructional materials to use with his own students. Although comprehensive, the listing is not complete as new materials are being developed and marketed almost daily. Nor have materials been evaluated beyond an initial screening to ensure that the subject matter is current. In the final analysis, the individual teacher and his students should be the evaluators of any material. This sourcebook is not an end but a means by which the teacher can locate extensive materials for his classroom and thereby provide improved representation and study of earth science phenomena.

R. O. U.
G. T. L.
H. O. A.

Contents

PART...1

Materials for the Teaching of Science

General Introduction

The tremendous amount of educational research dealing with the effectiveness of visual instructional materials has established the worth and the value of these materials in facilitating classroom learning. The fact that millions of dollars have been expended on them by school systems, especially since 1958, indicates that educators are beginning to take heed of the findings of researchers, and the horizons of students are beginning to expand as a result.

Many educators, however, have expressed disappointment in the adoption of visual instructional materials. They have discovered that projecting a film or a transparency does not automatically guarantee learning. These materials may not be a panacea for all the ills that affect education, but they are most effective when the following factors are given careful consideration:

1. Preparation of the teacher.
2. Preparation of the students.
3. Presentation of the material.
4. Follow-up activities to ensure the understanding of the materials presented.

Teacher Preparation

For greater impact on learning, visual materials should be closely correlated to the subject matter under consideration. Why make such an obvious point? It is amazing how often a teacher will use a film or filmstrip only because it happens to be handy and seems to provide an easy way of getting through a particularly difficult day. The careful, detailed planning of a lesson should precede the consideration of visual materials. The objectives of the lesson should be clearly set forth. The entrance behaviors and the terminal behaviors of the students should be spelled out. With these guidelines in hand the teacher then proceeds to search out those materials.

The purpose of this sourcebook is to make it convenient for the science teacher to locate and to select materials that appear to be useful. For that reason it should prove to be an invaluable aid. But the responsibility of the teacher does not stop with the location and selection. When received, the material should be carefully previewed by the teacher to ensure that the treatment of the material is geared to the level of understanding of the student, that it accomplishes the objectives outlined in the lesson, and that it provides only information that would be difficult or inconvenient for the teacher to present. When these determinations have been made, it is then the task of the teacher to integrate the material smoothly into the ongoing lesson.

Student Preparation

The principle of selective perception dictates that students be guided in observing the pertinent details of the visual material. The previous learning, attitudes, and interests of individual students will affect their perception of new information and their understanding of it. The teacher should pose various questions or state problems to be solved and establish cues that should be looked for: new vocabulary words or old words with new meanings should be introduced; the search for comparisons and contrasts and new relationships between new material and material already learned should be encouraged.

The purpose of presenting the visual material should be made explicit to the students. The teacher should make every effort to make the material understandable to the students and serve the objectives of the lesson.

Presentation of the Information

The circumstances connected with the viewing of visual materials can affect the amount of learning that results. The physical condition of the materials, the nature of the equipment, room-lighting and -darkening facilities, ventilation, the size of projection image, and the knowledge of operation of equipment—all are factors that should be carefully considered to guarantee effective utilization.

The materials should be inspected to eliminate the possibility of torn sprocket holes or faulty splices interrupting the presentation. Soiled transparencies should be cleaned to remove distracting elements from the screen; still pictures should be mounted or laminated to safeguard them against careless handling by students.

Equipment should be plugged in and the image properly framed on the screen before the start of a class presentation. The lens should be clean, dirt and dust removed from the aperture area, and an extra projection lamp kept handy.

Projected images will only be as bright as room-darkening conditions will allow. Blackout shades or drapes should be provided in those rooms where projected materials are used extensively. If possible, a low level of illumination should be maintained to permit quick reference to notes previously made or to jot down quick notes. However, general note-taking during movies or filmstrip presentations should not be encouraged. Where materials are being used by individuals or small groups, greater flexibility can be shown in lighting conditions and the rate of presentation.

The readability of visual material as affected by size should be given careful attention by the classroom teacher. Generally speaking, for viewing an overhead transparency, no one should be seated farther away than six times the width of the projected area. This means that in a standard classroom measuring 30 ft. the recommended screen size is 5 ft., or 60 in. The ratio for movies or filmstrips can be increased to 10 times. The best test of readability, however, is for the teacher to view the material from the farthest point in the classroom.

A smooth presentation of projected visual images requires that the operator be knowledgeable in the set-up and operation of the equipment. Learning is difficult when images are fuzzy or inverted, split frames are shown, projections are not properly centered, and the sound level is not adequate.

Follow-up

The lesson should not be considered complete when the lights come on or when the student turns away from his individual viewing of a picture or filmstrip. This is the critical moment for ensuring that the objectives spelled out for the lesson be achieved. Various activities should be planned to build on the informational background that was provided. These activities could involve the students in discussions, play-acting, demonstrations, planning and construction of bulletin boards, field trips, and written reports. The exact nature of the activity would be determined by the teacher's understanding of the basic needs and interests of the individual students as well as by the general nature of the subject matter.

The four factors outlined above provide a four-step system for not only effectively selecting the right materials to suit the needs of the students but also for ensuring that learning will take place when they view those materials.

The following sections concern the specific characteristics and availability of 16mm motion picture film, Super 8mm film loops, 35mm filmstrips, overhead transparencies, color photographs, and free and inexpensive materials. The specific advantages inherent in the use of each type of material are also considered.

16mm Motion Picture Films

Classroom use of motion picture films has reached unprecedented levels. The number of films available in the areas of science reflects the interest now being shown in this medium by educators and film producers.

The popularity of films in education can be traced to certain specific advantages of films:

1. Films combine action with sound to transmit information through two channels of communication instead of just one. Each reinforces the other to ensure greater learning and understanding of subject matter.
2. Films bring the action to the students, overcoming obstacles of distance and major expense.
3. Films bring expert presentations into the classroom providing front row seats to everyone in the room intent on viewing demonstrations and exhibits pertinent to scientific subject matter.
4. Films provide free-flowing action—a continuity of movement that is so necessary in many kinds of scientific observations and presentations—that cannot be duplicated through other channels of communication, especially print.
5. Films are important in their ability to reconstruct events and pace them for ease of understanding and study.
6. Films provide an attractive means for all in the class to share in common experiences that can then be used as the basis for further study.
7. Films can help to overcome barriers to learning, especially where students may not be verbally oriented but respond enthusiastically to visual, pictorial stimuli.
8. Films maintain interest and compel attention through various techniques incorporated in many scientific films: time lapse; microphotography, closeups, color montages, and flashbacks; use of time lapse for series of carefully controlled exposures of a single subject; stop motion; and animation involving a series of drawings to illustrate subject matter otherwise difficult to depict.

In the previous section we noted the need for following a definite system in the utilization of instructional materials in the classroom. The four-step plan emphasizes the importance of teacher preparation in the careful selection of material for class use.

Research has indicated that certain criteria can be followed in determining the quality of a film that is being previewed. The following elements, if contained in the film, will indicate that the film is well designed from a learning standpoint:

1. *Participation.* Are there procedures that might guide or control the viewers' behavior during the film? Are there printed or oral questions that students might answer either covertly or overtly? Are members of the audience involved in any other way? Are there situations where the anticipation of the audience might encourage them to structure the coming scene, or do the next section of an experiment?
2. *Knowledge of results.* Feedback generally goes hand in hand with participation. If participation is evident in the film, is feedback also incorporated into the film so that the students will know whether the answer they have "thought" is right or wrong? The better kind of feedback is the kind that gives a complete answer to the question. Example: "Yes, the circle represented the area that was covered with paint," which is better than just "Yes." Knowledge of results can also be given pictorially. Sometimes they will be given in both commentary and picture.
3. *Redundancy.* Redundancy is repetition. Does the film employ some form of repetition, either exact or varied? Repetition can occur in pictures (symbols), words, or sentences written and spoken, or in ideas. The better kind of repetition is varied.
4. *Attention-directing techniques.* These should be designed to focus the pupils' attention to certain bits of information in a film. Some examples are "pop-in" labels, moving arrows, and implosion techniques. Attention-directing can also be done with sound effects, i.e., the hiss of a snake simulating its characteristic sound. Music, like the music from "Peter and the Wolf," is also used where certain musical phrases are identified with particular characters. Slow or fast motion or humor is also used, but remember that it must relate to the specific information being transmitted; it must be relevant.
5. *Organizational outlines.*
   a. Is the film structured in some way so as to organize the information for the student?
   b. The most common way for this to be done is by actual outlining—usually printed—to separate the units of the film. Information usually breaks down into natural units in the kinds of films produced for classroom use. These should be outlined, either verbally or with printed information.
   c. The best kind of outlining is succinct. Too much outlining seems to be confusing, according to the research. The main

question is, is there some form of outlining incorporated into the film?

6. *Introductions.*

   a. Children learn better when they know what they are supposed to learn and have an objective of some kind. According to research, this is better done by the teacher, but it is believed that introductions within the film are helpful.

   b. The introduction should be a statement about the content of the film. It might be a brief overview of the important points; it might ask the students to observe certain things about the film; but generally it is exactly what it says it is—an introduction. Again, it may be verbal or pictorial or both, though usually it is printed with commentary.

7. *Reviews.*

   a. There are two kinds of review: spaced and massed. *Spaced review* occurs at the end of natural units of information within the film and usually occurs in films of greater length.

   b. *Massed review*, which is review that occurs at the end of the film, is the preferred kind. It should review the material that has preceded, noting the major points either verbally or with a written accompaniment. Sometimes the review is also combined with repetition; as the point is stressed, the scene in the film that represented the idea will be reviewed as the narrator repeats (reviews) the important points in the film.

   c. Either kind of review is good. A summary might be considered a review, although it is not as effective. A *summary* is a succinct statement at the conclusion of the film.

8. *Visual and audio.*

   a. The important question here is, do the video and audio complement each other; are they relevant to one another? If the pictures and the words do not match in information—if the audio is discussing something that is irrelevant to the visual or vice versa—then something is wrong.

   b. One thing should lead to the other so that the viewer can "switch his channels." Does the film contain lines like "Now watch what happens" and the picture (in a sense) takes over? There is no conclusive evidence on this, but it is a technique worth considering. Is it included in the film?

9. *Rate of development.* How long (in time) is a scene length? It should average about seven seconds. Consideration should be given here to camera angles, closeups and long shots, and use of camera movement.

10. *Color.* Research does not cite any specific advantages of color over black-and-white film. Exceptions occur when the subject matter or content has a definite color identity, and learning is

associated with maintaining a relation to that identity. Does the film, if in color, draw particular attention to the different tones or hues?

A preview of a film to determine its preproduction elements will guarantee the best possible learning film. In making your selection, you should keep certain general criteria in mind:

1. Is the film designed to effectively teach the information, attitudes, skills, or understandings pertinent at this point in the teaching-learning situation?
2. Can it be easily understood by the group to be taught?
3. Is it of suitable length for use with this age group or for this purpose in teaching?
4. Are the photographic and sound qualities good?
5. Is the film convincing in its presentation: clear, interesting, stimulating?
6. What will this group of children or young people learn from this film? What might some individuals in this group learn?
7. Is the film based on dependable information, is it a true representation of experience? Is it up to date; or, if dated, still useful?
8. Is this the best film available for this purpose and this group of learnings?

The film is an excellent medium for conveying information. Through practice evaluation of films, it is possible for the classroom teacher to considerably expand the boundaries of knowledge and information that are made available to the students in the area of earth science.

Directions for Use of 16mm Film Section

For the compilation of this section of the materials sourcebook, it was physically impossible to view all films listed. Therefore, the films listed are those, in the judgment of the authors (after reviewing the information supplied by their distributors), that are most pertinent and up to date. It is hoped that the array of films and accompanying information will provide the classroom teacher with a valuable aid in selecting films for his earth science class. For a more complete listing of 16mm films you might consult the film catalog of your local university or college which rents films.

Keyed Film Description

The nature and order of the information for each film listed appear as follows:

Title.
Brief description of context of film.
Specifics. Color or b/w (black and white), sd (sound) or si (silent), running time, date of release, intended audience (p- primary; i- intermediate; j- junior high; h- high school; a- adult; c- college), (name of supplier), free or no rental charges outside of postage costs. (Check individual supplier's restrictions as listed under Distributors.)

16mm Film Distributors[*]

A
Almanac Films, Inc.
29 East 10th St.
New York, N.Y. 10003

ABP
Arthur Barr Productions
1029 N. Allen Ave.
Pasadena, Calif. 91104

ACI
ACI Films
35 West 45th St.
New York, N.Y. 10036

AEF
American Educational Films
331 N. Maple Dr.
Beverly Hills, Calif. 90210

AEFS
Av-Ed Films for Schools
7934 Santa Monica Blvd.
Hollywood, Calif. 90046

AETNAC[1]
Aetna Life Affiliated Co.
Education Dept.
151 Farmington Ave.
Hartford, Conn. 06115

AF
Academy Films

748 N. Seward St.
Los Angeles, Calif. 90028

AIMS
Aims Instructional Media
   Services, Inc.
P.O. Box 1010
Hollywood, Calif. 90028

AISCI[2]
American Institute of Steel
   Construction, Inc.
Educational and Special Services
101 Park Ave.
New York, N.Y. 10017

AMS[3]
American Meteorological Society
45 Beacon St.
Boston, Mass. 02108

ANIB
Australian News and Information
   Bureau
Australian Embassy
1601 Massachusetts Ave.
Washington, D.C. 20036

API
American Petroleum Institute
1271 Ave. of the Americas
New York, N.Y. 10020

*Distributors are listed alphabetically by code.

[1] Lendee must pay return postage. Six weeks advance notice is required.

[2] Restricted to senior high schools. Lendee must pay return postage. Six months advance notice is required.

[3] Films are distributed through MLA or UE&VA.

ARC
Atlantic Richfield Company
Public Relations
717 Fifth Avenue
New York N.Y. 10022

ASF
Association — Sterling Films
866 Third Avenue
New York, N.Y. 10022

B
Brandon Films, Inc.
34 MacQuesten Pkwy. South
Mt. Vernon, N.Y. 10550

BARR
Arthur Barr Productions
c/o Aims Instructional Media
   Services, Inc.
P.O. Box 1010
Hollywood, Calif. 90028

BC
Boeing Co., Aero-Space Division
P.O. Box 3707
Seattle, Wash. 98124

BELL[4]
Bell Telephone Companies

BFA
BFA Educational Media
2211 Michigan Ave.
Santa Monica, Calif. 90404

BPNA
BP North America, Inc.
620 Fifth Avenue
New York, N.Y. 10020

BPR[5]
U.S. Dept. of Interior
Bureau of Reclamation

P.O. Box 360
Salt Lake City, Utah 84110

CBS
CBS Educational Holt Group
383 Madison Ave.
New York, N.Y. 10017

CCAI
Charles Cahill and Assoc., Inc.
P.O. Box 1010
5420 Melrose
Hollywood, Calif. 90028

CCC
Consolidated Coal Company
Public Relations Department
407 Monongahela Building
Morgantown, W. Va. 26505

CEF
Cenco Educational Films
2600 S. Kostner Ave.
Chicago, Ill. 60623

CF
Coronet Instructional Films
65 E. So. Water St.
Coronet Bldg.
Chicago, Ill. 60601

CFI
Carousel Films, Inc.
1501 Broadway
New York, N.Y. 10036

CGOC[6]
Consulate General of Canada
Film Library
310 S. Michigan Ave.
Chicago, Ill. 60604

Canadian Consulate General
Fifth Floor

*Contact your local telephone business office. Lendee must pay return postage. Advance notice must be given.

[5] Lendee must pay return postage. Advance notice of eight weeks must be given.

[6] Lendee must pay return postage. Advance notice of eight weeks is required. Orders must be placed from the office listed that serves your state.

500 Boylston St.
Boston, Mass. 02116
(For: Conn., Me., Mass., N.H.,
R.I., and Vt.)

Canadian Consulate General
Film Library
310 S. Michigan Ave.
Chicago, Ill. 60604
(For: Ill., Ind., Iowa, Kan., Ky.,
Minn., Mo., Neb., N.D., S.D.,
and Wisc.)

Canadian Consulate General
Film Librarian
1920 First Federal Building
Detroit, Mich. 48226
(For Mich. only)

Canadian Consulate General
510 West Sixth St.
Los Angeles, Calif. 90014
(For: Ariz. and Calif.)

Canadian Consulate General
Suite 2110 International Trade
Mart
2 Canal St.
New Orleans, La. 70130
(For: Ala., Ark., Miss., N.C.,
Okla., S.C., Fla., La., Tenn.,
and Tex.)

Canadian Consulate General
1308 Tower Building
7th Ave. and Olive Way
Seattle, Wash. 98101
(For: Alaska, Idaho, Mont., Ore.,
and Wash.)

Canadian Embassy
1746 Massachusetts Ave.
Washington, D.C. 20036
(For: Md., N.J., N.Y., Va., D.C.,
and W. Va.)

COC
Continental Oil Company
Public Relations Department
P.O. Box 2197
Houston, Tex. 77001

DFL[7]
United States Department of the
Interior
Geological Survey
Information Office
Washington, D.C. 20242

DISNY
Walt Disney Productions
Educational Film Division
500 S. Buena Vista Ave.
Burbank, Calif. 91505

DOUG
Douglass Productions
P.O. Box 878
Sedona, Ariz. 86336

EBEC
Encyclopaedia Britannica
Educational Corp.
425 N. Michigan Ave.
Chicago, Ill. 60611

EC
Ethyl Corporation
Corporate Public Relations
330 South Fourth Street
Richmond, Va. 23219

EDTS
Educational Testing Service
Cooperative Test Division
20 Nassau St.
Princeton, N.J. 08540

EF
Environmental Films, Inc.
P.O. Box 302
St. Johnsbury, Vt. 05819

[7] Advance notice of at least eight weeks is required.

EIDDN[8]
E. I. Du Pont de Nemours & Co.
Advertising Dept.
Motion Picture Section
Wilmington, Del. 19898

EMERY
Emery Pictures, Inc.
655 Madison Avenue
New York, N.Y. 10021

ESSA
Environmental Science Services
  Administration
Rockville, Md. 20852
(Distributed through MLA)

F
Films Inc.
1150 Wilmette Ave.
Wilmette, Ill. 60091

FAOC
Film Associates of California
11559 Santa Monica Blvd.
Los Angeles, Calif. 90025

FFI
Fleetwood Films, Inc.
34 MacQuesten Pkwy. South
Mount Vernon, N.Y. 10550

FPC
Florida Phosphate Council
P.O. Box 1565
Lakeland, Fla. 33802

HA
Harvard Films
Harvard University
Cambridge, Mass. 02138

HEW
U.S. Dept. of Health, Education
  and Welfare
330 Independence Ave. S.W.
Washington, D.C. 20201

HFC
Handel Film Corp.
8730 W. Sunset
Hollywood, Calif. 90069

HMP
John J. Hennessy Motion
  Pictures
1702 Marengo Ave.
So. Pasadena, Calif. 91030

HOC[9]
Humble Oil and Refining Co.
Humble Bldg.
Houston, Tex. 77002

IFB
International Film Bureau, Inc.
332 S. Michigan Ave.
Chicago, Ill. 60604

IOMS
Institute of Marine Sciences
Miami Seaquarium
Rickenbacker Causeway
Miami, Fla. 33149

ISO
International Screen Organization
1445 Eighteenth Ave., N.
St. Petersburg, Fla. 33704

ISOI [10]
Information Service of India
Consulate General of India
215 Market St.
San Francisco, Calif. 94105

  Film Section
  3 East 64th St.
  New York, N.Y. 10021

(For: Conn., Ill., Ind., Iowa,
  Me., Mass., Mich., Minn.,
  N.H., N.J., N.Y., Ohio, Pa.,
  R.I., Vt., Wisc.)

[8] Lendee must pay return postage. Advance notice of at least eight weeks is required.
[9] Lendee must pay return postage. Advance notice of eight weeks is required.
[10] Lendee must cover the total expense of mailing with the film to be insured for $100. Advance notice of one month is required. Order only from the office serving your area.

Film Section
215 Market St.
San Francisco, Calif. 94105
(For: Alaska, Ariz., Calif.,
  Hawaii, Idaho, Mont., Nev.,
  N.M., Ore., Utah, Wash., and
  Wyo.)

Film Section
975 National Press Bldg.
529 Fourteenth St., N.W.
Washington, D.C. 20004
(For: Ala., Ark., Colo., Del.,
  Fla., Kan., Ky., La., Md.,
  Miss., Mo., N.C., N.D., Neb.,
  Okla., S.C., S.D., Tenn.,
  Tex., Va., D.C., W. Va.)

IU
Indiana University
Audiovisual Center
Bloomington, Ind. 47401

JF
Journal Films
909 W. Diversey Pkwy.
Chicago, Ill. 60614

KING
King Screen Productions
320 Aurora Ave. N.
Seattle, Wash. 98109

McGH
McGraw Hill Text-Films
1221 Ave. of the Americas
New York, N.Y. 10020

MDC [11]
McDonnell Douglas Corp.
Film Library
Department 92, Room 167
P.O. Box 516
St. Louis, Mo. 63166

MF
Modern Film Corp.
729 Seventh Ave.
New York, N.Y. 10019

MLA [12]
Modern Learning Aids:
  811 8th Ave.
  Anchorage, Alaska 99501

  714 Spring St., N.W.
  Atlanta, Ga. 30308

  1168 Commonwealth Ave.
  Boston, Mass. 02134

  122 W. Chippewa St.
  Buffalo, N.Y. 14202

  129 Third Ave., S.W.
  Cedar Rapids, Iowa 52404

  503 N. College St.
  Charlotte, N.C. 28202

  160 E. Grand Ave.
  Chicago, Ill. 60611

  9 Garfield Pl.
  Cincinnati, Ohio 45202

  2238 Euclid Ave.
  Cleveland, Ohio 44115

  1411 Slocum St.
  Dallas, Tex. 75207

  1200 Stout St.
  Denver, Colo. 80204

  14533 Second Ave.
  Detroit, Mich. 48203

  1874 Leslie St.
  Metro Toronto
  Don Mills, Ont., Canada

  P.O. Box 3035
  928 N. Third St.
  Harrisburg, Pa. 17105

[11] Lendee must pay return postage. One month advance notice is required.
[12] Order films from office that serves your area.

742 Ala Moana Blvd.
Honolulu, Hawaii 96813

4048 Westheimer Rd.
Houston, Tex. 77027

102 E. Vermont St.
Indianapolis, Ind. 46204

3718 Broadway
Kansas City, Mo. 64111

1145 N. McCadden Pl.
Los Angeles, Calif. 90038

214 S. Cleveland St.
Memphis, Tenn. 38104

1696 N. Astor St.
Milwaukee, Wisc. 53202

114 Nicollet Ave.
Minneapolis, Minn. 55403

485 McGill St.
Montreal, P. Que., Canada

715 Girod St.
New Orleans, La. 70130

1410 Howard St.
Omaha, Neb. 68102

1234 Spruce St.
Philadelphia, Pa. 19107

910 Penn Ave.
Pittsburgh, Pa. 15222

3000 Ridge Road East
Rochester, N.Y. 14622

201 S. Jefferson Ave.
St. Louis, Mo. 63103

16 Spear St.
San Francisco, Calif. 94105

2100 N. 45th St.
Seattle, Wash. 98103

315 Springfield Ave. [13]
Summit, N.J. 07901

927 Nineteenth St., S.W.
Washington, D.C. 20006

MM
Martin Moyer Productions
900 Federal Ave.
Seattle, Wash. 98102

MOC
Marathon Oil Company
539 South Main St.
Findlay, Ohio 45840

MOIL [14]
Magnolia Petroleum Co.
Magnolia Building
P.O. Box 900
Dallas, Tex. 75221

MTPS [15]
Modern Talking Picture Service, Inc.
1212 Ave. of the Americas
New York, N.Y. 10036
(Manhattan and Bronx)

and

2323 New Hyde Park Rd.
New Hyde Park, L.I., N.Y. 11040

811 Eighth Ave.
Anchorage, Alaska 99501

714 Spring St., N.W.
Atlanta, Ga. 30308

1168 Commonwealth Ave.
Boston, Mass. 02134

122 W. Chippewa St.
Buffalo, N.Y. 14202

[13] Serving Conn., Northern N.J., Southern N.Y. State, and Boroughs of Brooklyn, Queens, and Richmond, in New York City.

[14] Lendee must pay return postage. One month advance notice is required.

[15] Lendee must pay return postage. Four weeks advance notice is required. Request film from the office that serves your area.

200 Third Ave., S.W.
Cedar Rapids, Iowa 52404

503 N. College St.
Charlotte, N.C. 28202

160 E. Grand Ave.
Chicago, Ill. 60611

9 Garfield Pl.
Cincinnati, Ohio 45202

2238 Euclid Ave.
Cleveland, Ohio 44115

1411 Slocum St.
Dallas, Tex. 75207

1200 Stout St.
Denver, Colo 80204

15921 West Eight Mile Rd.
Detroit, Mich. 48235

2009 N. Third St.
Harrisburg, Pa. 17105

742 Ala Moana Blvd.
Honolulu, Hawaii 96813

4084 Westheimer Rd.
Houston, Tex. 77027

115 E. Michigan St.
Indianapolis, Ind. 46204

3718 Broadway
Kansas City, Mo. 64111

1145 N. McCadden Pl.
Los Angeles, Calif. 90038

214 S. Cleveland St.
Memphis, Tenn. 38104

1696 N. Astor St.
Milwaukee, Wisc. 53202

9129 Lyndale Ave., S.
Minneapolis, Minn. 55403

715 Girod St.
New Orleans, La. 70130

1212 Ave. of the Americas
New York, N.Y. 10036
(Manhattan and the Bronx)

and

2323 New Hyde Park Road
New Hyde Park, L.I., N.Y.
11040

1410 Howard St.
Omaha, Neb. 68102

1234 Spruce St.
Philadelphia, Pa. 19107

910 Penn Ave.
Pittsburgh, Pa. 15222

201 S. Jefferson Ave.
St. Louis, Mo. 63103

16 Spear St.
San Francisco, Calif. 94105

1205 No. 45th St.
Seattle, Wash. 98103

315 Springfield Ave.
Summit, N.J. 07901
(For: Conn., Northern N.J., N.Y.
State, and Brooklyn, Queens,
and Richmond in New York
City)

927 19th St., N.W.
Washington, D.C. 20006

NACD
National Association of
Conservation Districts
League City, Tex. 77573

NAS[16]
National Academy of Sciences
2102 Constitution Ave., N.W.
Washington, D.C. 20418

---

[16] Lendee must pay return postage. Four weeks advance notice is required.

NASA [17]
National Aeronautics and Space
Administration
1520 H St.
Washington, D.C. 20025

NASA Ames Research Center
Public Affairs Office
Moffett Field, Calif. 94035
(For: Alaska, Calif., North of
Los Angeles, Idaho, Mont.,
Ore., Wash., and Wyo.)

NASA Electronics Research
Center
Educational Programs Office
Cambridge, Mass., 02139
(For: Conn., Me., Mass., N.H.,
R.I., Vt., and N.Y.)

NASA George C. Marshall Space
Flight Center—Public Affairs
Office
Huntsville, Ala. 36812
(For: Ala., Ark., La., Miss., Mo.,
and Tenn.)

NASA Goddard Space Flight
Center
Photographic Branch, Code 253
Greenbelt, Md. 20771
(For: Del., D.C., Md., N.J., Pa.,
and W. Va.)

NASA John F. Kennedy Space
Center
Code IS-DOC-2
Kennedy Space Center, Fla.
32899
(For: Fla., Ga., P.R., and V. I.)

NASA Langley Research Center
Public Affairs Office
Mail Stop 154
Langley Station

Hampton, Va. 23365
(For: Ky., N.C., S.C., and Va.)

NASA Lewis Research Center
Office of Educational Services
21000 Brookpark Road
Cleveland, Ohio 44135
(For: Ill., Ind., Iowa, Mich.,
Minn., Ohio, and Wisc.)

NASA Manned Spacecraft Center
Public Affairs Office, AP-2
Houston, Tex. 77058
(For: Colo., Kan., Neb., N.M.,
N.D., Okla., S.D., and Tex.)

NASA Pasadena Office
400 Oak Grove Dr.
Pasadena, Calif. 91103
[For: Ariz., Calif. (San Luis
Obispo, Kings, Tulare, and
Inyo counties), Hawaii, Nev.,
and Utah]

NBC
NBC Educational Enterprises
30 Rockefeller Plaza
New York, N.Y. 10020

NCAR
High Altitude Observatory
National Center for Atmospheric
Research
P.O. Box 1470
Boulder, Colo. 80302

NET: IU
National Educational Television
Film Service
Indiana University
Audio-Visual Center
Bloomington, Ind. 47401

NF
Northern Films
P.O. Box 98

[17] Lendee must pay return postage. Four weeks advance notice is required. Order only
from office serving your area.

Main Office Station
Seattle, Wash. 98111

NFBOC
National Film Board of Canada
680 Fifth Ave.
New York, N.Y. 10019

NORWOOD
Norwood Studios, Inc.
926 New Jersey Ave., N.W.
Washington, D.C. 20001

NSNC
North Shore News Company,
   Inc.
70 Mount Vernon St.
Lynn, Mass. 01901

OSU
The Ohio State University
Dept. of Photography and
   Cinema
Film Library
156 West 19th Ave.
Columbus, Ohio 43210

PE
Prism Productions
220 E. 23rd St.
New York, N.Y. 10010

PF
Pictura Films Corp.
4 W. 16th St.
New York, N.Y. 10011

PYRF
Pyramid Films
P.O. Box 1048
Santa Monica, Calif. 90406

RCP
Richard Cline Productions

3290 S. Williams St.
Englewood, Colo. 80110

RF [18]
Radim Films, Inc.
220 W. 42nd St.
New York, N.Y. 10036

SEF [19]
Sterling Educational Films
P.O. Box 8497
Universal City
Los Angeles, Calif. 91608

SF
Stuart Finley Films
3428 Mansfield Road
Falls Church, Va. 22041

SGPO
Sea Grant Program Office
University of Wisconsin
1225 W. Dayton St.
Madison, Wisc. 53706

SKP
Stacey Keach Productions
12240 Ventura Blvd.
Studio City, Calif. 91604

SOC [20]
Shell Oil Co.
450 N. Meridian St.
Indianapolis, Ind. 46204

TCF
Twentieth Century Fund
41 E. 70th St.
New York, N.Y. 10021

TELE
Teledyne Exploration Company
P.O. Box 36269
5825 Chimney Rock Rd.
Houston, Tex. 77036

[18] Lendee must pay return postage. Two weeks advance notice is required.

[19] Lendee must pay return postage. Six weeks advance notice is required.

[20] Lendee must pay return postage. Prefer 1-year advance notice but will accept one month.

TLF
Time Life Films
Rockefeller Center
1271 Ave. of the Americas
New York, N.Y. 10020

TLI
Total Leonard, Inc.
Advertising Department
Alma, Mich. 48801

TRW [21]
TRW Systems Group Motion
    Pictures
Bldg. 65, Rm. 1521
One Space Park
Redondo Beach, Calif. 90278

TSP
Trumbull Studio Productions
3297 Omyx Pl.
Eugene, Ore. 97405

UE&VA
Universal Education and Visual
    Arts
221 Park Ave. S.
New York, N.Y. 10003

UOI
University of Iowa
Audio-Visual Center
Division of Extension and
    University Services
Iowa City, Iowa 52240

UOM
University of Michigan
Audio-Visual Education Center
416 Fourth St.
Ann Arbor, Mich. 48103

UOT
University of Texas

Visual Instruction Bureau
Austin, Tex. 78712

UOW
University of Wisconsin
Department of Geology
207 Science Hall
Madison, Wisc. 53701

USAEC [22]
U.S. Atomic Energy Commission
Division of Public Information
Audio-Visual Branch
Washington, D.C. 20545

Albuquerque Operations Office
Office of Information
P.O. Box 5400
Albuquerque, N.M. 87115
(For: Ariz., N.M., Okla., and
    Tex.)

Chicago Operations Office
Office of Information
9800 S. Cass Ave.
Argonne, Ill. 60439
(For: Ill., Ind., Iowa, Mich.,
    Minn., Mo., N.D., Ohio, S.D.,
    and Wisc.)

Grand Junction Office
Public Information Office
Grand Junction, Colo. 81502
(For: Colo., Kan., Neb., and
    Wyo.)

Idaho Operations Office
Office of Public Information
P.O. Box 2108
Idaho Falls, Idaho 83401
(For: Idaho, Mont., and Utah)

New York Operations Office
Public Information Service

---

[21] Return postage required. Book two months in advance.

[22] Lendee must pay return postage. Three weeks advance notice is required. Order only from the office serving your area.

376 Hudson St.
New York, N.Y. 10014
(For: Conn., Me., Mass., N.H.,
   N.J., N.Y., Pa., R.I., and Vt.)

Oak Ridge Operations Office
Office of Public Information
P.O. Box E
Oak Ridge, Tenn. 37830
(For: Ark., Ky., La., Miss., and
   Tenn.)

Richland Operations Office
Division of Public Information
P.O. Box 550
Richland, Wash. 99352
(For: Alaska, Ore., and Wash.)

San Francisco Operations Office
Office of Public Information
2111 Bancroft Way
Berkeley, Calif. 94704
(For: Calif., Hawaii, and Nev.)

Savannah River Operations
   Office
Office of Public Information
P.O. Box A
Aiken, S.C. 29802
(For: Ala., Fla., Ga., N.C., and
   S.C.)

Division of Public Information
Washington, D.C. 20545
(For: Canada, Del., D.C., Md.,
   Va., and W. Va.)

USAF [23]
Air Force Film Library Center
8900 S. Broadway
St. Louis, Mo. 63125

USBM
Bureau of Mines

U.S. Department of the Interior
4800 Forbes Ave.
Pittsburgh, Pa. 15213

USC
University of Southern California
Dept. of Cinema
University Park
Los Angeles, Calif. 90007

USCE [24]
U.S. Corps of Engineers
First and Douglas Sts. N.W.
Washington, D.C. 20002

USCG [25]
U.S. Dept. of Treasury, Coast
   Guard
Old Southern Railway Bldg.
1300 E St. N.W.
Washington, D.C. 20226

Commander
First Coast Guard District
J. F. Kennedy Bldg.
Government Center
Boston, Mass. 02203

Commander
Second Coast Guard District
Federal Bldg.
1520 Market St.
St. Louis, Mo. 63103

Commander
Third Coast Guard District
Governors Island
New York, N.Y. 10004

Commander
Fifth Coast Guard District
Federal Bldg.
431 Crawford St.
Portsmouth, Va. 23705

[23] Postage paid by USAF.

[24] Lendee must pay return postage.

[25] Lendee must pay return postage. Four weeks advance notice is required. Order only
from the office serving your area.

Commander
Seventh Coast Guard District
Room 1203, Federal Bldg.
51 Southwest First Ave.
Miami, Fla. 33130

Commander
Eighth Coast Guard District
Customhouse
New Orleans, La. 70130

Commander
Ninth Coast Guard District
1240 E. Ninth St.
Cleveland, Ohio 44199

Commander
Eleventh Coast Guard District
Heartwell Bldg.
19 Pine Ave.
Long Beach, Calif. 90892

Commander
Twelfth Coast Guard District
630 Sansome St.
San Francisco, Calif. 94501

Commander
Thirteenth Coast Guard District
618 Second Ave.
Seattle, Wash. 98104

Commander
Fourteenth Coast Guard District
677 Ala Moana Blvd.
Honolulu, Hawaii 96813

Commander
Seventeenth Coast Guard District
F.P.O.
Seattle, Wash. 98771

USGS
U.S. Geological Survey
Coordinator-Motion Picture
    Films
18th and F Sts., N.W.
Washington, D.C. 20242

USN [26]
U.S. Navy Dept.
Office of Information
Pentagon Bldg.
Washington, D.C. 20350

USNAC
U.S. National Audiovisual Center
National Archives and Records
    Service
Washington, D.C. 20409

USWB [27]
U.S. Dept. of Commerce,
    Weather Bureau
Film Library
24th and M Sts., N.W.
Washington, D.C. 20025

WA
Western America Films
426 N. 10th Ave.
Bozeman, Mont. 59715

WI
John Wiley & Sons, Inc.
Education Services Department
605 Third Ave.
New York, N.Y. 10016

YA
Young America Films
(Distributed now by McGraw-
    Hill)

[26] Lendee must pay return postage.

[27] Lendee must pay return postage. Eight weeks advance notice is required.

35mm Filmstrips

Filmstrips have proved to be extremely popular and will continue to be so because they are relatively inexpensive, contain a great deal of information in a small package, are easy to present, and can be used for both group and individual instruction. Filmstrips are composed of a series of still pictures and captions placed in a fixed order on 35mm film. The number of pictures, or frames, varies from 20 to 60 frames. They come in color or black and white; they can be accompanied by sound on disc or tape; frame-change can be manual or automatically activated through the recording of inaudible impulses; and costs vary from $3 to $6 for a silent filmstrip to $12 to $16 for a sound filmstrip.

Filmstrips lend themselves to many kinds of instructional situations because of their specific characteristics. They:

1. *Provide a basis for understanding symbols.* The combination of captions, visual or pictorial elements, and sometimes sound combine to present the viewer and listener with a more understandable relationship between the concrete and the abstract.
2. *Help to teach skills.* Because of the capability of varying the speed of presentation, students are able (on an individualized study basis) to take as much time as needed to master a particular concept.
3. *Are comparatively inexpensive.* In terms of materials that they can replace, teaching through the use of filmstrips could save wear and tear on such things as wallmaps and expensive laboratory equipment.
4. *Present information.* Research studies of great variety and depth have proved this technique to be effective in presenting factual information in visual form.
5. *Broaden horizons.* They can be used to stimulate interest and encourage a more vigorous pursuit on the student's part toward acquiring a specific skill or body of factual information.
6. *Help to synthesize information.* They can provide meaningful summaries and reviews of information that might have been presented through other channels of communication.
7. *Are highly flexible.* Students have ample opportunity to practice basic skills using the information on the filmstrips. This fact, combined with their adaptability for individualized instruction makes this medium particularly attractive.

In selecting filmstrips for student use, the teacher should have several objectives and purposes in mind. These have to do with the content, cost, medium, and needs of the students:

1. Each filmstrip should be specific to the subject matter for which it is designed.
2. Its content should be accurate, truthful, and up to date.
3. The subject matter should be adaptable for presentation on filmstrip. A less expensive medium should be used if it is available and relevant.
4. The filmstrip should be designed to hold the interest and be understandable to the students for whom it is intended. The vocabulary, the conceptual level, and the pace of development should be carefully determined.
5. The filmstrip should be technically well designed, using close-ups, good composition and design elements in the graphic presentations.
6. The filmstrip should be educationally well conceived with logical organization, unity of content, and obvious emphasis on purpose. There should be thought-provoking captions, clear labeling, complete with review or self-test.
7. The filmstrip should encourage student participation and critical thinking as opposed to "passive" absorption of facts. [28]

The method of using filmstrips in the classroom follows the pattern already presented in the sections on films and in the general introduction to this chapter. There should be adequate teacher preparation regarding the content of the filmstrip and how best it could be integrated into the ongoing instruction. Students should be prepared regarding the probable general nature of the subject matter; they should be guided as to what to look for in the material that is being presented.

The most obvious variation in the plan of utilization of materials as previously presented has to do with the method of presentation. During group showing, students should be encouraged to participate by asking questions or commenting on the visual material. The teacher also could stimulate thinking by posing additional cues or problems to supplement those in the filmstrip. The filmstrip need not be shown in a fixed order of frames at a fixed pace. The comments or questions of class members should provide the impetus for returning to frames previously shown or for moving ahead rapidly to information of more immediate interest.

The filmstrip is a valuable instructional aid. But its effectiveness in instruction will depend on how carefully the teacher selects the material and how well it is fitted into the general construction of the lesson

[28] James W. Brown, Richard B. Lewis, and Fred F. Harcleroad. *A-V Instruction: Materials and Methods.* New York: McGraw-Hill Book Co., 1968, pp. 146–147.

or unit. With the filmstrip, as with any other material, careful planning will offer a greater likelihood of success.

Directions for Use of 35mm Filmstrip Section

Unfortunately, many listings of filmstrips from distributors do not give the full specifics of a filmstrip and/or a description of its contents. Thus it is necessary to include a number of filmstrips whose description is quite meager. The authors recommend that you request a filmstrip for preview purposes before purchasing. In this manner you can be sure that this particular aid will be appropriate for your particular earth science curriculum. In fact, the practice of ordering for previewing purposes is a good procedure no matter what media are under consideration.

Keyed Filmstrip Description

Title.

Specifics. Color or b/w, number of frames, captions or guide or record (if record, sd often used to indicate "sound"), date released, intended audience, and supplier.

35mm Filmstrip Distributors

BFA
BFA Educational Media
2211 Michigan Ave.
Santa Monica, Calif. 90404

BOW
Stanley Bowmar Co.
12 Cleveland St.
Valhalla, N.Y. 10595

C
Comma (Communication
 Materials Exchange)
1535 Ivar St.
Los Angeles, Calif. 90028

CEF
Cenco Educational Films
2600 S. Kostner Ave.
Chicago, Ill. 60623

CER
Community Educational

Resources
Dept. of Education
San Diego County
San Diego, Calif. 92101

CF
Coronet Films
65 E. S. Water St.
Coronet Bldg.
Chicago, Ill. 60601

CPC
Curtis Publishing Co.
Audiovisual Materials Div.
Independence Square
Philadelphia, Pa. 19105

EBEC
Encyclopaedia Britannica
 Educational Corp.
425 N. Michigan Ave.
Chicago, Ill. 60611

EG
Eye-Gate House, Inc.
146–01 Archer Ave.
Jamaica. N.Y. 11435

ELK
Herbert M. Elkins Co.
10031 Commerce Ave.
Tujunga, Calif. 91042

G
John W. Gunter
1027 S. Claremont St.
San Mateo, Calif. 94402

H
Haeseler Pictures
1737 W. Whitley
Hollywood, Calif. 90028

HANDY
Jam Handy Organization
2843 E. Grand Blvd.
Detroit, Mich. 48211

HEW
U.S. Department of Health,
   Education and Welfare
330 Independence Ave., S.W.
Washington, D.C. 20201

HM
Houghton Mifflin Publishing Co.
2 Park St.
Boston, Mass. 02107

IFB
International Film Bureau, Inc.
332 S. Michigan Ave.
Chicago, Ill. 60604

LEP
Life Filmstrips
Time & Life Bldg.
Rockefeller Center
New York, N.Y. 10020

LFS
Long Filmslide Service

7505 Fairmont Ave.
El Cerrito, Calif. 94530

McGH
McGraw-Hill Text-Films
1221 Ave. of the Americas
New York, N.Y. 10019

MIS
Moody Institute of Science
Educational Film Division
1200 E. Washington Blvd.
Whittier, Calif. 90606

NASA
National Aeronautics and Space
   Administration
1520 H St.
Washington, D.C. 20025

NYT
New York Times
Office of Educational Activities
229 W. 43rd St.
New York, N.Y. 10036

OSU
The Ohio State University Film
   Library
156 W. 19th Ave.
Columbus, Ohio 43210

PS
Popular Science Publishing Co.
Audio-Visual Division
355 Lexington Ave.
New York, N.Y. 10017

S
Sigma Educational Films
P.O. Box 1235
Studio City, Calif. 91604

Sc
Scribner and Sons
597 Fifth Ave.
New York, N.Y. 10017

SVE
Society for Visual Education,
  Inc.
1345 W. Diversey Pkwy.
Chicago, Ill. 60614

UNESCO
Unesco Publications Center
317 E. 34th St.
New York, N.Y. 10016

VEC
Visual Education Consultants,
  Inc.

2066 Helena St.
P.O. Box 52
Madison, Wisc. 53701

W
Ward's Natural Science
  Establishment, Inc.
P.O. Box 1749
Monterey, Calif. 93942

or

P.O. Box 1712
Rochester, N.Y. 14603

8mm Film Loops

Much of the early work in educational films had been done with 16mm film, but the costs of film and equipment hindered even greater adoption than was then becoming evident. The introduction of 8mm film in the early 1960s had little impact on the school market, although some educators were exploring the possibilities of local production of materials for classroom use.

Two developments occurred that provided the breakthrough as far as the adaptability of 8mm film was concerned. One was the invention of the film cartridge, and the other was the enhancement of the idea of the single-concept film. The cartridge obviates the need for anyone to be concerned with the mechanics of threading or operating the projector. One simply needs to insert the plastic container into the projector (it is designed to go in one way only) and turn on the switch. Focus can be adjusted by a turn of the lens; most units have stop action. Rewinding is not necessary because the end of the film is spliced to the beginning of the film, thus forming an endless loop; hence the name *film loop*. The length of film, in time, is from one to four minutes. Images may be projected on a wall, or the projector may have a self-contained rear-projection screen—the total unit resembling a small television receiver.

Educators have found a variety of concepts that can be presented through this medium. Content that gains value by repetition is especially well favored. Demonstrations of experiments on film reduce the need for expensive and time-consuming laboratory exercises; short incidents (dramatizations of problems) stimulate critical thinking on the solutions that might be effected.

Loop films, or single-concept films, are generally silent. Their design maximizes the visual flow of information. Sound may play an important part in the future development of this medium. But the emphasis at present is on compactness, reasonable cost, plus ease of operation of the silent cartridge projector. Some confusion existed for a time as to the nature of 8mm film that would be used. The industry has pretty well established itself on the use of the Super 8mm format. Users would be well advised to standardize on this format, especially if a school system is just beginning to use this medium.

Some special characteristics and advantages of the process are as follows:

1. Loop films are short sequences usually designed to be incorporated

with other learning materials in an integrated learning sequence; well adapted for use in the systems approach to lesson planning.

2. The films vary in length, are cartridged according to the specifications of manufacturers (Technicolor, Fairchild, and others), and are silent or sound.

3. They are typically expository, concentrating on a single point that would be difficult to communicate through any other technique.

4. Loop films also present short dramatic statements of problems to stimulate discussion. A visual presentation of "solutions" by consultants in the area could also be a part of the film.

5. The films have great potential in the area of self-testing. Problems can be posed requiring the overt or covert involvement of the viewer with answers supplied immediately to reinforce the action of the viewer. Programmed self-instruction is becoming increasingly popular, a technique to which the loop film can be applied.

6. They are excellent substitutions for the "live" presentation that may be too expensive or too dangerous to present to the individual student who may have a specific interest.

7. The films provide meaningful experiences that can be shared simultaneously in large-group viewing or can be watched by one viewer involved in individualized study.

The use of the loop film in the classroom requires thorough knowledge of the content of the film by the classroom teacher. The lack of sound track and minimum use of labeling in the film means that the film must be properly integrated into the learning unit. The purpose of the film should be clearly set forth and evaluative techniques developed that would demonstrate to the teacher and the student that the desired learnings have been accomplished.

Directions for Use of 8mm Film Loop Section

In compiling the materials for this sourcebook, no attempt was made to preview all loops listed in the text. Those you find listed were chosen to present comprehensive coverage of the topic, utilizing what loops are currently available. The description of each film loop contains the information supplied by the distributor in his literature. Preference was given to Super 8 loops and to those running up to 6 minutes. This decision was made in an attempt to keep within the framework of the "single-concept" loop. More lengthy loops were included where coverage by the shorter ones was not available. For a more detailed listing of 8mm film loops, you might consult the Technicolor listing of 8mm film loops or the NICEM Film Loop Index.

Sample Film Loop Description (Keyed)

Title.
Brief description.
Specifics. Color or b/w (black and white), sd (sound) or si (silent), running time in minutes, Sup 8 (super 8), cart (cartridge), date released, intended audience, and distributor.

8mm Film Loop Distributors

AEF
Animated Electronic Films
P.O. Box 2036
Eads Station
Arlington, Va. 22202

AL
Alpha Film Productions
115 Gaylord St.
Elk Grove Village, Ill. 60007

BFA
BFA Educational Media
2211 Michigan Ave.
Santa Monica, Calif. 90404

CEF
Cenco Educational Films
2600 S. Kostner Avenue
Chicago, Ill. 60623

CF
Coronet Films
65 E. Water St.
Coronet Bldg.
Chicago, Ill. 60601

DCI
Doubleday & Company, Inc.
School and Library Division
Garden City, N.Y. 11530

In Canada:

Audio Visual Systems
Division of Anglo-Photo

27 Haas Road
Rexdale
Toronto, Ont., Canada

E
Ealing Film-Loops
2225 Massachusetts Ave
Cambridge, Mass. 02140

EBEC
Encyclopaedia Britannica
    Educational Corp.
425 N. Michigan Ave.
Chicago, Ill. 60611

EG
Eye-Gate House, Inc.
146–01 Archer Ave.
Jamaica, N.Y. 11435

EMI
Educational Media, Inc.
106 W. Fourth Ave.
Ellensburg, Wash. 98926

FAOC
Film Associates of California
11559 Santa Monica Blvd.
W. Los Angeles, Calif. 90025

GEFL
Gateway Educational Films, Ltd.
470–474 Green Lanes
Palmers Green
London N. 13, U.K.

HR
Harper & Row, Publishers
2500 Crawford Ave.
Evanston, Ill. 60201

HSC
Hubbard Scientific Co.
P.O. Box 105
Northbrook, Ill. 60062

ICF
International Communications
    Films
1371 Reynolds Ave.
Santa Ana, Calif. 92705

IFB
International Film Bureau, Inc.
332 S. Michigan Ave.
Chicago, Ill. 60604

McGH
McGraw-Hill Book Company
Text-Film Division
1221 Ave. of the Americas
New York, N.Y. 10020

MLA
Modern Learning Aids
3000 Ridge Road East
Rochester, N.Y. 14622

MOODY
Moody Inst. of Science

1200 East Washington Blvd.
Whittier, Calif. 90606

PPAC
Potter's Photographic Applica-
    tions Co.
160 Herricks Rd.
Mineola, L.I., N.Y. 11501

RMC
Rand McNally Co.
P.O. Box 7600
Chicago, Ill. 60680

SKI
Science Kit, Inc.
P.O. Box 69
Tonowanda, N.Y. 14150

SRA
Science Research Associates
259 E. Erie St.
Chicago, Ill. 60611

UE&VA
Universal Education and Visual
    Arts
221 Park Ave. S.
New York, N.Y. 10003

USNAC
U.S. National Audiovisual Center
National Archives and Records
    Service
Washington, D.C. 20409

Overhead Transparencies

There are many reasons for the rapidly increasing use of the technique known as overhead projection. While they are in use, most projection techniques tend to replace the teacher, whereas the overhead projector complements his efforts. At all times the teacher controls this mechanical assistant and takes prominent part in the presentation. There is no need for a separate projector operator or constant instructions from the teacher to a classroom aide or assistant.

The optical system of the projector permits placing the projector close to the screen, thereby making it possible to project slides from the front of the room. Since the image is projected over the shoulder of the teacher, he faces the class at all times. A high light-output provides excellent screen visibility without darkening the room or impairing ventilation. With his class in full view the teacher can observe their reactions and adjust his program to meet their responses. He selects his own pace, extemporizing as he wishes, and commenting before, during, or after projection of a slide or transparency. He can alter the sequence of slides or return to a previously shown slide without awkward instructions to an assistant or cumbersome manipulation of materials.

A large, horizontal projection stage permits the classroom teacher to use the screen as a chalkboard. He can write or draw at will with a "grease pencil" on slides or on sheets of acetate without turning away from the class. He can also use a pointer or pencil to indicate important details of a transparency. The two techniques could also be combined. The clear acetate could be placed on a prepared transparency. When markings are made on the clear acetate, it appears as though the transparency itself is being written on. So the teacher can involve himself or the students through the addition of information more specific to a given situation than might be the case with the use of a prepared transparency only.

The construction of the transparency makes possible many different types of presentational techniques. Several sheets of film are easily superimposed on the stage, permitting many colors to be used to identify the different elements of the projected image. The teacher can unmask (peel off) transparencies in progressive disclosures of information or build up several components into a composite image.[29]

[29] Fred John Pula. *Application and Operation of Audiovisual Euipment in Education.* New York: John Wiley & Sons, 1968, pp. 86†87.

Transparencies should be selected by the teacher for the purpose of group presentation. Unlike other materials listed and discussed in this book, transparencies are not especially well suited for individualized instruction. They can be held in the hand by the student, but there are other materials that could impart the information in handier fashion less expensively. Single transparencies vary in cost from $1 to as much as $15. The best transparencies are those that are of simple, clean design, not cluttered with many pictorial or verbal elements. The purpose of the transparency is to supplement the presentation of the teacher. So it is the teacher who must bring meaning to a transparency. A good transparency is not necessarily one that is so completely labeled and detailed that it is self-explanatory.

In selecting transparencies, be certain that the images when projected under standard conditions can be read from the rear of the room. As pointed out in an earlier section, no one should be seated farther away than six times the width of the screen when viewing projected transparencies.

A prime advantage in the use of transparencies lies in the time saved in instruction and presentation. More material can be covered in less time because of the unique characteristics of the medium. But more important, good use of the medium requires the instructor to prepare more carefully the information that is to be presented—determining the objectives that are to be accomplished and seeking out those transparencies that will do the job most effectively.

Directions for Use of Overhead Transparencies Section

As you will notice, no descriptive material accompanies the transparancy titles, other than the distributor code. It is the authors' belief that, for the most part, the title is self-descriptive. It is anticipated, as with the 35mm filmstrips, that a teacher will order the transparencies for preview in order to ascertain their applicability to his teaching requirements. You may find more complete descriptions in the suppliers' catalogs; however, many do no more than simply list titles.

Overhead Transparencies Distributors

AI
Aevac, Inc.
500 Fifth Ave.
New York, N.Y. 10036

BPC
Buhl Projector Co., Inc.

1776 New Highway
Farmingdale, N.Y. 11735

CFD
Classroom Film Distributors
5610 Hollywood Blvd.
Hollywood, Calif. 90028

CV
Creative Visuals
P.O. Box 1911
Big Spring, Tex. 79720

DEP
DCA Educational Products, Inc.
Subsidiary of Display Corp. of
   America
4865 Stenton Ave.
Philadelphia, Pa. 19144

DG
Denoyer-Geppert Company
5235 Ravenswood Ave.
Chicago, Ill. 60640

EA-V
Educational Audio-Visual
29 Marble Ave.
Pleasantville, N.Y. 10570

EBEC
Encyclopaedia Britannica
   Educational Corp.
425 N. Michigan Ave.
Chicago, Ill. 60611

EDRECS
Educational Record Sales
157 Chambers St.
New York, N.Y. 10007

GMC
General Media Corp.
660 E. Powell Ave.
Monmouth, Ore. 97361

HI
Hammond, Inc.
Educational Div.
515 Valley St.
Maplewood, N.J. 07040

HM
Houghton Mifflin Publishing Co.
2 Park St.
Boston, Mass. 02107

IPC
Instructo Products Co.
1635 N. 55th St.
Philadelphia, Pa. 19131

JCA
John Colburn Associates, Inc.
P.O. Box 236
Wilmette, Ill. 60091

K&E
Keuffel & Esser Co.
20 Whittany St.
Morristown, N.J. 07960

MMAMC
Minnesota Mining and Manufac-
   turing Co.
Medical Film Library
2501 Hudson Rd.
St. Paul, Minn. 55119

MPC
Miliken Publishing Co.
611 Olive St.
St. Louis, Mo. 63101

N
A. J. Nystrom and Co.
3333 Elston Ave.
Chicago, Ill. 60618

PS
Popular Science Publishing Co.,
   Inc.
Audio-Visual Division
355 Lexington Ave.
New York, N.Y. 10017

PSC
Photo and Sound Co.
515 Sunset Blvd.
Los Angeles, Calif. 90028

T
Tweedy Transparencies
208 Hollywood Blvd.
East Orange, N.J. 07018

UNC
University of North Carolina
Bureau of Audio Visual
   Education
Chapel Hill, N.C. 27515

UTI
United Transparencies, Inc.
P.O. Box 688
Binghamton, N.Y. 13902

W
Ward's Natural Science

Establishment, Inc.
P.O. Box 1749
Monterey, Calif. 93942

WPC
Western Publishing Educational
   Services
Division of Western Publishing
   Co., Inc.
1220 Mound Ave.
Racine, Wisc. 53404

Color Photographs

Flat pictures of various kinds lend themselves well to many learning situations in the classroom. They can illustrate a multitude of ideas and can be adapted for different kinds of presentation and display.

Students have learned from infancy to look at and react to pictures. They recognize that regardless of language barriers, pictures communicate through a universal language based upon a common understanding of pictorial elements. Students generally pass through several phases of picture-reading ability:

1. Recognizing particular objects and calling them by name.
2. Determining details in a picture and describing what is seen.
3. Drawing inferences regarding past, current, or future action of people or objects shown, and making personal interpretations based on individual backgrounds.

In selecting pictures for classroom use, teachers probably play a more significant role than in the selection of other instructional materials. There needs to be developed a well-designed set of objectives and plan for the utilization of flat pictures. Techniques of use could involve students establishing comparisons between illustrations, or pointing out those aspects of illustrations that contribute toward a certain continuity in them.

Five important points about selecting pictures.

1. Is the picture sufficiently arresting to catch and hold the attention and interest of students with whom it will be used?
2. Is it sufficiently large and simple to be seen clearly?
3. Is the information it portrays important to the topic being considered?
4. Is the information accurate (truthful), and does it have a basis for needed size comparisons?
5. Is the picture well produced, realistic, and attractive? [30]

Studies on the use of pictures and graphs have shown that for maximum results, pictures should be relevant, large enough to be read easily in detail, simple, reproduced well, realistic rather than stylized, and integrated with whatever text materials are being used.

[30] Brown, Lewis, and Harcleroad, op. cit., p. 445.

There is also evidence that colored pictures attract more attention than black and white, and that the attention-attraction power varies with the viewer's sex, age, and personality.

Use of the pictures should call up as much creativity on the part of the teacher as of the student. Ingenuity and imagination are the keys to the use of flat pictures. However, it is important not to overwhelm students by using too many pictures. It is wise to be discriminating and highly selective when preparing a lesson from a large number of illustrations. Students should be helped in their perception of key elements through the use of various cues, including well-placed questions. Students should be encouraged to react in a creative manner to the illustrations that they view. Art activities can be stimulated, color and design studied, and transference from the pictorial to the real effected where the real objects of study are readily available.

Directions for Use of Color Photographs Section

A number of distributors carry what are commonly referred to as "curriculum color prints." Each print consists of a colored photo printed on an 18″ × 13″ card. Each card is laminated with clear plastic and contains a picture explanation and other background information on its reverse side.

Introducing each listing of photographs you will find a key that represents the arbitrary divisions, within the particular subject-matter area, paleontology, for example, which have been used throughout the sourcebook. Each set of prints is named (as Cenozoic Era) and identified as to distributor (CES, DG, etc.). Individual photos within each set are listed by name, and categorized as to subject matter.

Color Photograph Distributors

CES
Creative Educational Society, Inc.
Mankato, Minn. 56001

DG
Denoyer-Geppert Company
5235 Ravenswood Ave.
Chicago, Ill. 60640

EBEC
Encyclopaedia Britannica
  Educational Corp.

425 N. Michigan Ave.
Chicago, Ill. 60611

HSC
Hubbard Scientific Co.
P.O. Box 105
Northbrook, Ill. 60062

IAI
Instructional Aids, Inc.
P.O. Box 293
Owatonna, Minn. 55060

N
A. J. Nystrom and Co.
3333 Elston Ave.
Chicago, Ill. 60618

SP
Space Photos
2608 Sunset Blvd.
Houston, Tex. 77005

W
Ward's Natural Science
    Establishment, Inc.
P.O. Box 1712
Rochester, N.Y. 14603

or

P.O. Box 1749
Monterey, Calif. 93942

Free and Inexpensive Materials

The range of free and inexpensive materials is constantly increasing as are the number of contributors to this valuable source of instructional materials for the classroom. The problem of the teacher and student is to be discriminating in the selection of the material and the medium. More is involved than the planning of the lesson, preparation of the teacher and student, presentation of the lesson, and follow-up. Effective utilization of the material requires careful screening to eliminate as much blatant commercialism as possible. Much information being provided free of charge may have a built-in bias. Students and teachers should develop the talent to see through many of the devices used by the suppliers and gain some utility from the materials regardless.

Directions for Use of Free and Inexpensive Materials Section

It must be noted that the free and inexpensive materials listed in the sourcebook are *not* available from The Macmillan Company. They should be requested from those identified in the listing. When you wish to order any of these materials, you should follow these suggested general procedures:

1. Carefully record your *school address* as the return address.
2. Accurately list titles of materials and any identifying number that might accompany them.
3. Be sure to note the correct address of the individual supplier involved.

Additional Instructions for Requesting Free Materials

1. Utilize official school stationery for all requests.
2. Make specific note that materials will be utilized for classroom or other educational enterprise.
3. If possible, specify the subject-matter area materials will be used in and the estimated number of students involved.
4. Take note of restrictions that a particular supplier may have on all materials distributed (noted in key below), or restrictions on particular materials (noted in description of material).

Key to Restrictions or Limitations on Free Materials (noted in Distributor Index)

(a) No restrictions or none mentioned in material description.
(b) Single copy to individuals.
(c) Single copy to teachers only.
(d) Limited to teachers within the state.
(e) Limited to school libraries.
(f) No more than five different publications can be ordered at one time.
(g) Limited to five copies per teacher.
(h) Restricted to organizations within the state.
(i) No more than 10 copies per classroom.

Description of Free and Inexpensive Material Listing

Title.
Description of material.
Specifics. Individual restriction, number of pages or other notes concerning nature of material, date produced, name of distributor, and expense of material.

There has been a preliminary screening of the materials listed in this section of the sourcebook. For a more detailed listing of all free and inexpensive materials available in the area you can consult catalogs or publication lists available from distributors or from publications dealing only with free and inexpensive materials in science.

Free and Inexpensive Materials Distributors

AAS(a)
American Astronomical Society
211 FitzRandolph Rd.
Princeton, N.J. 08450

ADNR(a)
Alaska Department of Natural
  Resources
Division of Mines and Minerals
Box 1391
Juneau, Alaska 99801

AGA(a)
American Gas Association
Educational Services
605 Third Ave.
New York, N.Y. 10016

AGI(a)
American Geological Institute
Council on Education in the
  Geological Sciences
2201 M St. N.W.
Washington, D.C. 20037

AGU(a)
American Geophysical Union
2100 Pennsylvania Ave. N.W.
Washington, D.C. 20037

AIOA(a)
American Iron Ore Association
600 Bulkley Bldg.
Cleveland, Ohio 44115

AISI(c)
American Iron and Steel
Institute
Teaching Aids Distribution
Center
Bedford Hills, N.Y. 10507

AM-HP(a)
American Museum-Hayden
Planetarium
81st St. and Central Park West
New York, N.Y. 10024

AMS(c)
American Meteorological Society
45 Beacon St.
Boston, Mass. 02108

APCA(a)
Air Pollution Control Association
4400 Fifth Ave.
Pittsburgh, Pa. 15123

API(a)
American Petroleum Institute
1271 Ave. of the Americas
New York, N.Y. 10020

ASRC(a)
Atmosphere Sciences Resources
Center
State University at Albany
Albany, N.Y. 12203

BGA(g)
Barre Granite Association, Inc.
P.O. Box 481
Barre, Vt. 05641

BIS(a)
British Information Services
845 Third Ave.
New York, N.Y. 10022

CBA(c)
Copper and Brass Research
Association

420 Lexington Ave.
New York, N.Y. 10017

CDMG(e)
California Division of Mines and
Geology
Ferry Bldg.
San Francisco, Calif. 94111

CF(a)
The Conservation Foundation
1717 Massachusetts Ave., N.W.
Washington, D.C. 20036

CMC(a)
Criterion Manufacturing
Company
331 Church St.
Hartford, Conn. 06103

COO(a)
Mr. R. C. Vetter
Committee on Oceanography
National Academy of Sciences
National Research Council
2101 Constitution Ave. N.W.
Washington, D.C. 20418

CU(d)
Cornell University
New York State College of
Agriculture
Film Library
Ithaca, N.Y. 14850

DCC(a)
The Joseph Dixon Crucible
Company
Graphite and Lubricants Division
Jersey City, N.J. 07302

DG(d)
Denoyer-Geppert Company
5235 Ravenswood Ave.
Chicago, Ill. 60640

EKC(a)
Eastman Kodak Company
Sales Service Division
343 State St.
Rochester, N.Y. 14650

ESCO(a)
Edmund Scientific Co.
402 Edscorp Bldg.
Barrington, N.J. 08007

ESCP(a)
Earth Science Curriculum Project
P.O. Box 1559
Boulder, Colo. 80301

ESSA(g)
U.S. Coast & Geodetic Survey
Environmental Science Services
    Administration
Rockville, Md. 20852

FEEC(a)
Field Enterprises Educational
    Corp.
Head Librarian
Merchandise Mart Plaza
Chicago, Ill. 60654

FGS(f)
Florida Geological Survey
P.O. Box 631
Tallahassee, Fla. 32302

FPC(a)
Florida Phosphate Council
P.O. Box 1565
Lakeland, Fla. 33802

GCA(a)
The Garden Club of America
Conservation Committee
598 Madison Ave.
New York, N.Y. 10022

GDMMG(c)
Georgia Department of Mines,
    Mining and Geology
Agriculture Laboratory Bldg.

19 Hunter St., S.W.
Atlanta, Ga. 30303

GEC(a)
General Electric Company
P.O. Box 590A
540 Canal St.
Chicago, Ill. 60607

HORC(a)
Humble Oil and Refining Co.
Public Relations & Advertising
    Dept.
P.O. Box 2180
Houston, Tex. 77001

HRWI(a)
Holt, Rinehart and Winston, Inc.,
    Publishers
383 Madison Ave.
New York, N.Y. 10016

IBMG(d)
Idaho Bureau of Mines and
    Geology
Moscow, Idaho 83843

ICOO(d)
Interagency Committee on
    Oceanography
Federal Council for Science &
    Technology
Building 159 E, 4th Floor
Navy Yard Annex
Washington, D.C. 20390

IGS(a)
Indiana Geological Survey
Indiana Dept. of Conservation
611 N. Walnut Grove
Bloomington, Ind. 47405

IOCC(c)
Interstate Oil Compact
    Commission
P.O. Box 3127
Oklahoma City, Okla. 73101

IOGS(d)
Iowa Geological Survey
Geological Survey Bldg.
Iowa City, Iowa 52240

IPAA(a)
Independent Petroleum
   Association of America
1430 S. Boulder Ave.
P.O. Box 1019
Tulsa, Okla. 74104

ISGS(d)
Illinois State Geological Survey
Natural Resources Bldg.
Urbana, Ill. 61801

ISU(a)
Iowa State University
Publications Distribution Room
Morrill Hall
Ames, Iowa 50010

JRC(a)
Johnson Reprint Corp.
111 Fifth Ave.
New York, N.Y. 10003

KSU(d)
Kansas State University
Distribution Center
Umberger Hall
Manhattan, Kan. 66504

LCPC(a)
LaMotte Chemical Products Co.
Chestertown, Md. 21602

MAGS(a)
Maine Geological Survey
Dept. of Economic Development
State House
Augusta, Me. 04330

MDGSWR(a)
Missouri Division of Geological
   Survey & Water Resources
P.O. Box 250
Rolla, Mo. 65401

MFMGS(a)
Midwest Federation of Mineralo-
   gical & Geological Societies
c/o Verne Montgomery
830 Sheridan Pl.
Downers Grove, Ill. 60515

MGS(a)
Minnesota Geological Survey
University of Minnesota
Minneapolis, Minn. 55101

MGSD(a)
Michigan Geological Survey
   Division
Publications Room
Department of Conservation
Lansing, Mich. 48926

MIA(b)
Minnesota Institute of Agricul-
   ture
Bulletin Room
St. Paul, Minn. 55101

MSC(a)
Morton Salt Company
110 N. Wacker Dr.
Chicago, Ill. 60606

MSU(d)
Michigan State University
Bulletin Office
P.O. Box 231
East Lansing, Mich. 48823

N&C(d)
A. J. Nystrom and Co.
3333 Elston Ave.
Chicago, Ill. 60618

NASA(a)
NASA Goddard Space Flight
   Center
Educational Office
Greenbelt, Md. 20771

NAS/NRC(d)
NAS/NRC Committee on
   Oceanography
2101 Constitution Ave.
Washington, D.C. 20025

NCA(a)
National Coal Association
Education Division
Coal Bldg.
1130 17th St. N.W.
Washington, D.C. 20036

NCDMR(a)
North Carolina Division of
   Mineral Resources
Dept. of Conservation &
Development
P.O. Box 2719
Raleigh, N.C. 27607

NCSM(a)
North Carolina State Museum
101 Halifax St.
Raleigh, N.C. 27601

NCSU(b)
North Carolina State University
Department of Agricultural
   Information
P.O. Box 5037 State College
   Station
Raleigh, N.C. 27607

NDGS(a)
North Dakota Geological Survey
University Station
Grand Forks, N.D. 58201

NODC(a)
National Oceanographic Data
   Center
Washington, D.C. 20390

NODO(a)
Naval Oceanographic Distribution Office

5801 Tabor Ave.
Philadelphia, Pa. 19120

NSTA(a)
National Science Teachers
   Association
1201 16th St.
Washington, D.C. 20036

NYSMSS(a)
New York State Museum and
   Science Service
The State Education Department
The University of the State of
   New York
Albany, N.Y. 12224

ODGS(b)
Oregon State Dept. of Geology &
   Mineral Industries
State of Oregon Dept. of
   Geology & Mineral Industries
1069 State Office Bldg.
Portland, Ore. 97201

ODLS(c)
Ohio Division of Geological
   Survey
Dept. of Natural Resources
Columbus, Ohio 43215

ODMMR(b)
Oregon State Dept. of Mines &
   Mineral Resources
1069 State Office Bldg.
Portland, Ore. 97201

OGS(a)
Oklahoma Geological Survey
University of Oklahoma
Norman, Okla. 73069

OSHD(a)
Oregon State Highway Depart-
   ment
Travel Information Division
Salem, Ore. 97310

OSU(d)
Oklahoma State University
Extension Service
Stillwater, Okla. 74074

PPC(c)
Phillips Petroleum Company
Editorial Div.
Room 467, Adams Bldg.
Bartlesville, Okla. 74004

PTGS(d)
Pennsylvania Topographic &
  Geologic Survey
Dept. of Internal Affairs
Harrisburg, Pa. 17120

SA(d)
Science Associates
P.O. Box 216
Princeton, N.J. 08540

SCA(d)
Science Clubs of America
Science Service
1719 N St. N.W.
Washington, D.C. 20036

SCNC(a)
Secretariate of the Canadian
  National Committee
No. 8 Bldg., Room G-31
Carling Ave.
Ottawa 1, Canada

SCS(a)
Soil Conservation Service
Information Div.
U.S. Dept. of Agriculture
Washington, D.C. 20036

SEL(c)
Space Education Laboratories
Rosemont, Pa. 19010

SGSK(d)
State Geological Survey of
  Kansas

University of Kansas
Lawrence, Kan. 66045

SI(a)
Smithsonian Institution
Publications Distribution Section
Editorial and Publications
  Division
Washington, D.C. 20225

SIOO(a)
Scripps Institution of Oceanogra-
  phy
University of California
LaJolla, Calif. 92037

SLC(c)
Star-Liner Company
1106 S. Columbus Blvd.
Tucson, Ariz. 85711

SLI(a)
Spitz Laboratories, Inc.
Division of McGraw-Hill, Inc.
Yorklyn, Del. 19736

SOC(c)
Shell Oil Company
Community Activities Div.
50 W. 50th St.
New York, N.Y. 10020

SOCC(a)
Standard Oil Company of
  California
225 Bush St.
San Francisco, Calif. 94104

TAA(a)
The American Assembly
116th St. and Broadway
New York, N.Y. 10027

TAES(a)
Texas Agricultural Experiment
  Station
Department of Agricultural
  Information
College Station, Tex. 77840

TDG(a)
Tennessee Division of Geology
G-5 State Office Building
Nashville, Tenn. 37219

TGSC(a)
Texas Gulf Sulphur Co.
Agricultural Dept.
1801 Houston Club Bldg.
Houston, Tex. 77002

TIC(a)
Taylor Instrument Companies
Advertising Dept.
95 Ames St.
Rochester, N.Y. 14601

TSCS(a)
The Soil Conservation Society
7515 N.E. Ankeny Rd.
Ankeny, Iowa 50021

TSI(a)
The Salt Institute
33 N. LaSalle St.
Chicago, Ill. 60602

UAL(a)
United Air Lines, Inc.
School and College Services
O'Hare International Airport
Chicago, Ill. 60666

UCC(c)
Union Carbide Corp.
Consumer Products Div.
Advertising Dept.
270 Park Ave.
New York, N.Y. 10017

UK(a)
University of Kentucky
Agriculture Experiment Station
Lexington, Ky. 40506

USAEC(a)
United States Atomic Energy
  Commission
Division of Public Information

Audio-Visual Branch
Washington, D.C. 20025

USBM(a)(f)
Bureau of Mines
United States Department of the
  Interior
4800 Forbes Ave.
Pittsburgh, Pa. 15213

USC&CS(g)
U.S. Coast & Geodetic Survey
Department of Commerce
Washington, D.C. 20225

USCSC(a)
U.S. Civil Service Commission
Washington, D.C. 20415

USDA(b)
U.S. Department of Agriculture
Office of Information
Washington, D.C. 20250

USFS(b)
U.S. Department of Agriculture
Forest Service
Northern Region
Missoula, Mont. 59801

USGPO(a)
U.S. Government Printing Office
Superintendent of Documents
Washington, D.C. 20402

USGS(c)
U.S. Geological Survey
Information Office
Washington, D.C. 20242

USSC(a)
U.S. Steel Corporation
71 Broadway
New York, N.Y. 10006

USU(a)
Utah State University
Extension Services
Logan, Utah 84321

UVSAC(a)
University of Vermont & State
  Agricultural College
Vermont Agricultural Extension
  Service
Burlington, Vt. 05401

UW(d)
University of Wisconsin
Soil Survey Division
203 Soils Bldg.
Madison, Wisc. 53706

WDMG(a)
Washington Division of Mines
  and Geology
335 General Adm. Bldg.
Olympia, Wash. 98501

WGNHS(c)
Wisconsin Geological & Natural
  History Survey
170 Science Hall
The University of Wisconsin
Madison, Wisc. 53706

WHOI(a)
Woods Hole Oceanographic
  Institution
Woods Hole, Mass. 02543

WVGS(a)
West Virginia Geological Survey
P.O. Box 879
Morgantown, W. Va. 26505

Earth Science Suppliers

Directions for Use of Supplier and Distributor Index

The particular key which is used to denote the various subject-matter materials, i.e., equipment, supplies, and so on, that are available from the listed companies or agencies, can be found on the initial page of the Index. The designated materials were derived from a review of catalogs or other information available from the particular source. If you wish to obtain more complete descriptions of the materials, we suggest that you request a catalog from the particular company or agency involved.

KEY

A = Astronomy	1 = Equipment
M = Meteorology	2 = Supplies
O = Oceanography	3 = Maps/charts
P = Paleontology	4 = Models
PG = Physical Geology	5 = 35mm slides

	A	M	O	P	PG
William Ainsworth & Sons, Inc. 2151 Lawrence St. Denver, Colo. 80205					1
Allens Minerals McCoy, Colo. 80463					2
American Geological Institute 2201 M St. N.W. Washington, D.C. 20037					3
Astro Murals P.O. Box 7563 Washington, D.C. 20044	3				

	A	M	O	P	PG
Astronomy Charted 33 Winfield St. Worcester, Mass. 01610	1,2 3,5	5			
Astroscopics 521 California Dr. Claremont, Calif. 91711	1,2				
Belfort Instrument Co. 4 N. Central Ave. Balton, Md. 21202		1			
Bell Telephone (Contact your local Bell Telephone office)					1
Brown's Minerals 3030 E. 7th St. Joplin, Mo. 64801					2
Cal-Brea P.O. Box 254 Brea, Calif. 92621				1	2
Cambosco Scientific Co. 342 Western Ave. Boston, Mass. 02135	3,4	1,3,4		2,3,4	1,2 3,4
Cave Optical Co. 4137 Anaheim St. Long Beach, Calif. 90804	1,2				
Central Scientific Co. 1700 W. Irving Park Rd. Chicago, Ill. 60613	1,2 3,4	1,3,4	3	2,3,4	1,2 3,4
Cole-Parmer Instrument & Equipment Co. 7330 N. Clark St. Chicago, Ill. 60626					1,2
Colorado Geological Industries 1244 E. Colfax Denver, Colo. 80218				1,2	2,3,4
Wilt H. Curtin & Co. 4220 Jefferson Ave. Houston, Tex. 77023	1,2,4	1,3,4		2,3,4	1,2 3,4

	A	M	O	P	PG
Damon Corp. Educational Division 115 Fourth Ave. Needham Hts., Mass. 02194	1,4	1,4	1	1,3	1,3,4
David New — Minerals P.O. Box 7 Providence, Utah 84332					2
Denoyer-Geppert Co. 5235 Ravenswood Ave. Chicago, Ill. 60640		1,3,4	4	2 3,4	1,2 3,4
D. J. Mineral Kit Co. 901 Berkeley Ave. Menlo Park, Calif. 94025					2
Dynalab Corp. P.O. Box 112 Rochester, N.Y. 14601					1,2
Earth Science Center 230 Nassau St. Princeton, N.J. 18540	3,4				
Edmund Scientific Company 300 Edscorp Bldg. Barrington, N.J. 08007	1,2 3,4				1
Educational Materials & Equipment Co. P.O. Box 63 Bronxville, N.Y. 10708	1,2			2	1,2
Myron N. Emerson 52 Wheelock Rd. Waltham, Mass. 02154	1,2				
Estes Industries, Inc. P.O. Box 227 Penrose, Colo. 81240	1,2 3,4				
Faust Scientific Supply Co. 2801 Industrial Dr. Madison, Wisc. 53713	1,2,3 4,5	1,3,4		2,3,4	1,2 3,4
Filer's P.O. Box 487 Yucaipa, Calif. 92399					2,3,4

	A	M	O	P	PG
Fossils Unlimited 9925 Bankhead Highway Fort Worth, Tex. 76166				2	
Geological Enterprises P.O. Box 996 Ardmore, Okla. 73501				2	1,2 3,4
The Geological Society of America 801 Colorado Bldg., Box 1719 Boulder, Colo. 80302					3
Griegers, Inc. 1633 E. Walnut St. Pasadena, Calif. 91107				2	1,2
Hubbard Scientific Co. P.O. Box 105 Northbrook, Ill. 60062	1,2,3 4,5	1,3 4,5	3,4	2,3,4	1,2 3,4
Klister Graphics 400 Dahlia St. Denver, Colo. 80904					4
LaMotte Chemical Products Co. Chestertown, Md. 21602			1,2		2
Lapidary International, Inc. 1228 S. Beach Blvd. Anaheim, Calif. 92804					1,4
LaPine Scientific Co. 6001 S. Knox Ave. Chicago, Ill. 60629	1,2 3,4	1,3,4	3	2,3,4	1,2 3,4
LeMont Scientific, Inc. Pike St. Lemont, Pa. 16851					4
Macalaster Scientific Co. R. 111 Everett Tpk. Nashua, N.H. 03060				2,3,4	1,2 3,4
Mackinaw Geological Supply P.O. Box 375 Ishpeming, Mich. 49849					1,2

	A	M	O	P	PG
Malick's 5514 Plymouth Rd. Baltimore, Md. 21214				2	
Minerals Unlimited 1721 5th St. Berkeley, Calif. 94701					2
Miners Newcastle, Calif. 95658					2
Museum of Fossils P.O. Box 144 Sedona, Ariz. 86336				2	
NASCO Science and Mathematics 901 Janesville Ave. Fort Atkinson, Wisc. 53538	1,2 3,4	1,3,4		3,4	1,2 3,4
Nova Laboratories Division of Harmonic Reed Corp. Union Hill Park West Conshohocken, Pa. 19428	1,2				
A. J. Nystrom and Co. 3333 Elston Ave. Chicago, Ill. 60618					3,4
Ohaus Scale Corp. 1050 Commerce Ave. Union, N.J. 07083					1
The Optical Craftsmen 20962 Itasca St. Chatsworth, Calif. 91311	1,2				
Planetariums Unlimited Inc. 46 Broadway Holbrook, N.Y. 11741	1,2				
Questar New Hope, Pa. 18938	1,2				
Rand McNally Co. P.O. Box 7600 Chicago, Ill. 60680	1,2 3,4				3,4

	A	M	O	P	PG
Schortmann's Minerals 6 McKinley Ave. Easthampton, Mass. 01027					1,2
Science Associates, Inc. P.O. Box 216 Princeton, N.J. 08540		1			
Science Kit, Inc. 2299 Military Rd. Tonawanda, N.Y. 14150	1,2 3,4	1,3,4		2,3,4	2,3,4
Science Related Materials, Inc. P.O. Box 1009 Evanston, Ill. 60204					3,4
Scientific Educational Products Corp. 30 E. 42nd St. New York, N.Y. 10017					1
Scott Scientific, Inc. P.O. Box 2121 Fort Collins, Colo. 80512				2	2
Sepor Laboratory Supply P.O. Box 1366 Torrance, Calif. 90505					1,3,4
Silva, Inc. 704 Ridgeway St. La Porte, Ind. 46350					1
Soiltest, Inc. 2205 Lee St. Evanston, Ill. 60202	3,4	3,4		2,3,4	1,2 3,4
The Sort-Card Co. P.O. Box 901 Boulder, Colo. 80302					3,4
Southern Precision Instrument Co. 710 Augusta St. San Antonio, Tex. 78215	1,2				
Southwest Mineral Supply P.O. Box 323 Santa Fe, N.M. 87501					1,2

	A	M	O	P	PG
Space Photos 2608 Sunset Blvd. Houston, Tex. 77005	5				
Spitz Laboratories Division of McGraw-Hill Book Co. Yorklyn, Del. 19736	1,2				
Stansi Scientific Materials Division Fisher Scientific Co. 1231 N. Honore St. Chicago, Ill. 60622	1,2 3,4	1,3,4	3	2,3,4	3,4
Star Band Corp. Portsmouth, Va. 23704					2
Star Diamond Industries 1421 W. 240 St. Harbor City, Calif. 90710				1	1
Star-Liner Company 1106 S. Columbus Blvd. Tucson, Ariz. 85717	1,2				
Taylor Instruments Consumer Products Div. of Sybron Corp. 225 Fifth Ave. New York, N.Y. 10011		1			
Telescopics 6565 Romaine St. Los Angeles, Calif. 90038	1,2				
Tersch Enterprises P.O. Box 1059 Colorado Springs, Colo. 80901	5				
Thompson & Robinson 63A Waldron St. Cambridge, Mass. 02140				1	2
Trippensee Planetarium Co., Inc. S. Hamilton St. Saginaw, Mich. 48602	1,2 3,4				
U.S. Geological Survey 1200 S. Eads St. Arlington, Va. 22202					3

	A	M	O	P	PG
Unitron Instrument Co. 66 Needham St. Newton Highlands, Mass. 02161	1,2				
Ward's of California P.O. Box 1749 Monterey, Calif. 93941	1,2,3 4,5	1,3 4,5	3,4	1,2,3 4,5	1,2,3 4,5
or					
Ward's Natural Science Establishment P.O. Box 1712 Rochester, N.Y. 14603	1,2,3 4,5	1,3 4,5	3,4	1,2,3 4,5	1,2,3 4,5
Watkins Mineral Corp. 117 Pembroke Lane Wichita Falls, Tex. 76301				2	2
Webster Division McGraw-Hill Book Co. Manchester Rd. Manchester, Mo. 63011				2	
Williams & Heintz Map Corp. 8119 Central Ave. Washington, D.C. 20027					3
Wilkens-Anderson Co. 4525 W. Division St. Chicago, Ill. 60651	1,2 3,4	3,4	3,4	2,3,4	1,2 3,4
York River Mining Co. 9612 Parkman Rd. Windham, Ohio 44288					2

General Sources

A. ESCP (Earth Science Curriculum Project, Houghton Mifflin Publishing Co., Boston) Reference Series (ESCP) William Matthews, Ed.
  1. *Sources of Earth Science Information* (Matthews)
  2. *Selected References for Earth Science Courses* (Matthews)
  3. *Selected Earth Science Films* (Dort)
  4. *Selected Maps and Earth Science Publications* (Matthews)
  5. *Free Materials for Earth Science Teachers* (Matthews and Bartholomew)
  6. *Planetariums, Observatories, and Earth Science Exhibits* (Matthews)
  7. *Topographic Maps and How To Use Them* (Matthews)
  8. *Basic Data and Water Budget Computation* (Carter)
  9. *Selected Guides for Geologic Field Study* (Lokke)
B. Film catalogs from various University Film Rental Bureaus
C. *Educators Guide to Free Science Materials*, Educators Progress Service Inc., Randolph, Wisc., 1971.
D. NICEM (National Information Center for Educational Media, University of Southern California, University Park, Los Angeles, Calif. 90007): Film, Filmstrip, and Film Loop Indexes.

PART...2

Astronomy

Classroom Activities in Astronomy

1 Observing the Path of the Sun

Students are aware that the sun appears to travel across the sky during the daytime. There are, however, a number of misconceptions concerning the sun's apparent path. An example of one of these misconceptions involves the altitude of the sun at noon.

A very useful activity (developed by the Earth Science Curriculum Project), which can be used to illustrate the sun's position at noon or, for that matter, anytime during the day throughout the year, centers around the use of a clear plastic hemisphere. The hemisphere is attached to a cardboard or plywood square, taken outside, and oriented to a true north-south line.[1] (See Figure 2-1.)

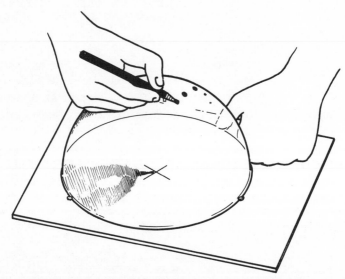

Figure 2-1 ESCP Plastic Hemisphere. From Earth Science Curriculum Project, *Investigating the Earth* (Boston: Houghton Mifflin Publishing Co., 1967, p. 27.)

The sun's position can be plotted at various times (including at noon) throughout the day using a grease pencil and placing a mark on the hemisphere where the tip of the pencil's shadow touches the X marked at the center of the square base. Care should be taken to

[1] A true north-south line can be established by noting the sun's directional position at solar noon. That direction will always be due south (in those regions whose latitude exceeds 23 1/2°). Once south is established the other points are easily determined.

ensure that the pencil is in contact with the hemisphere when the position of the sun is to be determined. Attention should also be paid to orienting the base with the true north-south line each time a reading is to be taken.

When the various positions of the sun, as recorded on the hemisphere, are connected, a quite reliable record of the sun's path during the day can be obtained. A record of the sun's position and/or path throughout the year; that is, its solstices and equinoxes may be obtained by keeping one hemisphere and using it to denote the varying positions.

2 Scale

One of the more important concepts in astronomy (but often one that is quite difficult for many students to grasp) is the enormity of astronomical distances. The difficulties with these great distances are similar to those commonly encountered with the vast expanses of geologic time. A very effective method that allows an individual student to bring these distances into an order of magnitude that he or she can grasp more easily involves devising a scale by which the distances can be represented.

This activity is made more meaningful to students if they devise the scale by which the distances can be represented. The students are given a chart of our solar system illustrating the distances between the various planets and the sun and are asked to choose an appropriate scale for these distances. If the students are unfamiliar with the concept of scaling, some explanations may be needed.

Once the students devise and discuss their various scales, there are several ways they can illustrate them graphically. One method utilizes adding-machine tape with one end being the sun and the planets being placed at respective distances along the tape. A second method often proves to be more fun for the students; they can go outside to a large open area (such as a football field) and mark off the respective distances there.

During the course of this activity the need to better represent the comparative diameters of the sun and planets often arises. Again, a scale devised by the students can be used quite effectively.

The utilization of student-devised scales cannot be stressed too heavily. Experience has shown that such scales allow the student to gain a much better grasp of this concept and provide a good deal more meaning to the activity.

3 Evidence for the Earth's Motion

One topic that invariable arises in any classroom discussion of astronomy is that of the earth's motions and how one can provide evidence to substantiate this movement. There are a number of traditional methods by which the motions can be evidenced; these include star trails, behavior of a pendulum, and the apparent movement of the sun. One activity has proved to be quite useful in bringing evidence to support earth movement, and it involves the students collecting data on the position of various stars (including Polaris) during a period of several hours in an evening.

This activity involves the use of an easily constructed device commonly called an "astrolab." The astrolab is made from a large-diameter drinking straw, a protractor, string or thread, a nut or washer, and masking tape or Scotch tape. The materials are put together in a manner similar to that depicted in Figure 2–2. The stars chosen by the students should be ones that have sufficient altitude to remain in sight during a three-hour period. The activity is also made even more effective if the stars chosen are bright, one of them is Polaris, and there is at least one in each of the four directions (north, south, east, and west).

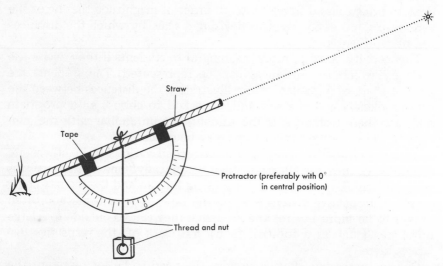

Figure 2–2 Astrolab.

Using the astrolab, the student sights in on the desired star (as depicted in Figure 2–2), presses the thread carefully against the surface of the protractor, and reads the angle above the horizon. The device can also be used to record the horizontal angle of a star by turning the astrolab horizontally, sighting the star through the straw, and positioning the string to true north.

When the students bring their data back to class and discuss their observations, a valuable insight into a number of concepts in addition to that of the earth's motion can be gained. Discussions about the changing or nonchanging (Polaris) stars lead to topics such as celestial sphere, why Polaris has not always been the "north star," determination of latitude, and many others.

4   Photographing the Moon

Students often are fascinated by the moon and its variety of faces or phases. When the topic of the moon arises in an earth science course, many teachers utilize pictures, movies, slides, or articles to describe the moon's phases. Some teachers have a school telescope which they can use to bring the class together at night to view the moon in greater detail.

Another activity that has proved very effective in the study of the moon and its phases involves the individual students themselves taking photographs of the moon and bringing them into class for display and discussion. (See Figure 2–3.)

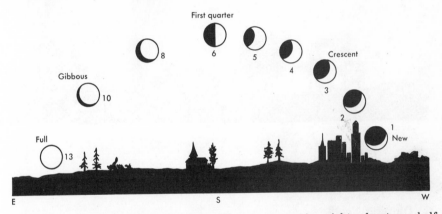

Figure 2–3 Apparent position of the moon on successive nights about one half hour after sunset. From Dean B. McLaughlin, *Introduction to Astronomy* (Boston: Houghton Mifflin Publishing Co., 1961, p. 124).

The cameras used in this activity are the Polaroid Swingers which take black-and-white photos and are quite inexpensive, and several would be well within the range of most school budgets. These cameras are easily operated by students and can be taken home on a revolving basis throughout several weeks so as to enable students to make complete photographic records of the phases. The Swinger can also be used quite easily with a telescope to make more detailed photos. There seems to be a great deal more relevancy added to the study of the moon and its phases when students, as in other activities, utilize materials that they have gathered themselves. Student interest is maintained for much longer periods of time with such an activity, and you may be quite certain that the students will obtain a better grasp of the subject matter than if they were merely lectured about the phases of the moon.

5 Skyline Silhouette

Students often are faced with the problem of orienting various objects in the sky from a given vantage point at different times during the year. Star charts, however, often prove confusing and difficult to manipulate for the beginning student. This situation can be greatly alleviated through the use of a *skyline silhouette* (see Figure 2-4). Such a silhouette can be constructed by a student at night by orienting himself directionally and sketching the silhouette of the features he can see on the skyline in each major direction (N,S,E,W). This sketch can then be transferred to a stencil and duplicate copies produced. These duplicate silhouettes in turn can be used as permanent pictorial records of observations made at that particular location for that date and time.

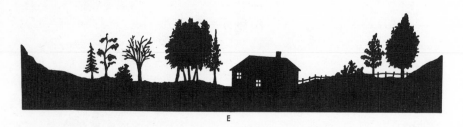

E

Figure 2-4 Skyline silhouette.

6 Dipping Needle

Locating the direction of the magnetic North Pole from a particular point on earth is only one aspect of studying the earth's magnetic field. Another dimension involves measuring the angle of tilt or inclination that the magnetic lines of force make with the earth's surface at that location.

A simple student-constructed device can be used to record this angle of "magnetic dip." This device is composed of a metal knitting needle, a long sewing needle, a cork, a protractor, two wooden blocks, and two wooden match sticks. The student strongly magnetizes the knitting needle and pushes it through the center of the cork. Then he pushes the sewing needle into the cork at a right angle to the knitting needle and adjusts the knitting needle until the apparatus is balanced. A wooden match stick is then glued to the two wooden blocks near the edge as illustrated in Figure 2-5. The match sticks will serve to reduce friction on the sewing needle and allow it to rotate more easily in response to the magnetic field. The protractor is then attached to one of the blocks so that measurement of the angle of dip can be made directly. The needle portion of the device is then positioned on the wooden blocks, and the complete device is magnetically oriented toward the magnetic North Pole by using a magnetic compass. When the device is oriented magnetically, the knitting needle will then dip a certain number of degrees approximating the angle that the earth's magnetic lines of force have at that particular point. The magnitude of the angle can then be read directly from the protractor.

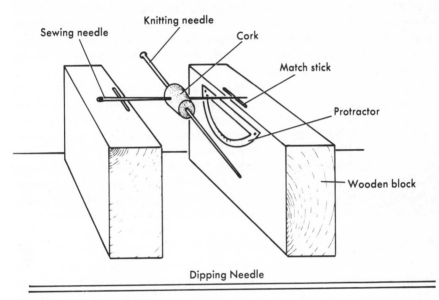

Figure 2–5 Dipping needle.

7   Position of the Moon

Noting the exact position of the moon on repeated observations during the same night or single sightings on successive nights, can provide the introductory student with valuable firsthand experience with lunar motion.

An activity like this can be introduced effectively by posing a question to the students, such as, "What, if anything, have you noticed concerning the position of the moon in the sky?" "Does it change from time to time or does it remain in the same position?" The ensuing discussion will provide sufficient dissonant opinions on lunar movement in such direction and degree as to give impetus to student observation of the phenomena. Following their observations, students can bring their observational records into class and compare and discuss their interpretations as to the nature and probable causes of lunar motions.

8   Planetarium and Field Trip

When you suggest a trip to a local planetarium, a teacher often gathers up images of stepping into a "canned" program which has little, if any, direct relevance to your own teaching objectives. This, however, need not be the case. Planetarium directors are usually most anxious to present a program within the limitations of his instruments that will parallel an individual teacher's program and therefore be of maximum benefit to the students. What happens all too often, however, is that a teacher makes an appointment for his class and this is, unfortunately, the last contact made with the director until his appearance before the students.

A planetarium can be a very effective educational tool in the study of astronomy. A large number of concepts such as retrograde motion, which are often very difficult to present in or outside of the classroom, can be replicated and repeated numerous times in the most planetariums. The planetarium should and can be used as a tool in a planned, organized, and integrated fashion in line with a teacher's objectives. The teacher should work with the planetarium director long before his scheduled class visit to ensure that the trip is of maximum value for the students and their understanding of astronomy.

9   Telescope or Binocular Observation

Student activities centered around observations of the actual environment are very important in astronomy as they are in any science. The telescope is a very important instrument, it extends the observational powers of the student. A large variety of telescopes are often within the budgets of many schools and are available from commercial sources. If these instruments are too costly for your science budget, there are a number of "do-it-yourself" kits that allow the novice astronomer to construct his own telescope (even including grinding the lenses, if desired!).

If the cost of these telescope kits is still prohibitive, don't give up. Binoculars can still provide the introductory student with an instrument with which he can achieve a sufficient degree of magnification which will greatly enhance his astronomical observations. Binoculars often can be acquired at reduced prices at Army surplus stores or government surplus depots in your area. The magnification power of binoculars may not be as great as that possessed by many telescopes, but they do have the distinct advantage of greater mobility and the capability of being easily and safely handled by students in their observations.

16mm Films

Forces, Movements, and Astronomical Phenomena

"Centripetal Force and Satellite Orbits" (color, sd, 11 min, 1962, h). Experiments illustrating the relationship between mass, velocity, and radius and magnitude of centripetal force (CF).

"Cosmic Ray" (color, sd, 20 min, 1960, h). Explains the modern concepts of atomic structure and cosmic rays. Describes the various methods of studying cosmic rays and their relationship to solar and outer space sources (McGH).

"Doppler Effect" (b/w, sd, 9 min, 1952, h). Shows the resultant frequency of sound waves as the source of the sound is varied in relation to the listener's ear (McGH).

"The Earth: Its Magnetic Field" (color, sd, 13 1/2 min, 1969, j-c). Utilizing charts, models, and animation, the film considers such topics as declination, inclination, intensity, and changes of the earth's magnetic field (CF).

"Earth in Motion, The" (color, sd, 12 min, 1963, j-h). Illustrates the tilt and rotation of the earth and their effects as well as how gravity and inertia affect the movements of the earth (CEF).

"Earth—Our Planet" (b/w, sd, 21 min, 1953, j-a). Presents the cosmic theory of the origin of the solar system and describes the changes of the earth's and moon's surface by volcanic activity (B).

"Earth in Space, The" (b/w, sd, 29 min, 1959, j-h). Presents via charts, models, photographs, and film clips the movements, physical characteristics, atmosphere, and seasons of the earth (NET:IU).

"Eclipse '65" (color, sd, 14 min, 1965, j-h). Traces a scientific plane flight taken to investigate a total solar eclipse (NASA), free.

"Eclipses of the Sun and Moon" (color, sd, 9 min, 1966, j-a). Depicts, via telescopic photography, both lunar and solar eclipses. Discusses their origin and the various knowledge that is obtained through studying them (EBEC).

"Elliptic Orbits" (b/w, sd, 19 min, 1959, h). Illustrates that the relationship between gravitational force and space satellites follows the inverse square relation (MLA).

"Flaming Sky, The" (b/w, sd, 29 min, 1960, j-a). Surveys the cause and characteristics of auroras. Describes their investigation through use of instruments, laboratory experimentation, and rocket research (McGH).

"Force of Gravity" (color or b/w, sd, 27 min, 1960, j-a). Outlines the historical and modern concepts of gravity as it is related to cosmology and geophysics (McGH).

"Galileo" (b/w, sd, 14 min, 1959, j-h). Follows Galileo's life from his break with a theory of Aristotle, verification of the Copernican theory, to his work with various concepts of mechanics (CF).

"Galileo's Laws of Falling Bodies" (b/w, sd, 6 min, 1953, j-h). Illustrates, with the use of slow-motion and freeze-frame photography, investigations with the inclined plane and free-falling bodies in air and a vacuum (EBEC).

"Gravity, Weight, and Weightlessness" (color, sd, 11 min, 1963, i-h). Discusses how scientists investigate gravity, weight, and the effects of free fall (FAOC).

"How We Know the Earth Moves" (color or b/w, sd, 12 min, 1960, i-j). Illustrates the concept and workings of a Foucault pendulum while providing evidence for the earth's rotation. Provides evidence for the earth's revolution around the sun through the phenomenon of star-shift (FAOC).

"How We Know the Earth's Shape" (color, sd, 10 min, 1960, i-j). Traces the development of various theories concerning the earth's shape. Includes methods by which man may gather evidence about the shape of the earth (FAOC).

"Laws of Motion" (color, sd, 13 min, 1953, j-h). Traces the development of Newton's three laws of motion. Examples of each are provided using demonstrations involving a variety of materials (EBEC).

"Magnetic Force" (color, sd, 28 min, 1960, j-h). Investigates the nature of the earth's magnetic field. Discusses the history and use of magnetism and geomagnetism (McGH).

"Magnetosphere" (color, 30 min, 1969, j-h). The film provides a general description of the space surrounding the earth at a distance of 600 miles or greater. Discusses the Van Allen belts, auroras, and the various programs which have attempted to study this area of space (McGH).

"Planets in Orbit—Laws of Kepler, The" (b/w, sd, 10 min, 1960, j-h). Discusses the development of Kepler's Laws accompanied by an account of man's earliest observations and beliefs about the universe (EBEC).

"Solar Radiation I: Sun and Earth" (color, sd, 18 min, 1967, h). Presents the basic concepts of the relationship of solar radiation to the earth (MLA).

"Van Allen Radiation Belts—Exploring in Space, The" (color or b/w, sd, 1963, j-a). Scientists provide an explanation as to the goals, instruments, and methods by which data are obtained in space flights with an emphasis on the radiation belts (EBEC).

"What Is an Eclipse?" (color, sd, 10 min, 1965, p-j). Explores the causes of both solar and lunar eclipses including relative inclination of orbits. Discusses the reason for not having monthly eclipses and for having only a relatively small area of the earth affected (FAOC).

Space Exploration

"Aeronautics" (color, sd, 28 min, 1971, j-h). Shows the technical problems of flight and the operational problems of commercial and private aviation that need to be solved and the areas of research that NASA will conduct during the 1970s (NASA), free.

"America on the Moon" (color, sd, 9 min, 1969, j-a). Traces all phases (from launch to splashdown and biological isolation) of America's first manned landing on the lunar surface. Includes photographs by the astronauts (UE&VA).

"America in Space—The First Decade" (color, sd, 18 min, 1968, j-a). Nontechnical survey of the research, accomplishments, and contributions made by NASA's studies of the moon, planets, and manned spaceflight (NASA), free.

"American Rendezvous, An" (color, sd, 20 min, 1966, j-h). Illustrates the flight of Gemini 7 during which the first rendezvous in space occurred (MDC), free.

"Anatomy of a Shoot" (color, sd, 26 min, 1968, j-h). Describes the last Surveyor space shot including the role that jet propulsion laboratories can play in future space flight (CBS).

"Apollo Mission Highlights" (b/w, sd, 12 min, 1969, j-h). Uses animation and special effects to trace an Apollo/Saturn from the flight to the moon, to the scientific studies to be conducted on the moon, and finally to splashdown and recovery (NASA), free.

"Apollo Nine: The Space Duet of Spider and Gumdrop" (color, sd, 28½ min, 1969, p-a). Traces the Apollo Nine Flight from the astronaut training program to the launching, rendezvous, and docking with the Lunar Module, reentry, and final recovery (NASA), free.

"Apollo 14: Mission to Fra Mauro" (color, sd, 28 min, 1971, j-a). A documentary account of the mission including its problems and their solutions, scientific activities on the moon, and the return journey to the earth (NASA), free.

"Apollo 15: In the Mountains of the Moon" (color, sd, 28 min, 1971, j-a). Story of the Apollo 15 flight including details of the three lunar surface expeditions, the experiment in lunar orbit, and the return to earth (NASA), free.

"Ariel—The First International Satellite" (color, sd, 12 min, 1963, j-a). Describes the solar effect on the earth's upper atmospheric layer, its effects on radio signals, and the international cooperation involved in the venture (NASA), free.

"Ariel II" (color, sd, 27 min, 1964, h-a). Follows the complete history of the cooperative satellite developed and launched by the United States and the United Kingdom (NASA), free.

"Assignment: Shoot the Moon" (color, sd, 28 min, 1967, j-h). A survey of the knowledge gained about the moon from the Ranger, Surveyor, and Lunar orbiter photographs and how it contributes to the manned flights. Includes photos of lunar surface features and the view of the earth (NASA), free.

"Atmospheric Penetration" (color, sd, 18 min, 1965, j-h). Meteoric phenomena and the relationship of thermokinetic energy to the construction and characteristics of reentry. Illustrates vehicles returning from outer space (USAF), free.

"Atomic Energy for Space" (color, sd, 17 min, 1967, i-a). Discussion of nuclear rockets and reactor electric power plants and their utilization in space exploration (HFC).

"Before Saturn" (color, sd, 15 min, 1962, h-a). Traces the development of rockets from the Chinese to the Saturn program (NASA), free.

"Biology in Space Science" (color, sd, 14 min, 1966, j-h). Describes the biological research conducted on men and animals to study their reactions to the conditions that would be experienced in space (CF).

"By-products of Space Research—Selected Examples" (color, sd, 16½ min, 1966, h). Illustrates many current applications of aeronautical and space technology (NASA), free.

"Cape Kennedy 1965" (color, sd, 27 min, 1965, i-h). Shows the various advances made in the Polaris, Saturn-Pegasus, Ranger, Apollo, Titan III, and Gemini projects at Cape Kennedy (USAF), free.

"Challenge of Unanswered Questions, The" (b/w, sd, 16 min, 1968, j-h). Describes the aurora: its characteristics, instruments used to study it, and the theories put forth to explain the phenomena (NASA), free.

"Debrief: Apollo 8" (color, sd, 28 min, 1969, h-c). Traces man's first journey to the moon with photographs of the moon's surface, earth, and activities of the three astronauts in the space capsule (NASA), free.

"Eagle Has Landed—The Flight of Apollo 11" (color, sd, 28 min, 1969, j-h). Traces the landing on the moon including first steps and planting of U.S. flag (NASA), free.

"Early Apollo Test No. 13" (color, sd, 13 min, 1968, j-h). Geologic traverses conducted at a cinder field near Flagstaff, Ariz., in order to define graphic aid criteria for lunar exploration (DFL), free.

"Experiment: Close-up of Mars" (color, 29 min, 1966, j-c). Surveys the attempt to study Mars by a "fly-by" from the design to the execution stages of the experiment (NET:IU).

"Exploration of the Planets" (color, sd, 25 min, 1971, j-a). Summary of the principal features of the planets; presents the various missions planned for their exploration during the decade of the 1970s (NASA), free.

"Explorations of the Moon" (color, 17 min, 1970, j-h). Traces the progress of the United States exploration program to present day (WI).

"Exploring the Moon" (color, 16 min, 1969, j). Presents a review of the history of man's attempts to learn more about the moon. The survey extends from the time of Galileo to the modern activities of the Apollo program (CF).

"Extra-vehicular Activity—Gemini IV, June 3, 1965" (NASA), free.

"First Soft Step" (color, sd, 14 min, 1968, p-h). Recounts the accomplishments of the Surveyor-B program to soft-land a craft capable of taking photographs on the moon's surface. Includes actual photos from the Surveyor (NASA), free.

"Flight of Apollo 7, The" (color, sd, 14 min, 1968, h). Describes all aspects of the first manned mission in the Apollo series with film of the astronaut's activities during the flight (NASA), free.

"Food for Space Travelers" (b/w, sd, 28½ min, 1966, h). Follows the progress and problems of providing food for lengthy trips into space (NASA), free.

"Four Days of Gemini 4, The" (color, sd, 27½ min, 1965, j-h). Includes prelaunch, launch, extravehicular "walk," photos of earth, and other investigations conducted by the astronauts during the Gemini-4 mission (NASA), free.

"How We Explore Space" (color, sd, 16 min, 1958, i-h). Depicts various astronomical methods and instruments used to investigate objects in space. Provides telescopic motion pictures of the sun, moon, Mars, Jupiter, and Saturn (FAOC).

"International Cooperation in Space" (color, sd, 23 min, 1965, j-a). Explains NASA's program of cooperation with numerous countries in launching international satellites, carrying out experiments on spacecraft, research with sounding rockets, and operating global tracking networks (NASA), free.

"It's You Against the Problem" (color, sd, 23 min, 1967, h). Emphasizes the challenge of basic research in ablative materials being carried out by a scientist and a graduate student. Provides insight into the education and life of a scientist (NASA), free.

"John Glenn Story, The" (color, sd, 30 min, 1963, j-h). Biography of the first American to orbit the earth (NASA), free.

"Knowledge Bank, The" (color, sd, 25 min, 1971, h-c). Takes a broad look at physics and astronomy research performed in space (NASA), free.

"Landing on the Moon" (b/w, sd, 28 min, 1966, j-h). A simulated trip in a Lunar Module to the surface of the moon with details of the landing and lift-off from the moon (NASA), free.

"Legacy of Gemini" (color, sd, 27½ min, 1967, i-h). Reviews the major achievements of the Gemini program and their relationship to the Apollo program (NASA), free.

"Life on Other Planets" (color, sd, 28 min, 1961, h-c). Discusses the possibility of other planets that could support life, how such life forms could originate, and in what forms this life might be found (McGH).

"Life from Outer Space" (color, si, 3 min, 1968, i-h). Depicts an alleged U F O being photographed as it undergoes changes in color and shape (MF).

"Lifeline in Space" (color, sd, 14 min, 1971, i-j). Describes the large supply operations in space and the intricate combination of men and machines that will be necessary to provide support for orbiting space stations (PYRF).

"Living in Space: Part I—Case for Regeneration, The" (color, sd, 12 min, 1967, j-h). Presents the concept of regenerative life support in order to provide man with usable products such as air, water, and food during flights of long duration (NASA), free.

"Living in Space: Part II—Regenerative Processes" (color, sd, 20 min, 1967, j-h). Illustrates the principles of science that are utilized in a regenerative life-support system (NASA), free.

"Living in Space: Part III—A Technology for Spacecraft Design" (color, sd, 12 min, 1967, j-h). Points out the various characteristics a spacecraft must possess to enable it to carry out a manned space flight of long duration (NASA), free.

"Log of Mariner IV" (color, sd, 27 min, 1967, j-h). Recounts the Mars fly-by of Mariner IV, including the various problems incurred during the flight (NASA), free.

"Lunar Orbiter" (color, sd, 14 min, 1967, j-h). Deals with the nature of the Lunar Orbiter from launch to receival of photographs (BC), free.

"Man in Space: The Second Decade" (color, sd, 28 min, 1971, j-h). Reviews the achievements of manned space flight during its first decade and shows the programs for manned flight during the 1970s and beyond 1980 (NASA), free.

"*Mare Tranquillitatis*: Flagstaff, Arizona" (color, sd, 12 min, j-a). Shows the construction of a simulated lunar surface by the Geological Survey using explosives to produce the crater field (DFL), free.

"One Hundred and Nine Days to Venus" (b/w, sd, 32 min, 1963, i-h). Gives an account of the Mariner mission to Venus and a brief history of exploration of the solar system (CFI).

"Orbiting Solar Observatory" (color, sd, 25 min, 1962, j-h). Discusses the mission of the OSO spacecraft in gathering data dealing with the effect of the sun on the earth (NASA), free.

"Path to Space" (b/w, sd, 28 min, 1961, j-a). Traces the astronaut training program and the flight of astronaut Shepard (USAF), free.

"Pathfinders from the Stars" (color, sd, 48 min, 1967, j-a). Follows man's progress in determining his position on the earth's surface by utilizing the stars. Describes the use of satellite triangulation to obtain a greater degree of precision in positional determination (ESSA), free.

"Planetary Entry" (color, sd, 8 min, 1966). Discusses the problems that must be solved in order that landings may be made on the moon, Mars, and other planets (MDC), free.

"Pioneers and Modern Rockets" (color, sd, 24 min, 1970, h-c). An account of the technological advances in rocketry during the first half of the twentieth century, with particular emphasis on the efforts of engineering technology and theoretical design (ACI).

"Project Apollo—Manned Flight to the Moon" (color, sd, 13 min, 1963, j-c). Compares the Gemini and Apollo spacecrafts and boosters. Illustrates the events of a manned lunar landing (NASA), free.

"Ranger VII Photographs the Moon" (b/w, sd, 7 min, 1964, j-h). Illustrates and explains the photographs taken of the moon by the Ranger VII spacecraft (NASA), free.

"Ranger VIII Television Pictures of the Moon" (b/w, sd, 7½ min, 1965, j-h). Presents the photographs taken of the moon by the Ranger VIII spacecraft accompanied by a description of each photo (NASA), free.

"Ranger IX Television Pictures of the Moon" (b/w, sd, 6½ min, 1965, j-h). Presents the photographs taken of the moon by the Ranger IX spacecraft accompanied by a description of each photo (NASA), free.

"Research by Rockets" (color, sd, 29 min, 1960, j-c). Traces the history of research by rockets and the present emphasis of current research, namely, atmospheric, solar radiation, cosmic radiation, and auroral investigations (McGH).

"Rocket Flight" (color, sd, 5½ min). Demonstration of three flights of the Bell Rocket Belt in Arizona accompanied by a description of the Belt's operation (DFL), free.

"Satellite Astronomy: Progress and Promise" (color, sd, 17 min, 1969, j-a). Summarizes the results of unmanned satellite explorations of the moon, nearby planets and stars during the last decade (NASA), free.

"Seeds of Discovery" (color, sd, 28 min, 1970, j-c). Provides a summary of the planetary exploration and research planned by NASA for the 1970's including expeditions to Mars, Jupiter, outer planets, and solar trips (NASA), free.

"Space Medicine" (b/w, sd, 28½ min, 1962, j-h). Problems and progress of manned space flight with emphasis on the space suit and life support system (NASA), free.

"Space Navigation" (color, sd, 21 min, 1967, j-h). Depicts the equipment, procedures, and mathematics used to provide space navigation for all types of missions (NASA), free.

"Space Orbits" (color, sd, 18 min, 1960, j-h). Deals with the fundamental aspects of orbital forces and patterns in relation to the equipment and/or men involved in space flight (USAF), free.

"We Came in Peace" (color, sd, 38 min, 1970, j-h). Documentary of space exploration from Jules Verne to the moon landing of Apollo 11 (ASF), free.

Solar System

"Asteroids, Comets, and Meteorites" (color, sd, 11 min, 1960, i-a). Deals with minor members of the solar system; their characteristics, methods of study, and theories of origin (FAOC).

"Beyond the Moon" (color, 10 min, 1971, i-j). Takes the viewer through the solar system and introduces him to the planets, asteroids, and some of the planetary satellites (BFA).

"Closeup of Mars" (color, sd, 30 min, 1966, j-c). Discusses questions concerning Mars, the system to be used to record photographs of the planet, and the significance of such photos (IU).

"Clouds of Venus, The" (color, sd, 30 min, 1963, h). Documentary of the Mariner II flight to Venus including known features of the planet, complete description of the flight, and some preliminary findings from the data collected (NASA), free.

"Controversy Over the Moon" (color, sd, 16 min, 1971, j-c). Reviews the different theories that have been formulated to explain the moon's surface features. Geologists, representing both the impact and the volcanism theories, discuss each viewpoint with the use of earth features, moon phenomena, and lunar samples (EBEC).

"Dark Line Planets—Astronomical Observation Spectroscopy" (color, sd, 20 min, 1965, j-h). Illustrates the investigation of planetary atmospheres with the use of a 150-foot spectrographic tube (CEF).

"Experiment: Close-Up of Mars" (color, sd, 29 min, 1966, j-h). Surveys the development, experimentation, and usage of the camera used on a Mars fly-by to take photos of the planet's surface. Actual photos of Mars included in the film (NET:IU).

"Man Looks at the Moon" (color, sd, 15 min, 1971, j-h). Traces man's understanding of the moon from ancient myth to the first manned lunar landing and examines the (1) moon's highlands and craters, (2) importance of lunar rocks, and (3) framework for further study of our solar system (EBEC).

"Mariner — Mars 69" (color, sd, 21 min, 1971, j-a). Reviews the principal features of Mars that were known prior to 1969 and those that were determined by the two Mariner spacecrafts in 1969 (NASA), free.

"Men Encounter Mars" (b/w, sd, 29 min, 1965, j-a). Traces the work of scientists and engineers in planning and executing the flight of Mariner 4 to photograph the surface of Mars (NASA), free.

"Minor Members of the Solar System" (b/w, sd, 29 min, 1959, j-h). Discusses, with the aid of a variety of visual methods, the characteristics and origin of asteroids, comets, and meteors. Emphasizes the major comets of the solar system and meteors (NET:IU).

"Moon, The" (b/w, sd, 29 min, j-h). Utilizes a wide variety of audiovisual aids in considering the physical characteristics of the moon as well as eclipses of the moon and sun (NET:IU).

"Moon, The" (b/w, sd, 11 min, 1953, j-h). Illustrates, with observatory photographs, the various features of the lunar surface and the phases of the moon (ISO).

"Moon, The Adventure in Space," 3rd ed. (color, 16 min, 1971, i-h). Summarizes what we know about the moon as the result of recent exploration programs (AIMS).

"Museum of the Solar System" (color, 23 min, 1970, j-a). A review of what scientists have gained through the study of lunar samples.

Describes what procedures these individuals follow as they attempt to unravel the geologic past of the moon (SF).

"Origin of Our Solar System" (color, sd, 11 min, i-c). Presents, via animation, historical and more current theories concerning the origin of our solar system (DOUG).

"Planets, The" (color, sd, 11 min, 1961, i-j). Illustrates the movements of the planets in relation to the sun, comparative sizes of planets, distances from the sun, rotations, and satellite systems (IFB).

"Red Planet—Mars, The" (color, sd, 17 min, 1967, j-a). Discusses the history of scientific studies of Mars, possible interpretations of its seasons, and fluctuations in its polar caps and clouds. Illustrates specific details of the experiment carried out by Mariner 4 (IFB).

"Solar System, The" (b/w, sd, 11 min, 1953 j-h). Illustrates, via astronomical photographs, the moons of Jupiter, Uranus, and Neptune; the discovery of Pluto, Halley's and Brook's Comets, Saturn, the orbital motion of Venus, and variations in the appearances of Mars (ISO).

"Solar System, The" (color, 21 min, 1970, j-a). Utilizes time-lapse photographs, diagrams, and animated drawings to describe our solar system, its relation to the Milky Way, history of the Ptolemaic System, and various types of astronomical investigation (IFB).

"Solar System—The Giant Planets, The" (b/w, sd, 29 min, 1968, j-h). Describes the physical characteristics, movements and satellites of Jupiter, Saturn, Uranus, and Neptune (NET:IU).

"Solar System—Its Motions, The" (color, sd, 11 min, 1969, j-h). Discusses the theories of Newton, Kepler, Brahe, Copernicus, and Ptolemy with the patterns of motion of the various members of our solar system (McGH).

"Solar System—The Small Planets, The" (b/w, sd, 29 min, 1968, j-h). Describes the physical characteristics, movements, and satellites of the five smallest planets of our solar system (NET:IU).

"Sun, Earth, and Moon" (color, 11 min, 1968, i-j). Introduces some of the relationships that exist between the sun, the earth, and the moon. Includes diagrams, maps, and models. (McGH).

Solar and Stellar Aspects

"Active Sun, The" (color, 27 min, 1969, j-h). Provides a study of the nature and characteristics of sunspots, prominences, and granules that provide evidence for the instability of this important star (McGH).

"Experiment: Invisible Planet, The" (b/w, sd, 30 min, 1966, j-a). Surveys the 24-year photographic study of a star field containing a star (Bernard's star) whose variation in orbit is hypothesized to be caused by an unseen planet (IU).

"Explosions on the Sun" (b/w, si, 16 min, 1949, j-h). Motion pictures and photographs of solar prominences taken at the Climax Observatory with a coronagraph bifringent filter (HA).

"Fingerprints of the Stars" (b/w, sd, 29 min, j-h). Traces the development of the telescope and discusses the importance of photography, radio astronomy, and the spectroscope in investigating objects in space (NET:IU).

"How We Study the Sun" (color, sd, 15 min, 1966, i-h). Shows how astronomers study the sun using its light, radio energy, and various instruments positioned beyond the atmosphere of the earth (FAOC).

"Jupiter, Saturn, and Mars in Motion" (color, si, 10 min, 1960, j-a). Illustrates the significant features of the three planets including Jupiter's rotation and orbit, changing weather conditions of Saturn, Mars' polar cap, and a planet-wide dust storm (EBEC).

"Mystery of the Sun" (b/w, sd, 26 min, 1960, j-c). Indicates the scientific findings (to 1959) on the effects of the solar flare activity on radio waves on the earth (CFI).

"Nature of the Stars, The" (b/w, sd, 29 min, 1959, j-h). Deals with the classification of stars, their physical properties, brightness, size, origin, and evolution (NET:IU).

"Nearest Star" (color, sd, 28 min, 1960, j-a). Considers the importance of the sun to the earth, utilization of various instruments to study the sun, and the analysis of solar flares and their influence on the earth (McGH).

"Portrait of the Sun" (color, sd, 18 min, 1960, i-h). Depicts the major characteristics and features of the sun such as its corona, sunspots, solar prominences, and the sun's relationship to the earth (AF).

"Quiet Sun, The" (color, sd, 27 min, 1968, j-c). Surveys the knowledge that was acquired from studies of the sun during the International Year of the Quiet Sun. Includes location in space, composition, structure, and solar phenomena (McGH).

"Shadow Across the Sun" (color, sd, 27 min, 1971, h-a). Tells the story of scientific expeditions attempting to study the March 7, 1970 solar eclipse (NCAR).

"Solar Eclipse Expedition" (color, sd, 32 min, 1967, j-c). The film describes the study of the sun, the aurora, and the events of near space in an attempt to learn more about the sources and effects of nuclear energy (AEC), free.

"Solar Flares" (b/w, sd, 13 min, 1958, h-a). Illustrates, with the use of time-lapse photography, the major solar phenomena such as spots, filaments, phases, and prominences. Discusses the nature of flares and their effects on the magnetic field of the earth (UOM).

"Solar Prominences" (b/w, sd, 11 min, 1948, h-a). Discusses the origin, characteristics and general types of solar prominences (UOM).

"Stars and Star Systems" (b/w, sd, 16 min, 1960, j-h). Uses stars and star systems as devices to clarify present concepts of the universe. Emphasis is placed on the degree to which astronomers rely on direct observation as well as theoretical analysis in attempting to explain the phenomena of outer space (EBEC).

"Sun, The" (b/w, sd, 29 min, 1959, j-h). Describes the significance, nature, and phenomena of the controlling body of our solar system (NET:IU).

"Sun As a Star, The" (color, 13½ min, 1970, j). Charts, models, and photographs are used to depict the sun as a star with certain known physical characteristics; that is, mass, size, temperature, brightness, and rotation (CF).

"Sun Watchers, The" (color, 27 min, 1968, i-h). Surveys the work of astronomers as they study the sun from the world's major solar observatories (McGH).

Galactical and Universal Topics

"Depths of Space—Exterior Galaxies, The" (b/w, sd, 11 min, 1953, h). Presents an investigation of photographs of the galaxies taken through the Mt. Palomar telescope (ISO).

"Exploring the Milky Way" (color, sd, 28½ min, j-h). Considers the use of Mira variable stars in formulating an hypothesis concerning the origin and evolution of the Milky Way. Describes the use of the Lick telescope and its spectrographic equipment (MLA).

"Exploring the Universe" (b/w, sd, 11 min, 1937, i-a). Explains the nature of reflecting and refracting telescopes as well as the motions of intragalaxy stars (EBEC).

"Galaxies and the Universe" (b/w, sd, 29 min, 1959, j-h). Surveys the current concept of the universe, physical characteristics of the Milky Way including its motions, theories concerning the evolution of galaxies, methods of classifying galaxies, and the likelihood of life on other planets (NET:IU).

"Galaxies and the Universe" (color, 13½ min, 1969, j). Describes what is known about galaxies and illustrates the modern theories concerning their origin and evolution (CF).

"Interplanetary Space" (color, 23 min, 1969, j-c). Presents an animated overview of the present knowledge of the members of our solar system including a detailed discussion of the solar wind (McGH).

"Nebulae and Clusters" (b/w, sd, 29 min, 1959, j-h). Describes star groupings, double and multiple stars, galactic and globular clusters, size and characteristics of the Milky Way, size and shape of other galaxies, star clusters, nebulae, and cosmic dust clouds (NET:IU).

"Our Milky Way Galaxy" (b/w, sd, 29 min, 1959, j-h). Recounts the historical development of man's conception of our galaxy. Explains how the investigation of other galaxies has led to a greater understanding of our own (NET:IU).

"Radio View of the Universe, A" (color, sd, 28½ min, j-a). Explains the use of the radio line of atomic hydrogen in determining the total content of hydrogen in galaxies outside of our own (MLA).

"Sound Waves and Stars—The Doppler Effect" (color, sd, 12 min, 1964, i-a). Discusses the Doppler Effect and points out how it is utilized by scientists to investigate the universe (FAOC).

"To the Edge of the Universe" (color, sd, 23 min, 1971, h-c). Describes the building of a precision instrument for measuring distant objects, new techniques of long-base interferometry and cosmology, specifically concerning quasars (McGH).

"Universe" (b/w, sd, 28 min, 1960, j-h). Deals with the nature of the solar system, Milky Way, and galaxies beyond (NASA), free.

"Universe, The" (b/w, sd, 29 min, 1959, h-c). Discusses the earth's place in the solar system and universe, chemical composition of the universe, means of investigating its theories of age, origin, and source of stellar energy (NET:IU).

"View from Space, The" (Parts I and II) (color, 59 min, 1969, j-a). Considers the comparative value of the present space program to mankind in lieu of extreme cost. Included in the film are features of the earth's surface as seen from outer space and views of the 1968 voyage of astronauts Anders, Borman, and Lovell (McGH).

"Violent Universe, The" (5 parts) (color, 2 1/2 hr, 1969, h-c). Offers a complete survey of astronomy including its theories, researchers, and discoveries (NET:IU).

General Topics

"Exploring the Night Sky" (b/w, sd, 11 min, 1956, i-j). Describes the fundamental concepts of astronomy, how astronomers investigate the night-time sky, major constellations and the relationship between stellar motion and time (EBEC).

"Measurement of the Speed of Light" (b/w, sd, 7 min, 1955, h-a). Explains the basic formulas that utilize the speed of light and illustrates the methods scientists have used to determine its speed (McGH).

"Measuring in Astronomy: How Big, How Far" (color, sd, 12 min, i-j). Describes the use of geometry and trigonometry in measuring large distances on the surface of the earth (FAOC).

"Measuring Large Distances" (b/w, sd, 29 min, 1959, h-a). Discusses the importance of the inverse square law, triangulation, and parallax in measuring distance in space (MLA).

"Measuring Time and Distance" (b/w, sd, 29 min, 1959, j-h). Describes the various methods, both natural and artificial, of measuring time and distance. Discusses the relationship between earth and moon motions to time and how the speed of light and magnitude of stars is used to determine distances in space (NET:IU).

"Nuclear Radiation in Earth Studies" (color, sd, 15 min, 1961, h-a). Illustrates the use of radiation-detecting devices in prospecting principles of radiation theory, atomic theory, particle emission, and carbon-14 dating (CF).

"Nuclear Radiation in Outer Space" (color, sd, 16 min, 1961, h-a). Describes the types of radiation in outer space, their relationship to solar activity and altitude of a body above the earth, preparation and exposure of living cells to these radiations, and Dr. Van Allen's work (CF).

"Radio Astronomy Explorer" (color, sd, 30 min, 1968, j-h). Design and operation of the R A E satellite designed to detect and relay radio waves coming to it from the sun, earth, and other planets (NASA), free.

"Radio Waves" (color, sd, 27 min, 1960, h-a). Discusses the history of radio waves (both natural and artificial), their characteristics, and how they are influenced and used in astronomical research (McGH).

"Rediscovering America" (color, 27 1/2 min, 1970, j-h). Describes the various information that can be obtained by remote sensing of the earth (TRW), free.

"Science in Space" (color, sd, 28 min, 1960, j-a). Describes the construction, functioning, and the various uses of satellites as research tools (McGH).

"Seas of Infinity" (color, sd, 14½ min, 1969, j-h). Planning, development, launching, and operation of the Orbiting Astronomical Observatory. The OAS being composed of a series of orbiting telescopes to be used in studying our solar system and other stars (NASA), free.

"Star Gazing" (b/w, sd, 29 min, j-h). Describes the appearance of the night-time sky, the location of individual stars in constellations, the celestial sphere, and the use of star charts and telescopes (NET:IU).

"Story of Palomar" (color, sd, 39 min, 1960, h-a). Traces the construction and functioning of the 200-inch Hale telescope (EBEC).

"Time Is" (color, sd, 30 min, 1964, j-c). Points out the dispute between physicists and philosophers concerning the concept of time. Discusses the effects of time on our lives (McGH).

35mm Filmstrips

Forces, Movements, and Astronomical Phenomena

"Earth and Its Motions, The" (23 frs, color, captions, 1954) (EG).

"Earth and Its Movements, The" (52 frs, color 12½ min, record and guide, 1965). Rotation and other movements in the context of the solar system (SVE).

"Earth's Magnetism" (61 frs, color, captions, 1962). Reviews various radiation belts, the origin and renewal of the earth's magnetic field, and the type of material coming to the earth from outer space (LEP).

"How Earth's Movements Affect Us" (61 frs, color record, 1965). Depicts the cause of day and night and the seasons (SVE).

"How Light Travels" (39 frs, color, captions, 1959). Illustrates via demonstrations how light travels (PS).

"How Satellites Stay in Orbit" (42 frs, color, record, 1967) (CF).

"Motions of the Earth in Space" (66 frs, color, captions, 1958) (McGH).

"On the Sky" (52 frs, color, captions, 1961) (McGH).

"Revolution" (47 frs, color, guide, 1966) (W).

"Rotation" (27 frs, color, guide, 1966) (W).

Space Exploration

"Atoms in Space" (39 frs, color, captions, 1960) (EG).

"Current Events in Space" (47 frs, color, captions, 1968). Function of satellites; information gathered, moon launch and launching of satellite (SVE).

"Decade in Space" (51 frs, b/w, captions, 1967). Surveys first ten years of exploration in space (NYT).

"Exploring the Space Around Earth" (52 frs, color, captions, 1958) (McGH).

"Flight to Mars" (49 frs, color, captions, 1959) (EBEC).

"Geology from Space" (24 frs, color, sd, 1967). Geologic features of the earth depicted in photographs taken during the Gemini flights (NASA), free.

"Hazards in Space Travel" (26 frs, color, captions, 1960) (EG).

"How Man Explores Space" (60 frs, color, 16 min, record and guide, 1965). Overcoming the pull of gravity; rockets, rocket stages, and space capsule (SVE).

"Information from Satellites" (52 frs, color, captions, 1958) (McGH).

"In Sight of the Giant Steps" (40 frs, color, sd, 1967). Paintings and sketches by leading artists depicting man's exploration of space (NASA), free.

"Leaving the World" (41 frs, color, captions, 1960). Illustrates recently launched man-made satellites, describes aspects of rocketry as well as defining *perigee*, *apogee*, and *ellipse* (SVE).

"Man and the Moon" (49 frs, color, captions, 1959) (EBEC).

"Man in Space" (47 frs, color, 1960). How man is trained for space flight and problems he faces in such a flight (SVE).

"Man in the Universe" (52 frs, color, 1962) (McGH).

"Meteorology from Space" (22 frs, color, sd, 1967). Various cloud formations and related weather phenomena as photographed by Tiros satellites (NASA), free.

"Nuclear Propulsion in Space" (77 frs, color, captions, 1968). Development, nature, and uses of the rocket engine (NASA), free.

"Satellites" (42 frs, color, captions, 1964). Discusses the types, uses, launching, and orbiting of satellites (PS).

"Space Navigation" (69 frs, color, captions, 1967). Planning of trajectories, use of computers and other devices in space flights (NASA), free.

"Space Travel A.D. 2000" (52 frs, color, 1962). Nature of space and time to distance traveled, atomic, plasma, and photon power (SVE).

Solar System

"Between the Planets" (52 frs, color, captions, 1962) (McGH).

"Beyond Pluto" (37 frs, color, record, 1967). Depicts the nature of space outside the most distant planet of the solar system (EG).

"Comets and Meteors" (56 frs, color, captions, 1953) (SVE).

"Earth, The" (47 frs, color, guide, 1966). Nature of the earth (size, shape, structure) (W).

"Earth As a Planet" (52 frs, color, captions, 1958) (McGH).

"Earth Is Born, The" (74 frs, color, captions, 1955) (LEP).

"Earth's Nearest Neighbor" (45 frs, color, guide, 1956). Moon, its characteristics and relationship to the earth; comparison of the characteristics of human beings on earth with those while on the moon (SVE).

"Earth's Satellite—The Moon" (66 frs, b/w, captions, 1953) (SVE).

"Earth's Shape and Size, The" (52 frs, color, captions, 1958) (McGH).

"Exploring the Moon" (33 frs, b/w, captions, 1961). Photographs taken at the Mount Wilson and Palomar Observatories (EBEC).

"Giant Planets: Jupiter, Saturn, Uranus and Neptune" (80 frs, color, captions, 1960) (McGH).

"How Did Our Solar System Begin?" (32 frs, color, captions, 1956). Discusses the collision, tidal wave, double star, nebular, and whirlpool theories concerning the origin of the solar system (SC).

"Introduction to the Solar System" (52 frs, color, captions, 1960) (McGH).

"Mars" (52 frs, color, captions, 1960) (McGH).

"Mercury and Venus" (52 frs, captions, color, 1960) (McGH).

"Moon, The" (46 frs, color, guide, 1966). Phases, eclipses, and reason for color of the earth's shadow during a lunar eclipse (W).

"Moon and Its Relation to the Earth, The" (59 frs, color, 15 min, record, guide, 1965). Size of moon; distance from earth; reasons for lack of lunar atmosphere (SVE).

"Neighbors in Space" (41 frs, color, captions, 1961). Discusses the features of the members of the solar system (EG).

"Our Earth" (46 frs, color, captions, 1956) (EBEC).

"Our Solar System" (54 frs, color, 16 min, record, guide, 1965). Planets to meteor particles (SVE).

"Planets and Comets" (33 frs, b/w, captions, 1961) (EBEC).

"Solar System, The" (48 frs, color, captions, 1956) (EBEC).

"Solar System and the Universe" (23 frs, color, captions, 1954) (EG).

"Sun and Its Family, The" (46 frs, color, captions, 1956). Various members of the solar system, gravity, and solar energy (SVE).

Solar and Stellar Aspects

"Abnormal Stars" (52 frs, color, captions, 1961) (McGH).

"Between the Stars" (52 frs, color, captions, 1962) (McGH).

"Constellations" (46 frs, color, captions, 1955). Construction of star finder to locate constellations with the aid of star charts. Major constellations in both hemispheres are illustrated throughout the year (PS).

"Exploring the Sun" (33 frs, b/w, captions, 1961). Photographs taken at Mount Wilson and Palomar Observatories (EBEC).

"How Far Are the Stars?" (52 frs, color, captions, 1961) (McGH).

"Life of a Star, The" (54 frs, color, captions, 1961) (McGH).

"More About Stars" (52 frs, color, captions (1961) (McGH).

"Our Sun" (52 frs, color, captions, 1960) (McGH).

"Pictures in the Sky" (46 frs, color, captions, 1956). Constellations, their locations, locating first magnitude stars, relating rotation to summer and winter skies (SVE).

"Solar Storehouse—Light, Heat, Power" (23 frs, color, captions, 1954). Follows solar energy from the sun through plants, coal, oil, natural gas, and electricity (MIS).

"Stars, The" (46 frs, color, captions, 1956) (EBEC).

"Stars and Outer Space" (61 frs, color, 13 min, record, guide, 1965). Andromeda, galaxies, and other features (SVE).

"Sun, The" (46 frs, color, captions, 1956) (EBEC).

"Sun and Its Energy, The" (61 frs, color, 12 min, record, guide, 1965). Relationship of heat to earth energy (SVE).

"Why the Stars" (55 frs, color captions, 1961). Discusses the origin and nature of stars (McGH).

Galactical and Universal Topics

"Galaxies" (52 frs, color, captions, 1962) (McGH).

"Milky Way Galaxy, The" (46 frs, color, captions, 1962) (McGH).

"Milky Way and Other Galaxies, The" (33 frs, b/w, captions, 1961). Photographs taken at the Mount Wilson and Palomar Observatories (EBEC).

"Nebulae" (33 frs, b/w, captions, 1961). Photographs taken at the Mount Wilson and Palomar Observatories (EBEC).

"Stars and Galaxies" (43 frs, color, captions, 1953) (SVE).

"Universe, The" (52 frs, color, captions, 1962) (McGH).

"You and the Universe" (43 frs, color, captions, 1956). Nature and number of galaxies, earth as a member of a galaxy (SVE).

General Topics

"Astronomer at Work, The" (39 frs, color, captions, 1957). Construction of refracting and reflecting telescopes; how other sciences contribute to the study of astronomy (PS).

"Astronomy Through the Ages" (48 frs, color, captions, 1956). History of the science of astronomy (EBEC).

"Earth, Moon, Sun and Stars" (49 frs, color, record, 1961) (ELK).

"Exploring the Sky" (32 frs, color, captions, 1957). Describes the use of telescopes in studying the stars and constellations (SC).

"Eyes and Ears (Telescopes and Antennas)" (52 frs, color, captions, 1962) (McGH).

"Light" (48 frs, color, guide, 1966). Nature and behavior of light (W).

"Looking at the Stars" (50 frs, b/w, captions, 1951) (McGH).

"Man Becomes an Astronomer" (49 frs, color, captions, 1959) (EBEC).

"Measuring Time" (47 frs, color, guide, 1966) (W).

"Mount Wilson and Palomar Telescopes" (33 frs, b/w, captions, 1961). Photographs of the structure and operation of two observatories (EBEC).

8mm Film Loops

Forces, Movements, and Astronomical Phenomena

"Day and Night" (color, si, 1 1/2 min, cart, 1949). Effect of sun's light on the earth's surface (UE&VA).

"Day and Night" (color, si, Sup 8, cart). The earth's rotation viewed from a stationary satellite above the North Pole at solstice and equinox positions. A location marker at mid-United States latitude scribes a circle in space with each rotation (HSC).

"Earth and the Sun's Rays" (color, sd, Sup 8, cart, 1951) (BFA).

"Earth: Rotation and Revolution" (color, si, Sup 8, cart). An earth model rotates and revolves about a sun model for several complete revolutions. The marked equator and poles enable the viewer to see the parallelism of the axis as it revolves and rotates (HSC).

"Eclipse of the Moon" (color, si, 3½ min, Sup 8, cart, 1965). Uses time-lapse photography of a lunar eclipse to illustrate the role the earth's shadow plays in its formation. Demonstrates the direct relationship between the tilt of the moon's orbit and the time intervals between eclipses (FAOC).

"Eclipse of the Sun" (color, si, 3½ min, Sup 8, cart). Depicts how the motion of the moon in its orbit can position the moon between the earth and the sun. Shows motion picture of an eclipse and various sun features visible only during eclipses (FAOC).

"Flaming Sky-Aurora" (color, sd, 27 min, reel, h-a). Illustrates the nature of the aurora; presents theory on what it is; its cause; relationship to the earth's magnetic field, radio waves, and solar activity (McGH).

"Force of Gravity, The" (color, sd, 27 min, reel, h-c). Traces the concept of gravity from early thinking to present day thought, from Newton through Einstein. Examines the relationship of gravitational field to planetary motions, effect of sun and moon on earth, and significance of satellite orbits (McGH).

"Gravity: The Mighty Pull" (color, 14 min, Sup 8, cart, 1961, p-h) (UE&VA).

"Gravity, Weight, and Weightlessness" (color, sd, cart, 1963, i-h) (BFA).

"Kepler's Laws" (color, si, 4 min, cart, 1968 j-a). Kepler's three laws are illustrated by computer-produced orbits displayed on C.R.T. (E).

"Lunar Eclipse—Total Eclipse of the Moon" (color, 3 min, Sup 8, cart, 1969, i-j) (EBEC).

"Meteors and Meteorites" (color, si, 4 min, Sup 8, cart, 1967). Shows, by animation and motion-picture footages, how meteors enter and vaporize in the atmosphere, and three types of meteorites (FAOC).

"Moon: Motion and Phases" (color, si, Sup 8, cart). Rotation and revolution of the moon about a spinning earth is examined from overhead and side views (HSC).

"Night and Day" (color, 1 min, Sup 8, cart, 1966). Presents the relationship between the rotation of the earth and day and night (CEF).

"Planetary Motion" (color, si, Sup 8, cart). Kepler's three laws of planetary motion are studied with the use of animation, matched with artwork (HSC).

"Retrograde Motion—Geocentric Model" (color, si, Sup 8, cart, 1967, j-a). The model is presented with pictures taken by a camera positioned as a fixed earth (E).

"Retrograde Motion—Heliocentric Model" (color, si, Sup 8, cart, 1967, j-a). The model is presented with the camera revolving around the sun (E).

"Retrograde Planetary Motion" (color, si, Sup 8, cart, 1967). Animated depiction of the motion of Mars and Mercury (E).

"Seasons" (color, si, Sup 8, cart). Summer solstice, winter solstice, spring equinox, and summer equinox are examined. Close-up side and overhead views at each seasonal position, aided by animated lines and the natural terminator. Examines the basis for the equator, the Arctic and Antarctic circles, and the tropics of Cancer and Capricorn (HSC).

"Summer and Winter" (color, si, 2½ min, cart, 1966). The relative position of the earth and sun during the Northern Hemisphere's summer and winter seasons is presented along with the earth's axis, shown by animation (PPAC).

"Time and Dateline" (color, si, Sup 8, cart). The concepts of 24 time zones, each 15° of longitude and representing one hour of rotation is shown with a rotating earth (HSC).

"What Is an Eclipse?" (color, sd, 11 min, Sup 8, cart, 1965, i-a) (BFA).

"Zero Gravity" (color, si, Sup 8, cart). Demonstrations of the effects of weightlessness by astronauts inside Apollo 10 spacecraft (HSC).

Space Exploration

"Apollo Mission: To the Moon" (color, si, Sup 8, cart). Photos of launch and staging. Animation of flight through landing on the moon, including docking operations, flight path, and orbit (HSC).

"Apollo Mission: From the Moon" (color, si, Sup 8, cart). Animation of return flight from lunar surface. Photos of re-entry, splashdown, and recovery (HSC).

"Apollo 11: Man on the Moon, Part I" (color, si, Sup 8, cart). Highlights of launch and flight to lunar surface including views of and from the lunar landing site (HSC).

"Apollo 11: Man on the Moon, Part II" (color, si, Sup 8, cart). Highlights of return from lunar surface, including views of and from lunar landing site (HSC).

"Earth from Space, The" (color, si, Sup 8, cart). Views of the earth from various altitudes including lunar orbit. Time-lapse views of day and night (HSC).

"Experimental Aircraft" (color, si, Sup 8, cart). Early experimental aircraft: supersonic transport, B-70, vertical takeoff aircraft, and pilot's view of low-level flight (HSC).

"Exploring the Moon" (color, 4 min, Sup 8, 1969, i-c). Illustrates Apollo 11 astronauts as they explore the surface of the moon (E).

"Flight to Mars" (color, si, Sup 8, cart). Model of Mariner IV spacecraft. Launch and tracking. Animation of flight and photographic mission. Photographs taken are superimposed in sequence on drawing of planet Mars (HSC).

"Flight to Venus" (color, si, Sup 8, cart). Model of Mariner II spacecraft: lift-off, diagram of flight, animation of staging, receiving telemetry, and animation of Venus flight (HSC).

"Geology from Space" (color, si, Sup 8, cart). Views of various landforms and terrain including special filtering and film techniques for landform interpretation (HSC).

"Moon from Space, The" (color, si, Sup 8, cart). Vertical and oblique photos of lunar surface from Apollo 10 and Ranger 9 photos of lunar surface to impact (HSC).

"Putting a Spacecraft into a Desired Orbit" (color, 2 min, Sup 8, cart, 1969, i-j) (EBEC).

"Rockets and Satellites" (color, sd, Sup 8, cart, 1960, p-h) (BFA).

"Saturn V" (color, si, Sup 8, cart). Detail view of entire Saturn V booster blast-off, staging, and tracking as seen from ground and from the booster (HSC).

"Space Walk" (color, si, Sup 8, cart). Astronaut Ed White's space walk. EVA by Astronauts Gordon and Alden (HSC).

"Trajectory of a Moon Probe" (color, 2 min, Sup 8, cart, 1969, i-j) (EBEC).

"A Walk in Space, Part I" (color, si, cart, 1965). America's first walk in space by astronaut McDivitt of the Gemini 4 mission. Includes Gemini 4's orbits (CEF).

"A Walk in Space, Part II" (color, si, 4 min, cart, 1965). Continues with space walk and follows flight to splashdown and transfer to waiting helicopter (CEF).

Solar System

"Asteroids, Comets, and Meteorites" (color, sd, Sup 8, cart, 1960, i-c) (BFA).

"Comet Orbits" (color, si, 3 min, Sup 8, cart, 1965). Demonstrates, via animation, the peculiar nature of comet orbits (FAOC).

"Jupiter Satellite Orbit" (color, si, 4 min, Sup 8, cart, 1968, j-a). Illustrates, via time-lapse photography, Jupiter's Satellite 10 and shows how the mass of Jupiter can be calculated from data in the film (E).

"Mars and Jupiter" (color, si, 3½ min, tech Sup 8, cart, 1965). Depicts, via time-lapse photography, the general features of Mars and Jupiter, their rotation, and a transit of one of Jupiter's moons (PPAC).

"Planets Around Our Sun" (color, sd, 14 min, Sup 8, cart, 1961) (UE&VA).

"Solar System—Inner Planets" (color, 4 min, Sup 8, cart, 1969, i-j) (EBEC).

Solar and Stellar Aspects

"Nearest Star, The Sun and Solar Activity" (color, sd, 27 min, reel, h-a). Discusses the various properties of the sun and relationship to such solar activities as sunspots, flares, and particle radiation. Illustrates the launching of a "sun-seeker" telescope by skyhook balloon and rocket firings during the Danger Island Eclipse Expedition, and activities of an airborne geophysical laboratory (McGH).

"Portrait of the Sun" (color, 18 min, Sup 8, cart, 1968, i-h). Traces a solar eclipse through time-lapse and special animation (DCI).

"Solar Eclipse—Total Eclipse of the Sun" (color, 2 min, Sup 8, cart, 1968, i-j) (EBEC).

"Solar Flares" (color, si, 3 min, Sup 8, cart, 1965). Traces solar flares by motion pictures from their appearance to disappearance (FAOC).

"Solar Prominence" (color, si, 3 min, Sup 8, cart, 1965, h-a). Solar prominences are illustrated by time-lapse telescopic motion pictures (FAOC).

"Solar Prominences and Sunspots" (b/w, 3 min, Sup 8, cart, 1970, j-h). Describes how man investigates the sun, and emphasis is on the nature of prominences and sunspots (DCI).

"Solar Radiation (Sun and Earth)" (color, sd, Sup 8, cart, 1966, i-c) (UE&VA).

"Solar System—Outer Planets" (color, 3 min, Sup 8, cart, 1969, i-j) (EBEC).

"Sun As a Source of Light" (color, si, 1½ min, Sup 8, cart) (UE&VA).

"Sun's Energy, The" (color, sd, 16½ min, Sup 8, cart, 1968, i-h). Discusses the importance of solar energy to life and as a source of all industrial energy (ICF).

"What Are Stars Made Of?" (color, sd, 16 min, cart, h). Follows a Mount Wilson and Palomar Observatory astronomer as he investigates the chemical nature of stars (IFB).

Galactical and Universal Topics

"Milky Way, The" (color, sd, 13 min, Sup 8, cart, 1961, i-h) (UE&VA).

General Topics

"Astronomer, The" (color, 16 min, cart, h). Discusses the work of present-day astronomers—especially while they are away from the telescopes—such as measurement and analysis. Demonstrates the construction and functions of the Hale telescope, the Schmidt-type telescope, and refractor, reflector, and radio telescopes (IFB).

"Four Telescope Arrangements" (b/w, si, 4 min, cart). Discusses the principle of the Schmidt corrector comparison between a parabolic and spherical reflector. Illustrates the Cassegrainian and Newtonian arrangements of reflecting telescopes using a raystreak (BFA).

"How We Know the Earth Moves" (color, sd, 11 min, i-h) (BFA).

"How We Study the Sun" (color, sd, 15 min, 1966, j-h) (BFA).

"Measuring the Speed of Light" (color, sd, Sup 8, cart, j-h) (GEFL).

"Radio Waves" (color, sd, 27 min, reel). Depicts both man-made and natural radio waves from the nineteenth century to the present. Discusses the influence of the ionosphere, earth's magnetic force, and solar activity on radio waves (McGH).

"Telescope at Mount Palomar, The 200-in." (b/w, si, 5 min, cart). Comparison of actual photos of the Hale telescope with a model (PPAC).

"Telescopes" (color, sd, Sup 8, cart, j-h) (GEFL).

"Time and Eternity" (color, sd, Sup 8, 1958, i-h) (MOODY).

Overhead Transparencies

Forces, Movements, and Astronomical Phenomena

"Astronomical Twilight" (WPC)

"Because the Earth Revolves Around the Sun" (UNC)

"Causes of Seasons" (PSC)

"Changing Pole Stars" (WPC)

"Comparative Movements of Earth and Moon" (EA-V)

"Daily Path of Pole Star" (WPC)

"Day and Night" (MMAMC)

"Day and Night" (MPC)

"Different Parts of the Moon Visible During the Month, The" (MMAMC)

"Earth As a Magnet, The" (MPC)

"Earth Rotates Once Every 24 Hours, The" (MMAMC)

"Earth's Magnetic Fields" (EDRECS)

"Earth's Satellite" (PS)

"Eclipse" (EA-V)

"Eclipse" (PSC)

"Eclipse" (WPC)

"Eclipse of the Moon" (N)

"Eclipse of the Moon and Sun" (EA-V)

"Eclipse of the Sun" (N)

"Eclipse of Sun and Moon" (HI)

"Eclipse of the Sun and the Moon, An" (UTI)

"Eclipses" (UTI)

"Eclipses" (WPC)

"Eclipsing a Star" (WPC)

"Fall" (MMAMC)

"Favorite Summer" (WPC)

"First Law of Inertia" (WPC)

"First Quarter Phase" (IPC)

"Force Vectors" (WPC)

"Full Moon" (IPC)

"Full Moon" (MMAMC)

"G-Force" (WPC)

"Giant Corkscrew Path" (WPC)

"Gravitational Pull" (WPC)

"Gravitational Pull, Falling Bodies" (WPC)

"Half-Moon" (MMAMC)

"Kepler's Laws" (DG)

"Kinds of Orbits" (WPC)

"Light and the Seasons" (WPC)

"Light Rays and the Seasons" (WPC)

"Lunar Eclipse" (MMAMC)

"Lunar and Solar Eclipses" (T)

"Meteor Showers" (WPC)

"Meteors and Meteorites" (MPC)

"Moon Circles Earth in 28 Days, The" (MMAMC)

"Moon Phases" (DG)

"Moon Phases" (UTI)

"Moon's and Earth's Rotations, The" (MMAMC)

"Moon's Revolution and Rotation Rates Are the Same" (MMAMC)

"Motions of the Earth—Revolution and Rotation" (T)

"Movement of the Earth Around the Sun" (EA-V)

"Myths—Phases of the Moon" (WPC)

"New Moon" (MMAMC)

"Noise Conditions" (DG)

"Occurrence of Neap Tides" (EA-V)

"Occurrence of Spring Tides" (EA-V)

"Orbits and Gravity" (WPC)

"Path of the Sun on the Sky at New York City" (W)

"Phases and Eclipses" (PS)

"Phases of the Moon" (EA-V)

"Phases of the Moon" (HI)

"Phases of the Moon" (T)

"Phases of the Moon As Seen from the Earth" (N)

"Planetary Magnetic Fields" (DG)

"Polar View of Rotation" (WPC)

"Poles of the Earth" (WPC)

"Possible Orbits" (UTI)

"Possible Orbits of a Planet Deflected by the Sun or a Planet" (EA-V)

"Principles of Orbit" (PSC)

"Procession of the Earth's Axis" (EA-V)

"Proof—A Turning Earth" (WPC)

"Proof—Sun Rotates" (WPC)

"Proof of the Sun's Rotation" (WPC)

"Quarter Moon" (MMAMC)

"Rays of the Setting Sun Are Reflected by the Earth's Atmosphere" (UTI)

"Refraction of Sun's Rays" (UTI)

"Regions of the Atmosphere" (WPC)

"Revolution" (IPC)

"Seasonal Star Clock" (WPC)

"Seasonal Variation in the Period of Daylight" (EA-V)

"Seasons" (EA-V)

"Seasons—2" (MPC)

"Seasons of the Earth" (T)

"Seasons, Northern Hemisphere" (MMAMC)

"Seasons on Planet Earth" (WPC)

"Seasons of the Year" (HI)

"Second Law of Inertia" (WPC)

"Semi-Daily Tide Curve" (W)

"Shadows Change with the Position of the Sun" (MMAMC)

"Signals in Noise" (DG)

"Solar Eclipse" (MMAMC)

"Solar/Lunar Eclipse" (T)

"Solstice and Equinox" (W)

"Solstice and Equinoxes" (MMAMC)

"Some Earth Motions (Rotation and Revolution)" (WPC)

"Speed of Earth at Different Latitudes" (WPC)

"Spring" (MMAMC)

"Spring Tides" (UNC)

"Star Clock" (WPC)

"Star Clock—24 Hours" (WPC)

"Stratosphere and Ionosphere" (MMAMC)

"Summer" (MMAMC)

"Summer Sky—South" (CV)

"Summer Solstice" (EA-V)

"Sun at Midnight, The" (WPC)

"Tidal Bulge of the Earth" (EA-V)

"Tidal Forces on the Earth" (W)

"Tides" (DG)

"Tides" (MPC)

"Tides, The" (HI)

"Total Eclipse of Moon" (WPC)

"Total Solar Eclipse" (IPC)

"Total Solar Eclipse—Bailey's Beads" (WPC)

"Twilight" (W)

"Umbra and Penumbra" (UTI)

"Van Allen Radiation Belt" (UTI)

"What Causes Day and Night" (MMAMC)

"Why the Sky Is Blue" (WPC)

"Winter" (MMAMC)

"Winter Sky—South" (CV)

Space Exploration

"Air Slows Satellites" (WPC)

"Apollo—Lunar Landing"
(EA-V)

"Apollo Program" (MPC)

"Apollo—Return to Earth"
(EA-V)

"Apollo-Spacecraft" (EA-V)

"Basic Life-Support System—The
Spacecraft" (WPC)

"Communication on the Moon"
(MMAMC)

"Communications Satellite Orbit" (UTI)

"Deep Space Communication"
(DG)

"Degenerate Orbital Re-entry
Pattern" (WPC)

"Destination Mars—The Red
Planet" (WPC)

"Destination Unknown" (WPC)

"Direct Re-Entry Pattern"
(WPC)

"Earth to Moon" (MMAMC)

"Escape Orbit Explained" (UTI)

"From Space into Outer Space"
(T)

"Gemini" (CV)

"Gemini Capsule" (EA-V)

"Gemini Docking" (EA-V)

"Gemini Return to Earth"
(EA-V)

"General Science-Space Science—
A Series" (T)

"How a Rocket Remains in Orbit" (EA-V)

"How a Spaceship Maneuvers—
Pitch Axis" (WPC)

"How a Spaceship Maneuvers—
Roll Axis" (WPC)

"How a Spaceship Maneuvers—
Yaw Axis" (WPC)

"ICBM Mechanics" (DG)

"Ion Rocket" (WPC)

"Jet Propulsion" (WPC)

"Launching and Staging" (T)

"Man in Space" (MPC)

"Man in Space" (T)

"Man-Made Satellites Also Orbit
the Earth" (MMAMC)

"Manned Space Stations" (MPC)

"Mariner—Venus" (DG)

"Mariner II" (WPC)

"Mariner II Flight to Venus"
(EA-V)

"Mars from Mariner" (IPC)

"Mars and Venus Probes" (MPC)

"Mercury Capsule, The" (WPC)

"Mercury and Gemini Programs"
(MPC)

"Mercury—Orbital Flight"
(EA-V)

"Mercury—Suborbital Flight"
(EA-V)

"Midway to Mars and Moon"
(DG)

"Mooncrafts" (MPC)

"On a Lunar 'Sea' " (MMAMC)

"Orbiting a Rocket" (EA-V)

"Orbits of Friendship 7" (UTI)

"Possible Satellite Orbits to Venus and Mars" (EA-V)

"Principles of Rocket Flight" (T)

"Project Apollo—Spacecraft"
(WPC)

"Project Gemini—Docking"
(WPC)

"Project Gemini—Return to
Earth" (WPC)

"Project Mercury—Orbital
Flight" (WPC)

"Project Mercury—Suborbital
Flight" (WPC)

"Project Syncom" (EA-V)

"Project Syncom" (WPC)

"Ranger Flight Profile" (DG)

"Ranger—Lunar Approach"
(DG)

"Ranger VII—Flight to the
Moon" (EA-V)

"Ranger VII Flight to the Moon" (WPC)
"Re-entry Patterns" (T)
"Rockets—Present and Future" (MPC)
"Roll, Pitch, and Yaw" (WPC)
"Satellite Heights" (WPC)
"Satellite—Rocket   Cut-Away" (PSC)
"Solar System and Space Travel, The (A Series)" (MPC)
"Sonic Boom" (WPC)
"Space   Flights   (A   Series)" (EA-V)
"Space Launch Azimuths" (DG)
"Space Pictures (A Series)" (IPC)
"Space Science—Astronomy and Space Exploration (A Series)" (DG)
"Space Science—Communications (A Series)" (DG)
"Space Science—Flight Mechanics (A Series)" (DG)
"Space Vehicles—Man-Made Satellites" (T)
"Spacecraft Communication" (DG)
"Spacecraft Maneuver" (DG)
"Spacecraft Navigation" (DG)
"Spacecraft Orbits" (UTI)
"Spaceflight" (DG)
"Staging in Rocketry" (WPC)
"Steps into Space—Rockets and Explorations" (MPC)
"Ten-Month Drive to the Moon, A" (MMAMC)
"Three Days to the Moon by Rocket" (MMAMC)
"Three Weeks by Plane— Four-and-a-Half Months by Train" (MMAMC)
"Tiros Weather Satellite" (WPC)
"Transit 1-B Satellite" (UTI)
"Two Possible Ways to Escape from the Earth" (EA-V)

"Types of Orbits" (T)
"Types of Rockets—Launch Vehicles" (T)
"Types of Satellite" (MPC)
"Types of Satellites" (T)
"Typical Missile" (WPC)
"Typical Rocket" (WPC)
"Typical Space Station" (WPC)
"U.S.   Space   Program—Terrain Photos (A Series)" (IPC)
"Voyager Approach and Landing" (DG)
"Voyager—Mars" (DG)
"Weather Satellites" (MPC)
"Weightlessness" (WPC)

Solar System

"Apparent Path of the Sun" (WPC)
"Approximation   of   Relative Sizes and Distances of Planets to Sun" (MMAMC)
"Asteroid Belt" (UTI)
"Asteroid Orbits" (W)
"Asteroids, Comets, and Meteors" (DG)
"Astronomical Unit, The" (WPC)
"Atmosphere of the Earth, The" (MMAMC)
"Comet Mrkos" (IPC)
"Comets" (MPC)
"Comparative Size of United States and Moon" (WPC)
"Crater Copernicus" (IPC)
"Curve of the Earth" (WPC)
"Declination of Celestial Sphere" (W)
"Earth" (MPC)
"Earth, The" (MMAMC)
"Earth Ellipsoid, The" (W)
"Earth from Gemini" (IPC)
"Earth As a Magnet, The" (K&E)
"Earth and Moon from Lunar Orbiter" (IPC)

"Earth-Moon Pair" (W)
"Earth's Orbit" (PS)
"Earth's Shape" (WPC)
"Flat, Round Earth" (WPC)
"Full Moon Illusions" (WPC)
"Galileo's Notebook" (WPC)
"Galileo's Notebook (Four Moons of Jupiter)" (WPC)
"Geoid and the Ellipsoid, The" (W)
"Halley's Comet" (IPC)
"Halley's Comet 1910" (WPC)
"Halley's Comet Orbit" (WPC)
"Heavenly Bodies" (PS)
"Importance to Earth—Moon" (PS)
"Inclination of the Axis of Some of the Planets" (EA-V)
"Inclination of the Moon's Orbit" (W)
"Inclination of Planetary Orbits" (WPC)
"Location of North Star" (MMAMC)
"Mars and the Asteroids" (MPC)
"Mercury and Venus" (MPC)
"Moon" (MPC)
"Moon from Close Up, The" (MMAMC)
"Moon Has Only 1/6 the Gravity of Earth, The" (MMAMC)
"Moon Has Only Reflected Light, The" (MMAMC)
"Moon Is Both Very Hot and Very Cold, The" (MMAMC)
"Moon (A Series)" (MMAMC)
"Moon's Orbit, The" (WPC)
"Movement of Planets" (PS)
"North Star Position" (UTI)
"Orbit of the Moon with Respect to Earth's Orbit" (EA-V)
"Orbits of the Earth-Moon System" (W)
"Orbits of the Nine Planets" (W)

"Phases of Venus" (W)
"Plane of Orbit—Biela's Comet" (WPC)
"Plane of Planet Orbits" (UTI)
"Ptolemaic System" (UTI)
"Relative Size of Planets" (EA-V)
"Relative Size of Planets" (WPC)
"Relative Sizes of Planets" (IPC)
"Saturn's Ring" (WPC)
"Seeing the Moon from a Distance" (MMAMC)
"Size of U.S. and Moon" (MPC)
"Solar System" (PSC)
"Solar System" (UTI)
"Solar System, The" (EA-V)
"Solar System, The" (HI)
"Solar System, The" (IPC)
"Solar System, The" (JCA)
"Solar System, The" (MMAMC)
"Solar System, The" (T)
"Solar System Map Making" (DG)
"Solar System Origin" (DG)
"Solar System of Planets, The" (WPC)
"Space Stones" (WPC)
"Surface of the Moon" (IPC)
"Uranus, Neptune, and Pluto" (MPC)
"Variation in Distance Between Earth and Sun" (EA-V)

Solar and Stellar Aspects
"Andromeda and Triangulum" (CV)
"Aquila" (CV)
"Aries and Triangulum" (CV)
"Astral Parallax" (WPC)
"Autumn Sky—South" (CV)
"Band of Stars" (WPC)
"Band of Stars—Zodiac" (WPC)
"Big Dipper, The" (MMAMC)
"Big Dipper Stars" (WPC)

"Big Dipper's Seasonal Changes, The" (MMAMC)

"Big Triangle, The" (MMAMC)

"Bootes" (CV)

"Canis Major" (CV)

"Canis Minor" (CV)

"Cassiopeia" (CV)

"Cassiopeia" (WPC)

"Cassiopeia, From Alpha Centauri" (WPC)

"Cepheus" (CV)

"Cepheus, Cassiopeia and Cygnus" (MMAMC)

"Chemical Analysis of a Star" (EDRECS)

"Chemical Analysis of a Star" (WPC)

"Comparative Size—Sun and Some Stars" (WPC)

"Comparison of the Actual Sizes of Some Well-known Stars, A" (UNC)

"Comparison of the Size of Stars" (EA-V)

"Composition of Stars" (PS)

"Constellation Star Chart" (UTI)

"Constellations-1" (MPC)

"Constellations-2" (MPC)

"Constellations-3" (MPC)

"Constellations-4" (MPC)

"Constellations-5" (MPC)

"Constellations—Winter" (UTI)

"Cygnus, the Swan" (MMAMC)

"Cygnus and Lyra" (CV)

"Dipper Through the Ages" (MMAMC)

"Distance of the Stars" (MPC)

"Double Stars" (WPC)

"Draco" (CV)

"Early Solar Theory" (UTI)

"Favorite Spring Constellations" (WPC)

"Favorite Summer Constellations" (WPC)

"Hercules and Corona Borealis" (W)

"Hydrogen-Helium Reactions" (EA-V)

"Leo, the Lion" (MMAMC)

"Leo and Leo Minor" (CV)

"Location of the Dragon" (MMAMC)

"Location of Magnitude Stars, No. 1" (MMAMC)

"Location of Magnitude Stars, No. 2" (MMAMC)

"Location of Magnitude Stars, No. 3" (MMAMC)

"Location of Magnitude Stars, No. 4" (MMAMC)

"Location of Magnitude Stars, No. 5" (MMAMC)

"Location of the Northern Crown" (MMAMC)

"Lyra, The Lyre" (MMAMC)

"Measurement—Star Mass" (UTI)

"Morning Star—Venus" (WPC)

"Nearby Star" (WPC)

"Night Sky Appearance" (EA-V)

"North Circumpolar Sky" (CV)

"North Pole Constellations, The" (CV)

"Orion" (CV)

"Orion, A Winter Constellation" (CV)

"Parallax Effect" (DG)

"Pegasus" (CV)

"Pegasus, The Winged Horse" (CV)

"Perseus" (CV)

"Pisces" (CV)

"Polaris" (MPC)

"Probable Structure of the Sun" (EA-V)

"Sagittarius" (CV)

"Scorpius, The Scorpion" (MMAMC)

"Series of Thermonuclear Reactions" (EA-V)

"Size of Sunspots" (WPC)
"Sizes and Colors of Stars" (MPC)
"Solar Energy" (MMAMC)
"Solar Flares and Magnetic Field" (DG)
"Solar Prominences" (IPC)
"Star Brightness" (MPC)
"Star Chart (I)" (DG)
"Star Chart—Northern Skies" (DG)
"Star Chart—Southern Skies" (DG)
"Star Colors" (WPC)
"Star and Constellation Recognition (A Series)" (MMAMC)
"Star Finder—Northern Skies" (DG)
"Star Finder—Southern Skies" (DG)
"Star Neighborhood" (WPC)
"Stars (A Series)" (UNC)
"Stars and Constellations— North" (JCA)
"Stars and Constellations— South" (JCA)
"Stars and the Milky Way" (IPC)
"Stars and Space Science (A Series)" (MPC)
"Stellar Evolution" (HM)
"Structure of the Sun" (HI)
"Structure of the Sun" (T)
"Sun" (EA-V)
"Sun" (DG)
"Sun" (PSC)
"Taurus" (CV)
"Types of Stars" (MPC)
"Ursa Major" (CV)
"Ursa Minor" (CV)
"Using the Big Dipper" (WPC)
"Variable Stars" (DG)
"What Is a Star?" (MPC)
"Where Is the Sun?" (WPC)
"Zodiac" (N)

Galactical and Universal Topics

"Andromeda Galaxy" (IPC)
"Barred Spiral" (IPC)
"Comet Orbits" (W)
"Crab Nebula, The" (IPC)
"Drawing Showing the Probable Appearance of Our Own Galaxy, A" (UNC)
"Earth-Centered Universe" (WPC)
"Expanding Universe Theory" (UTI)
"Galaxies" (N)
"Galaxies" (WPC)
"Milky Way, The" (WPC)
"Milky Way Galaxy" (DG)
"Milky Way Galaxy" (MPC)
"Nature of the Universe" (T)
"Our Solar System in a Galaxy" (WPC)
"Ring Nebula, The" (IPC)
"Pleiades, The" (IPC)
"Pleiades and Hyades, The" (MMAMC)
"Probable Appearance of Our Galaxy" (EA-V)
"Spectrum and Doppler Shift" (DG)
"Spiral Galaxy, Side View" (IPC)
"Theories of the Origin of the Universe" (MPC)
"Types of Galaxies" (WPC)
"Types of Galaxies" (DG)
"Universe (A Series)" (IPC)
"Universe—Big Bang Hypothesis" (UTI)
"Whirlpool Galaxy" (IPC)

General Topics

"Celestial Coordinate System" (W)
"Celestial Navigation" (WPC)
"Comparing Diameters" (MMAMC)

"Comparison of Fission and Fusion" (K&E)

"Distortion of High-Latitude Regions by Mercator Projection" (EA-V)

"Divisions of Space" (WPC)

"Equal Areas" (WPC)

"Eratosthenes' Measurement of the Earth" (W)

"First Sextant, A" (WPC)

"Frequencies and Wave-lengths Range" (EA-V)

"General Science (A Series)" (MMAMC)

"General Science—Astronomy (A Series)" (T)

"Great Pyramid at Giza" (WPC)

"Hemispheres" (T)

"How Telstar Works" (WPC)

"Importance to Man—Stars and Planets" (PS)

"Kepler's Laws of Planetary Orbits" (W)

"Latitude Lines of Parallels" (MMAMC)

"Latitude and Longitude—Earth" (MMAMC)

"Latitude and Star Observing" (WPC)

"Lines of Latitude of Parallels" (MMAMC)

"Lines of Longitude or Meridians, No. 1" (MMAMC)

"Lines of Longitude or Meridians, No. 2" (MMAMC)

"Longitude and Latitude" (T)

"Measuring Altitude of Stars" (WPC)

"Measuring Astral Distances" (WPC)

"Measuring Distant Stars (Parallax)" (WPC)

"Modern Earth Sciences—Astronomy (A Series)" (EA-V)

"Naming the Days" (WPC)

"Orbiting Telescope" (IPC)

"Projector Lens System" (UTI)

"Radiations in the Atmosphere" (WPC)

"Reflecting and Refracting Telescopes" (T)

"Reflecting Telescope, A" (UTI)

"Refracting Telescope Lens System" (UTI)

"Sextant" (WPC)

"Sextant—How It Works" (WPC)

"Solar Still" (UTI)

"Standard Time Zones of the Earth" (EA-V)

"Standard Time Zones for North America" (EA-V)

"Standard Time Zones of the United States" (T)

"Telescope" (PSC)

"Telescope" (UTI)

"Telescope, The" (T)

"Telescopes" (EA-V)

"Three-Station Network" (DG)

"Time" (DG)

"Time Can Be Told by the Movement of the Sun" (MMAMC)

"Time on the Globe" (W)

"Time Zones" (EA-V)

"Time Zones" (HI)

"Tools of the Astronomer" (MPC)

Color Photographs

Key

(1) Forces, Movements, and Astronomical Phenomena
(2) Space Exploration
(3) Solar System
(4) Solar and Stellar Aspects
(5) Galactical and Universal Topics
(6) General Topics

13″ x 18″ B/W Study Print (with texts and questions) (EBEC)

1. Comets (3)
2. Day and Night (1)
3. Earth, The (3)
4. Heating and Cooling of the Earth's Surface (6)
5. How the Equatorial Region Is Established (1)
6. Jupiter (3)
7. Lunar Crater, A (3)
8. Mars (3)
9. Midnight Sun I, The (1)
10. Midnight Sun II, The (1)
11. Moon, The (3)
12. Revolution of the Earth (1)
13. Saturn (3)
14. Summer Solstice in the Northern Hemisphere (1)
15. Summer Solstice in the Southern Hemisphere (1)
16. Sun, The (Solar Surface) (4)
17. Sun and the Planets, The (3)
18. Venus (3)
19. Winter Solstice in the Northern Hemisphere (1)
20. Winter Solstice in the Southern Hemisphere (1)

13″ x 18″ Color Curriculum Prints (CES, DG, IAI, N, W).

1. Gas and Dust of Space, The (5)
2. Moon, The (3)
3. Solar System, The (3)
4. Stars, The (4)
5. Sun, The (4)
6. Universe of Galaxies, The (5)

Crew of Apollo 11 (SP).

24″ x 36″ (b/w or color) Photographs (Astro Murals).

1. Andromeda Galaxy (b/w) (5)
2. Canes Venatici Spiral (b/w) (5)
3. Composite Photo of Third Quarter Moon (21 days) (b/w) (3)
4. Crab Nebula in Taurus (color) (5)
5. Edge-on Spiral in Andromeda (b/w) (5)
6. Full Moon (b/w) (3)
7. Orion Nebula (b/w) (5)
8. Saturn Rings (b/w) (3)
9. Veil Nebula in Cygnus (color) (5)

8″ x 10″ B/W Mount Wilson and Palomar Observatories Photographs: Galaxies, Nebulae, Star Clusters (HSC).

1. Galaxy, type Ep, in Cassiopeia (5)
2. Galaxy, type SBab(s), in Cetus (5)
3. Galaxy, type E pec/So., in Andromeda (5)
4. Galaxy, type sh, in Andromeda (2 photos) (5)
5. All of the Great Galaxy in Andromeda and Satellite Galaxies NGc 205 and 221 (5)
6. Galaxy, type Sc, in Sculptor (5)
7. Gaseous Nebula in Orion; the "Horsehead" Nebula South of Zeta Orionis (5)
8. Gaseous Nebula in Gemini (photographed in redlight) (5)
9. Galaxy, type Sab, in Pisces (5)
10. Supernova in type Sb/SBb galaxy, in Coma Berenices (4)
11. Galaxy, type Sb, in Canes Venatici (5)
12. Galaxy, type Sb, in Coma Berenices (5)
13. Galaxy, unusual type, in Centaurus (5)
14. Galaxy, the "Whirlpool," type Sc, in Canes Venatici (5)
15. Globular Star Cluster, in Canes Venatici (5)
16. Galaxy, type Sc, in Virgo (5)
17. Galaxy, type Sc, in Ursa Major (5)
18. Supernova in type Sc galaxy, in Ursa Major (4)
19. Galaxy, type SO$_3$, in Bootes (5)
20. Star Cluster, open type, in Libra (5)
21. Group of Five Galaxies with Unusual Connecting Clouds, in Serpens (5)
22. Star Cluster, globular, in Hercules (5)
23. Gaseous Nebula in Serpens (5)
24. Gaseous Nebula, the "Omega" nebula, in Sagittarius (5)

25. Planetary Nebula, the "Dumbbell" Nebula, in Vulpecula   (4)
26. Gaseous Nebula—"Veil" Nebula, in Cygnus (3 photos)   (5)
27. Gaseous Nebula, the "North America" Nebula, in Cygnus   (5)
28. Galaxy, type Sb, in Pegasus   (5)
29. Galaxy, type Sc, in Pisces 200-inch   (5)
30. Galaxy, type Sb, in Andromeda (seen edge-on)   (5)
31. Galaxy, type SBc (sr), in Cetus   (5)
32. Galaxy, type SO, in Fornax   (5)
33. Galaxy, type E + Sb, in Perseus   (5)
34. Galaxy, type SBb(s), in Eridanus   (5)
35. Galaxy, type SBb(r), in Fornax   (5)
36. Pleiades, an open-star cluster, in Taurus   (5)
37. Star Merope in the Pleiades Cluster, in Taurus (showing nebulosity)   (4)
38. Planetary Nebula in Taurus; the "Crab" Nebula, remains of supernova of AD 1054   (4)
39. The "Crab" Nebula in Taurus (montage of 4 views in polarized light)   (4)
40. The "Crab" Nebula in Taurus (montage of 4 views in blue, yellow, red, and infrared light)   (4)
41. Gaseous Nebula, the "Rosette" Nebula, in Monoceros   (5)
42. Enlarged section of the "Rosette" Nebula, in Monoceros (showing fine absorption detail)   (5)
43. Gaseous Nebula, Hubble's Variable Nebula, in Monoceros   (5)
44. Gaseous Nebula, the "Cone" Nebula, in Monoceros, situated in south outer region of NGC 2264   (5)
45. Planetary Nebula in Gemini   (4)
46. Galaxy, type Sc, in Camelopardus   (5)
47. Galaxy, type SBc(s), in Puppis   (5)
48. Galaxy, type Sc pec, in Cancer   (5)
49. Star cluster, open type, in Cancer   (5)
50. Galaxy, type So, in Uras Major   (5)
51. Galaxy, type Sa, in Hydra   (5)
52. Galaxy, type Sb, in Ursa Major   (5)
53. Galaxy, type SBo, in Leo Minor   (5)
54. Galaxy, type Sc, in Leo   (5)
55. Galaxy, type Sc, in Ursa Major   (5)
56. Galaxy, type Sb, in Ursa Major   (5)
57. Galaxy, type Sb, in Ursa Major, member of group—4 galaxies including NGC 3031, 3034, and 3077   (5)
58. Galaxy, type Irr, in Ursa Major   (5)
59. Galaxy, type Sbz(s), in Leo   (5)
60. Galaxy, type Sa, in Leo   (5)
61. Galaxy, type E, in Leo   (5)

62. Planetary Nebula in Hydra (photographed in red light)   (4)
63. Galaxies, type Sc pec, in Corvus   (5)
64. Supernova (1937) in a galaxy, in Virgo   (4)
65. Galaxy, type Sb, in Canes Venatici   (5)
66. Galaxy, type Eo pec, in Virgo   (5)
67. Galaxy, type Sba(s) pec, in Coma Berencies   (5)
68. Galaxy, type Sb, in Coma Berenices   (5)
69. Galaxy, type Sa/Sb, in Virgo   (5)
70. Galaxy, type Sc, in Canes Venatici   (5)
71. Planetary Nebula in Aquarius   (4)
72. Galaxy, type Sb, in Pegasus   (5)
73. Gaseous Nebula in Cygnus   (5)
74. WW CYGNI Variable star at maximum and minimum   (4)
75. Whole constellation of Orion and surrounding region   (4)
76. The Milky Way in Sagittarius (3 photos)   (5)
77. Mosaic of the Milky Way (composed of several wide-angle photographs)   (5)
78. Nova Persei (1901) showing expanding nebulosity surrounding star   (4)
79. Radio source in Cassiopeia; faint wisps of gas in the position of a source of radio noise (red light photograph)   (5)
80. The Cygnus "A" source of radio noise   (5)
81. Galaxy, a faint dwarf system, in Sextans   (5)
82. Unusual cluster of galaxies in Hercules   (5)
83. Portion of a large cluster of galaxies in Coma Berenices   (5)
84. Cluster of galaxies in Corona Borealis   (5)
85. Cluster of galaxies in Hydra   (5)
86. A faint cluster of galaxies at a distance of well over a billion light years   (5)
87. Picture and spectrum of the most distant object 3C295 in Bootes   (5)
88. An area in Coma Berenices showing faint galaxies   (5)
89. Populations I and II illustrated by means of photographs of a spiral arm of NGC 224 and NGC 205   (5)

Four Solar Phenomena (HSC).

1. Sunspot (7 photos)   (4)
2. Solar Disk (2 photos)   (4)
3. Spectroheliogram (4 photos)   (4)
4. Solar Flare   (4)
5. Solar Granulations   (4)
6. Prominences (5 photos)   (4)
7. Corona   (4)
8. Magnetogram Photos (2 photos)   (4)

The Moon, Planets, and Comets (HSC).

Moon:

1. Crescent Phase (3 + 5 days) (3)
2. Crescent Phase (8 days) (3)
3. Gibbous Phase (11 days) (3)
4. Full Phase (14 days) (3)
5. Gibbous Phase (17 days) (3)
6. Crescent Phase (23 + 26 days) (3)
7. Northern Region (8 days) with Caucasus Mountains + Alpine Valley (21 days), from Copernicus to Limb (3)
8. Central Region (21 days) Ptolemy and Eratosthenes Craters (3)
9. Southern Region (21 days) Ptolemy and Tycho regions (3)
10. Southern Region (21 days) from Ptolemaeus to Limb (3)
11. Crater Copernicus (2 photos) (3)
12. Crater Clavius (3)
13. Mosaic of Entire Crescent at Last Quarter (3)

The Planets and Comets:

1. Venus (6 views) (3)
2. Venus (thin crescent) (3)
3. Mars (3 photos) (3)
4. Mars, Jupiter, Saturn, and Pluto (3)
5. Jupiter (4 photos) (3)
6. Saturn (3)
7. Pluto (3)
8. Halley's Comet (3 photos) (3)
9. Cunningham Comet (3)
10. Arend-Roland Comet (2 photos) (3)
11. Mrkos Comet (3)

Instruments and Buildings:

1. Palomar Observatory, including exterior, interior, and instrument (6)
2. Mount Wilson Observatory, including exterior, interior, and instrument (6)

Supplementary Reading Materials

The supplementary reading materials contained in the following extensive listing are almost exclusively paperbound volumes. Although not all-inclusive, the listings do represent a major portion of the currently available paperback books that should be of interest to both teachers and students. These materials constitute an economical source that is often overlooked. These available paperbacks span all levels of instruction from the junior high school to reference works for the teacher. No attempt has been made to indicate the grade or reading level because many are useful for a wide range of abilities. Prices are subject to fluctuation, but most of these publications are reasonably priced. A brief annotation is included for most titles.

Adler, Irving. *Seeing the Earth from Space.* New York: New American Library of World Literature, 1962, 144 pp. Summarization of the data on man-made satellites and the information they have revealed about the earth's shape, gravity, atmosphere, cosmic rays, and so forth.

Ahrendt, M. H. *The Mathematics of Space Exploration.* Space Science Series. New York: Holt, Rinehart and Winston, 1965, 160 pp. Deals with force and motion, the nature of space, and the mathematics of launching rockets, rocket orbits, and flights in space.

Ahrens, Louis H. *Distribution of the Elements in Our Planet.* McGraw-Hill Earth and Planetary Science Series. New York: McGraw-Hill Book Co., 1965, 125 pp. Explores the origin of the universe and the evolution of the solar system. Explains how the abundance of elements are determined, and analyzes the principal structural components of the planet. Geochemical methods of classifying elements are introduced and actual and theoretical aspects of element distribution are discussed.

Asimov, Isaac. *The Kingdom of the Sun.* New York: Collier Books, 1962, 157 pp. History of man's ideas about the solar system. Shows how scientific investigation has answered old questions and raised new ones.

Bates, D. R., ed. *The Earth and Its Atmosphere.* New York: John Wiley & Sons, 1961, 324 pp. Covers knowledge in geophysical sciences including: composition of interior and deep crust of the earth; circulation of the oceans and atmosphere; causes of auroras and magnetic storms; climatology; meteorology; cosmic radiation; and the geomagnetic field of the earth. Also covers the ice ages and the origin of our planet and its probable end.

Bondi, Hermann. *The Universe at Large.* Garden City, N.Y.: Doubleday & Co., 1960, 154 pp. Discusses the origin and size of the universe. Also age of the galaxies and stars.

Branley, Franklyn M. *Exploration of the Moon.* Garden City, N.Y.: Doubleday & Co., 1963, 146 pp. Discusses knowledge of the moon prior to manned landings on the moon. Looks into the possibilities of establishing a permanent lunar colony using current knowledge. Emphasis on science rather than rocketry.

Broms, Allan. *Our Emerging Universe.* New York: Dell Publishing Co., 1964, 260 pp. Tells the story of the creation—how the universe and our solar system and the earth were formed and how they are now cooling. The evolution of the earth, from its preplanetary state of swirling gases to its present substance. Presents theories of the birth of the planets, the making of oceans, the movement of continents, speculations about life on other planets, the existence of other solar systems, and the future of our universe.

Butler, S. T., and H. Messel, eds. *A Journey Through Space and the Atom.* Elmsford, N.Y.: Pergamon Press, 1963, 495 pp. Consists of four sections, each by a different author. Section titles are "Life in the Galaxy," "Are We Alone?," "Space Rocketry," and "Elementary Atomic Energy."

_____, eds. *Light and Life in the Universe.* Elmsford, N.Y.: Pergamon Press, 1965, 344 pp. Discusses origins of life and the possibility of life on other planets. Includes atoms and universe, life in the galaxy, and the replication of living molecules.

da Andrade, E. N. *Sir Isaac Newton: His Life and Work.* Garden City, N.Y.: Doubleday & Co., 1965, 160 pp. Explains how the famous mathematician, astronomer, physicist, and natural philosopher revolutionized scientific thinking with his laws of universal gravitation, his innovations in integral calculus, and his experiments with light.

Daniels, Farrington. *Direct Use of the Sun's Energy.* New Haven: Yale University Press, 1964, 374 pp. Discusses possibilities of converting the sun's rays into mechanical and electrical power and describes the full range of experimental work on collectors of solar radiation.

Dexter, William A. *Field Guide to Astronomy Without a Telescope.* ESCP Pamphlet Series PS-9. Boston: Houghton Mifflin Co., 1971.

Ebbighausen, E. G. *Astronomy,* 2d ed. Merrill Physical Science Series. Columbus, Ohio: Charles E. Merrill Publishing Co., 1971, 150 pp. An introduction to astronomy written for beginning college-level courses.

Eddington, Sir Arthur. *Expanding Universe.* Ann Arbor: University of Michigan Press, 1958, 142 pp. Presents an earlier view on the theory that the whole material universe of stars and galaxies of stars is dispersing. Also proposes that the galaxies are scattered and occupying an ever increasing volume.

_____. *Internal Constitution of the Stars.* New York: Dover Publications, 1959, 407 pp. Detailed exposition of the theory of radiative equilibrium for stellar interiors and of evidence for existence of diffuse matter in interstellar space. Studies quantum theory, polytropic gas spheres, mass-luminosity relations, and variable stars.

_____. *The Nature of the Physical World.* Ann Arbor: University of Michigan Press, 1958, 382 pp. Discusses the downfall of classical physics; relativity; time; gravitation; man's place in the universe; the quantum theory; reality; causation; science and mysticism, etc.

Emme, Eugene, M. *A History of Space Flight.* Space Science Series. New York:

Holt, Rinehart and Winston, 1965, 224 pp. A narrative of the dramatic efforts in the development of space flight on a world-wide basis. A concise history of major milestones in space.

Faget, Max. *Manned Space Flight.* Space Science Series. New York: Holt, Rinehart and Winston, 1965, 176 pp. Deals with spacecraft, navigation and control, tracking and communication, and power generation in space.

Fanning, A. E. *Planets, Stars and Galaxies,* rev. ed. New York: Dover Publications, 1966, 189 pp. A book for those with a beginning interest in astronomy. Includes descriptions of the solar system, stars and galaxies, and discussions of methods used by today's astronomers to gather knowledge.

Gamow, George. *Creation of the Universe.* New York: Bantam Books, 1956, 144 pp. Presents theories of general cosmology, including the conversion of energy into atoms, the evolution of stars and other stellar bodies, the structure of galaxies, and the theory of an expanding universe.

_____. *Gravity.* Garden City, N.Y.: Doubleday & Co., 1962, 157 pp. Discusses work of Galileo, Newton, and Einstein in discovering the nature of gravity. Places concepts and techniques of science in terms understandable to students.

_____. *One, Two, Three . . . Infinity,* rev. ed. New York: Bantam Books, 1961, 352 pp. Summation of the basic theories and some of the facts of modern science. Presents such diverse topics as the origin and size of the universe, genetics, and relativity.

_____. *A Planet Called Earth.* New York: Bantam Books, 1963, 256 pp. Presents theories on the evolution of the solar system and the successive reformations of the earth's surface. Includes origin of earth and origin and evolution of life.

_____. *A Star Called the Sun.* New York: Viking Press, 1964, 208 pp. Traces the vital stages in the history of the sun and other stars and discusses the sun's relation to the grand panorama of cosmic evolution. Introduces the fundamentals of nuclear chemistry and quantum physics.

Gardner, Marjorie H. *Chemistry in the Space Age.* Space Science Series. New York: Holt, Rinehart and Winston, 1965, 176 pp. The chemistry of the solar system and beyond, with an introduction to the possibilities of life on other planets.

Garland, G. D. *Earth's Shape and Gravity.* Elmsford, N.Y.: Pergamon Press, 1965, 188 pp. Presents knowledge of earth's form and interior that can be obtained from measurements of gravity. Introduction to modern work being carried out in fields of geophysics and geodesy.

Geymonat, Ludovico. Translated by Drake Stillman. *Galileo Galilei.* New York, McGraw-Hill Book Co., 1965, 288 pp. Sets forth known facts of Galileo's life, explains his sporadic teaching career, and examines the research that lay behind his famous treatises on astronomy and mechanics.

Goodwin, Harold L. *The Images of Space.* Space Science Series. New York: Holt, Rinehart and Winston, 1965, 189 pp. The effects of space exploration successes and failures on the struggle between the democratic and communistic ideologies. Interesting historical space events; their political, economic, social, and moral implications, and their contribution to national images.

Gurney, Gene. *Walk in Space: The Story of Project Gemini.* New York: Random House, 1967, 192 pp. An account of the space flight of Project Gemini, emphasizing achievements that brought America closer to a manned landing on the moon.

Haber, Heinz. *Stars, Men, and Atoms.* New York, Washington Square Press. This book presents the exciting story of how man has probed the secrets of his own and other planets—from the heretical assertions of Copernicus, through formulations of Bruno and Newton, to the dramatic effect of artificial satellites upon present-day theories.

Harbeck, Richard M., and Lloyd K. Johnson. *Earth and Space Science.* New York: Holt, Rinehart and Winston, 1965, 296 pp. The last half of this book discusses space science and considers the moon, planets, stars, theories of the universe and extraterrestrial life, and the mechanics of escaping from earth.

Heide, Fritz. *Meteorites.* Translated by Edward Anders and Eugene Dufresne. Chicago: University of Chicago Press, 1964, 144 pp. Covers many aspects of meteorites: fall phenomena; frequency of fall; recognition of meteorites, their size, shape, and composition; classification, origin, and age; and historical anecdotes.

Henry, J. P. *Biomedical Aspects of Space Flight.* Space Science Series. New York: Holt, Rinehart and Winston, 1966, 184 pp. Presents the many physiological problems facing men as they go into space and how these are being solved.

Honegger, Gottfried, and Peter van de Kamp. *Space.* New York: Dell Publishing Co., 1962, 120 pp. Investigates astronomy. Illuminates the relationship of man to his expanded universe.

Hunter, M. W. *Thrust into Space.* Space Science Series. New York: Holt, Rinehart and Winston, 1966, 224 pp. Covers the basic concepts and laws of rocketry, including requirements for interplanetary and interstellar travel. Investigates the problems, mechanics, and dynamics of various types of space flights.

Hymoff, E. *Guidance and Control of Spacecraft.* Space Science Series. New York: Holt, Rinehart and Winston, 1966, 176 pp. Explanations of the systems used to guide and control spacecraft on various types of missions, both manned and unmanned.

Jaffe, L. *Communications in Space.* Space Science Series. New York: Holt, Rinehart and Winston, 1966, 176 pp. Describes space power supplies, communications satellites, ground stations, and the future of communications satellites.

Jeans, Sir James. *Through Space and Time.* New York: John Wiley & Sons, 1963, 224 pp. Exciting journey into nature of the physical universe.

Johnson, Gaylord, and Irving Adler. *Discover the Stars,* rev. ed. New York: Sentinel Books, 1965, 128 pp. A beginner's guide to astronomy with emphasis on the moon and its movements. Includes instructions for making and using a telescope and explains astronomical terms, using simple analogies.

Kiepenheuer, Karl. *The Sun.* Ann Arbor: University of Michigan Press, 1959, 160 pp. Includes information on the solar system, surface of the sun, changing face of the sun, interior of the sun, radio waves from the sun, and earth-sun relationships.

Kondo, Herbert. *Adventures in Space and Time.* New York: Holiday House, 1966, 93 pp. Einstein's theory of relativity is explained in language and in a style that is readily understandable to children. Older readers will find the explanations and analogies helpful. Brief biography of Einstein included.

Korff, Serge A., ed. *Astronomy.* New York: Washington Square Press. Contains contributions by several well-known astronomers. Covers origin and magnitude of universe and man's place in it, as well as space exploration and discoveries, and question of life on other planets.

Kruse, W., and W. Dieckvoss. *The Stars.* Ann Arbor: University of Michigan Press, 1957, 202 pp. Covers the world of the stars, our island in the universe, and the greater universe. Includes celestial position, brightness, and color of stars.

Ley, Willy. *Watchers of the Skies: An Informal History of Astronomy from Babylon to the Space Age.* New York: Viking Press, 1963, 640 pp.

Lundquist, Charles A. *Space Science.* New York: McGraw-Hill Book Co., 1966, 116 pp. Introduction to space science. Discusses spacecraft and their orbits, the earth and its many fields (magnetic, radiation, ionosphere, and so forth), the moon, interplanetary space, and applied and manned space science.

McDonald, R. L., and W. H. Hesse. *Space Science.* Merrill Physical Science Series. Columbus, Ohio: Charles E. Merrill Publishing Co., 1970, 154 pp. A fairly complete introduction to space science. Covers subject from the thinking of ancient Greeks through Apollo moon landings. Includes discussion of space technology, applications of space knowledge, and the future of space programs.

McKinley, D. W. R. *Meteor Science and Engineering.* New York: McGraw-Hill Book Co., 1963, 309 pp. Covers major observational and theoretical developments in meteor science. Includes discussion of meteor particles and their effect on atmosphere.

Maloney, Terry. *Telescopes—How to Choose and Use Them.* New York: Sterling Publishing Co., 1968, 160 pp. How different types of telescopes work, how to go about studying astronomy, what to observe, including stars in the daytime. Thoroughly illustrated with diagrams, drawings, star charts, and photographs.

Marks, Robert W., ed. *The New Dictionary and Handbook of Aerospace.* New York: Bantam Books, 1969, 531 pp. A practical dictionary and handbook that should provide handy reference for students, technicians, and interested laymen. Contains over 50,000 definitions in the basic sciences of aerospace and 64 pages of color illustrations.

Mehlin, T. G. *Astronomy and the Origin of the Earth.* Brown Foundations of Earth Sciences Series. Dubuque, Iowa: William C. Brown Co., 1968, 131 pp. Comprehensive introduction to astronomy designed to give the reader a basic understanding of the sun, moon, planets, stars, and galaxies, in addition to discussing the origin of the universe and the solar system.

Moore, Charleton B. *Meteorites.* ESCP Pamphlet Series PS-10. Boston: Houghton Mifflin Co., 1971.

Motz, Lloyd. *This Is Astronomy.* New York: Columbia University Press, 1963, 279 pp. An account of space and the planets.

Munitz, Milton K. *Theories of the Universe.* New York: Free Press of Glencoe,

1965, 448 pp. Covers breadth of historical development of man's curiosity and discoveries about the nature of the universe.

Naugle, J. E. *Unmanned Space Flight.* Space Science Series. New York: Holt, Rinehart and Winston 1965, 176 pp. Discusses exploration of the earth's environment, the solar system, and interplanetary space.

Newlon, Clarke. *1001 Answers to Questions About Space,* rev. ed. New York: Grosset and Dunlap, 1966, 362 pp. Many aspects of space travel and the technology behind it are explained in question-and-answer form. Information is organized under 18 major headings.

Ohring, George. *Weather on the Planets. What We Know About Their Atmospheres.* Science Study Series. Garden City, N.Y.: Doubleday & Co., Anchor Books, 1966, 146 pp. Describes how meteorologists obtain information about planetary atmospheres and how it is used by earth-bound meteorologists and climatologists.

Orr, Clyde, Jr. *Between Earth and Space.* New York: Collier Books, 1961, 253 pp.

Osgood, T. H., A. E. Ruark, and E. Hutchinson. *Atoms, Radiation, and Nuclei.* New York: John Wiley & Sons, 1964, 503 pp. The atomic nature of matter, the Bohr model of the atom, x-rays, waves, the periodic system, applications of nuclear physics, and so on.

Page, L. W. *Astronomy: How Man Learned About the Universe.* Reading, Mass.: Addison-Wesley, 1969, 208 pp. Provides a survey of astronomy from ancient theories through to modern astronomical thought.

Page, Thornton, ed. *Stars and Galaxies: Birth, Aging, and Death in the Universe.* Englewood Cliffs, N.J.: Prentice-Hall, 1962, 163 pp. Discussion by leading astronomers of new discoveries and revised theories of the universe, and concepts of stellar evolution.

Payne-Gaposchkin, Cecelia. *Stars in the Making* New York: Pocket Books, 1959, 162 pp. An interesting and authoritative story of the origin of the stars, their expenditure of light and heat, and their eventual disintegration. Well illustrated.

Rapport, Samuel, and Helen Wright, eds. *Astronomy.* New York: New York University Press, 1965, 364 pp. Selection of essays that reveal spectacular sweep of the astronomer's domain.

Schwarzchild, Martin. *Structure and Evolution of the Stars.* New York: Dover Publications, 1965, 296 pp. Summary of stellar evolution theory. Descriptions of methods employed and results obtained from investigations in the field.

Scientific American, eds. *The Universe.* New York: Simon and Schuster, 1957, 142 pp. Answers many questions about the universe from its origin up to question, "Is it expanding or evolving at the present time?"

Sharpe, Mitchell R. *Living in Space: The Astronaut and His Environment.* Garden City, N.Y.: Doubleday & Co., 1969, 192 pp.

Stern, P. D. *Our Space Environment.* Space Science Series. New York: Holt, Rinehart and Winston, 1965, 160 pp. Brief history of astronomy from ancient Egyptians to the present. Summarizes knowledge of the solar system, stars, and galaxies.

Strong, James. *Flight to the Stars.* New York: Hart Publishing Co., 1965, 178 pp. Inquiry into the feasibility of interstellar flight, based on knowledge drawn from the science of astronomy, astrophysics, cosmobiology, geology, and nuclear engineering.

Stumpff, Karl. *Planet Earth.* Ann Arbor: University of Michigan Press, 1959, 192 pp. Explains the interaction between the earth and other terrestrial bodies through radiation and gravity, the origin, movements, size, shape, and structure of the earth.

Sutton, R. M. *The Physics of Space.* Space Science Series. New York: Holt, Rinehart and Winston, 1965, 176 pp. Discusses physics of motion, gravitation, rocket propulsion, weightlessness, time and radiation in space, in terms which the student and layman can understand.

Watson, Fletcher G. *Between the Planets.* Garden City, N.Y.: Doubleday & Co., 1962, 226 pp. Gives description of phenomena of asteroids, comets, and meteors.

Whitrow, G. J. *Structure and Evolution of the Universe: An Introduction to Cosmology.* New York: Harper & Row, 1959, 212 pp. Discusses concepts of space, time, relativity, the structure of galaxies and related topics.

Young, Richard S. *Extraterrestrial Biology.* Space Science Series. New York: Holt, Rinehart and Winston, 1966, 121 pp. Discussion of the possibilities of life on other planets with respect to ancient and recent theories of the origin of life. Descriptions of experimental investigations being carried on in laboratories and in space.

Free and Inexpensive Materials

Space Exploration

"Astrosolar Map" (38½" × 29"). Latest data from space vehicles, abstracted articles, and various hypotheses concerning recent discoveries in space science (GEC), free.

"Gemini Pictorial" (1 p., 21" × 48" folded, Cat. #NASA 1.20:4/1, 1966). Twenty photos taken during Gemini flights with a brief narrative of each photo (USGPO), 20c.

"Journey to the Moon" (21" × 48" folded, Cat. #NASA 1.20:NF-40, 1968). Describes, in simplified terms, the lunar journey from launch to recovery (USGPO), 30¢.

"Lunar Charts of Far Side of Moon"
1. Scale 1:5,000,000. (27" × 43", Cat. #D301:LFC-1/967-Z). (USGPO), 50¢.
2. Scale 1:10,000,000. (29" × 23", Cat. #D301:49/4:LFC-Z). (USGPO), 35¢.

"Lunar Map" (approx. 10½" sq.). Map of the moon with over 300 lunar mountains and craters identified (AM—HP), 30¢.

"Man and the Moon Information Space Pack" (GPO) 0-378-973, 1970). A circular describing the various NASA publications available (USGPO), free.

"Mars: Mariner 69 Mars Chart" (Scale 1:25,000,000 at equator, 30" × 35", Cat. #D301:49/4:MEC-2, 1967), (USGPO), 35¢.

"Moon Map" (35" × 45", mailed folded). Map of lunar surface with hundreds of formations indexed and keyed (AM-HP), $1.25.

"NASA Aerospace Bibliography" List of NASA and other publications pertinent to aerospace (NASA), free.

"NASA Educational Publications" (0-382-416, 1970). Pamphlet describing available NASA educational aids (USGPO), free.

"NASA Facts" Educational Publicational Folder (NASA), free.

"Nuclear Propulsion for Space" (56 pp.). Discusses the application of nuclear energy for space exploration (USAEC), free.

"Ranger VII Lunar Charts" (Cat. #301:49/4 RLC1-5, 1964). (USGPO), $1.75/set.

"Space Resources for Teachers: Space Science" (144 pp., 1969, Pub.

#1969:0- 358- 799). Guide outlining the understandings, fundamental concepts, and activities for space science in Grades 10- 12 (USGPO), $2.00.

"Space Sciences and Satellite Tracking" Describes the research programs of the Smithsonian Astrophysical Laboratory as well as photographs of several satellites with the laboratory tracks (SI), free.

"Space—The New Frontier" (96 pp.). Discusses the potential, unexplored areas of space exploration (NASA), free.

"Space Travel" (Cat. #SA- 1794). Traces the development of space exploration with emphasis on satellites and other probes (FEEC), free.

"Steps to the Moon" Provides a summary of man's attempts to better understand the moon (USGS), free.

Solar System

"Meteorites" (1 p., Information Circular #52- 7). (NCSM), free.

General Topics

"Astronomy and You" Relates astronomy to the everyday needs of man (ESCO), free.

"Astrophotography with Your Camera" (16 pp., Pub. #C- 20). Survey about use of telescope and camera in studying astronomy (EKC), free.

"Career in Astronomy, A" Educational requirements and opportunities in Astronomy (AAS), free.

"Fifteen Questions About Planetariums and Nova III" General discussion concerning the various factors one should consider before purchasing a planetarium (SEL), free.

"Key Administrative Considerations for the Proposed Planetarium Classroom" (15 pp.) (SLI), free.

"More About Nova III" Designed as supplement to "Fifteen Questions" (SEL), free.

"Planetarium Lectures and Course Outlines Bibliography" (25 pp.). Overall review of planetariums, their addresses, outlines, and guides accompanied by a selected bibliography (SLI), free.

"Power from Radioisotopes" (40 pp.). Discusses the conversion of heat (from decay of radioisotopes) into electricity (USAEC), free.

"Seeing the Universe" Various materials dealing with telescopes, their construction, and sources of accessories and telescopes (CMC), free.

"Short Glossary of Space Terms" (NASA), free.

"SLI Physical Science Classroom" (4 pp.). Philosophy, use, and construction of a planetarium classroom (SLI), free.

"Snap Nuclear Space Reactors" Discusses a method by which heat (obtained from small nuclear reactors) is converted into electricity (USAEC), free.

"Space Radiation" (58 pp.). Discusses the importance, description, and research performed on radiation from space (USAEC), free.

"Space Science Classroom, A" (14 pp.). Outlines the role of astronomy in the science curriculum and the place of a planetarium in the classroom. Accompanied by description of the research, development, and implementation of planetariums (SLI), free.

"Star-Liner Telescopes" (24 pp.). Selection, utilization, and care of telescopes (SLC), free.

"Telescope Operation Manual" (4 pp.). Operation and use of telescopes especially in photographing stars (SLC), free.

"Unity of the Universe, The" (paperback). Describes how our present picture of the universe came about (AM- HP), $1.25.

"Weather, Astronomy and Meteorology" (Publication list of the U.S. Government Printing Office, Washington, D.C.), free.

PART...3

Meteorology

Classroom Activities

The study of weather phenomena can prove to be very meaningful to students, especially when they use data that they themselves have collected. A wide variety of meteorological phenomena can easily be observed by the students during the school day, observations recorded, and used by the entire class in discussing the topic of meteorology.

Student-Constructed Weather Stations

A suggested activity involves organizing each class into groups whose responsibility for a given time will be to observe and record a specific meteorological phenomenon; air temperature, for example. During the first five minutes of a period, each group will make and record their observations on a class station model using symbols that the class has agreed upon to represent that particular phenomenon. In order to give students a wider variety of experience in observation, a system can be devised whereby the various groups rotate between observing specific phenomena.

Space on a blackboard or bulletin board can be set aside for each class station model. These station models are retained from day to day and the students can make copies of them for their own records. Each basic station model sheet contains only a large circle on which the students will record their observations. For most phenomena little if any equipment is needed that would not normally be available in an earth science classroom. Data can be collected during the weekends or vacation periods through the use of newspaper reports or monthly summary sheets which are available from your local weather bureau.

The student-collected data can be utilized in a variety of ways when one discusses weather phenomena: their causes and relationships. Experience with this activity has shown that the students are better able to discuss and relate the data to the underlying concepts than if one introduced the topics in the more traditional manner.

Daily Weather Maps

Collection and interpretation of local meteorological data gives a good picture of weather in the student's community. However, time should also be spent relating these observations to the phenomena occurring on a larger scale, such as the entire United States. This can be accomplished quite easily with the use of *Daily Weather Maps* (weekly series) published by ESSA (Environmental Science Services Administration).

The charts in this publication are a continuation of the principal charts of the Weather Bureau publication, *Daily Weather Map.*. They include the Surface Weather Map, the 500-Millibar Chart, the Highest and Lowest Temperatures Chart, and the Daily Precipitation Chart. All the charts for one day are arranged on a single page of this publication. They are copies from operational weather maps prepared by the National Meteorological Center, Weather Bureau. The symbols used on the Surface Weather Map and the 500-Millibar Chart are the same as those used previously in *Daily Weather Map*. An explanatory sheet is available, and single copies may be obtained without charge by writing to: Environmental Science Services Administration, Publications Section, AD 143, Rockville, Maryland 20852. Bulk copies may be ordered from the Superintendent of Documents, Government Printing Office, Washington, D.C. 20402, at a cost of $3.75 per 50 copies. Checks should be made payable to the Superintendent of Documents.

The Surface Weather Map presents station data and the analysis for 7:00 a.m./e.s.t. The tracks of well-defined low pressure areas are indicated by chains of arrows; the locations of these centers at times 6, 12, and 18 hours preceding map time are indicated by small black squares enclosing white crosses. Areas of precipitation are indicated by shading. The weather reports that are printed here are only a fraction of those that are included in the operational weather maps, and on which the analyses are based. Occasional apparent discrepancies between the printed station data and the analyses result from those station reports that cannot be included in the published maps because of lack of space.

The 500-Millibar Chart presents the height contours and isotherms of the 500-millibar surface at 7:00 a.m./e.s.t. The height contours are shown as continuous lines and are labeled in degrees Celsius. The arrows show the wind direction and speed at the 500-millibar level.

The Highest and Lowest Temperatures Chart presents the maximum and minimum values for the 24-hour period ending at 1:00 a.m./e.s.t. The names of the reporting points can be obtained from the Surface Weather Map. The maximum temperature is plotted above the station location, and the minimum temperature is plotted below this point.

The Precipitation Areas and Amounts Chart indicates by means of shading the areas that had precipitation during the 24 hours ending at 1:00 a.m./e.s.t. Amounts in inches to the nearest hundredth of an inch are for the same period. Incomplete totals are underlined. "T" indicates a trace of precipitation. Dashed lines, in season, show the depth of snow on the ground in inches as of 7:00 a.m./e.s.t. of the previous day.[1]

The Weekly Series as described above by ESSA are recommended because they are less bulky and therefore more easily used in the classroom. The series allows the students to compare their own obser-

---

[1] Environmental Science Services Administration, Publication Section, AD 143, Rockville, Md.

vations with conditions in other cities and to relate them to overall weather patterns. The use of the maps also creatively enhances the ability of students to interpret phenomena represented by the maps. All in all, the maps, whether daily or weekly series, prove themselves very effective in the study of meteorology.

Pressure Differences

Basic to a number of meteorological phenomena is the influence of air pressure. The importance of differences in air pressure is quite often a difficult one to introduce to students. An activity that graphically represents the force that can be exerted by air pressure, the direction of this force (from an area of high pressure to an area of low pressure), and the influence of heating on air pressure involves hard-boiled eggs and a glass quart milk bottle.

The peeled hard-boiled egg is placed in the mouth of the bottle immediately after a piece of burning paper has been inserted in the container (see Figure 3–1). When the paper stops burning, the egg will be pushed into the bottle because the air pressure outside is greater than that inside. The egg in turn can be removed from the bottle by positioning it in the neck of the bottle, holding the bottle at a high angle and blowing quite hard into it (see Figure 3–2). The pressure gradient created in the demonstration can be compared to that in operation in frontal systems, land and sea breezes, and other weather phenomena caused by differences in air pressure. The activity proves to be very enjoyable, but at the same time an effective introduction into the concept of air pressure.

A Trip to the Local Weather Station

In most areas there is a local U.S. Weather Bureau station, university weather station, Air Force base, or airport weather installation in which certain observational equipment is used by trained meteorologists. A trip to such a facility offers students the opportunity to relate their own observations and conclusions to those of a trained scientist. It also affords them an opportunity to see a good deal of the operating equipment which the practicing meteorologist has at his disposal.

Most facilities are open to the public for tours on a pre-scheduled basis. The tour is usually conducted by a staff member who will answer all questions posed to him by your students. You will find, however, that if the trip is scheduled after your students have been collecting their own data, interpreting their observations, and relating it to actual weather maps, the questions asked will be quite pertinent, penetrating, and to the point. It is suggested that you check thorough-

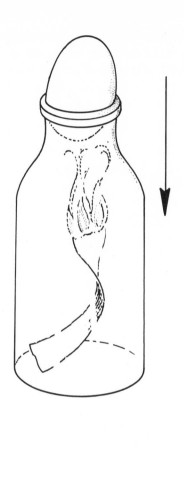

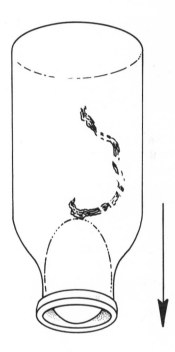

Figure 3-1   Figure 3-2

ly with the local station's personnel as to date, time, and number of students they can accommodate at one time.

Temperature Inversion

In recent years there has been an obvious increase in concern over air pollution and certain meteorological conditions which tend to increase pollution levels within a particular geographic area, such as a city. One of these physical conditions involves a meteorological phenomenon referred to as a *temperature inversion* (cold air overlain by warmer air). This phenomenon can become a major contributor to drastic increases in pollution levels because of the fact that the inversion acts as a "lid" and prevents the air in that locality from rising and carrying pollutants out of the immediate environment. Instead, the air is trapped and the polluted air remains.

An activity which demonstrates the formation of a temperature inversion involves the use of a shallow container, such as a cake tin, and a clear hollow plastic cylinder at least 12 inches in height and 2 inches in diameter. A small hole is placed in the cylinder about 6 inches from one end. This hole should be sufficiently large to allow smoke to be blown through it into the cylinder.

A normal noninverted condition can be demonstrated by placing hot water in the pan, filling it one-half full. The cylinder is then placed into the water in an upright position as illustrated in Figure 3–3. Masking tape may be used to give stability to the apparatus.

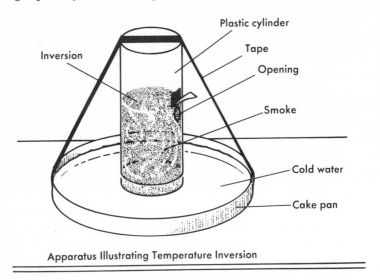

Apparatus Illustrating Temperature Inversion

Figure 3–3 Apparatus illustrating temperature inversion.

After two or three minutes, the normal circulation pattern is established and cigarette smoke may then be introduced through the hole in the side of the tube. Once the smoke has been introduced, the hole is then sealed with tape to prevent the smoke from escaping or establishment of disturbing currents in the tube. The smoke will rise slowly out of the tube, indicating the general flow pattern of the warm air traveling upward. This is caused by the warm air being less dense than the overlying cooler air in the cylinder and therefore rising, carrying the smoke particles with it.

Creation of an inversion involves the addition of ice cubes to the water in the pan and the introduction of more smoke into the tube if necessary. As the lower air becomes cooler through contact with the water, an interface will be formed with the relatively warmer air overlying it. The smoke will be trapped at this contact zone, thus illustrating a temperature inversion at that location. This inversion in turn can be destroyed in much the same manner as it is in nature (1) by blowing along the top of the cylinder, thus causing mixing of the air, or (2) by reheating the bottom air by increasing the temperature of the water.

This demonstrational model of temperature inversion can provide the foundation for a discussion of actual inversions in the environment and their importance to pollution.

Measurement of Wind Velocity

Determination of wind velocity can be accomplished by using a simple student-constructed anemometer. This device can be made by using two pieces of wood (each 12 X ½ X ¼ inches), small nails, the glass portion of a medicine dropper, small (3–4 inch) aluminum pans, and strong wire. An equal-armed cross is constructed from the wood and small nails; and a hole, just big enough for the glass tube of the dropper to fit through, is bored in the center of the cross. Next, the aluminum pans are attached to the wooden arms as illustrated in Figure 3–4. The small end of the glass dropper is sealed by heating it in an open flame and then inserted into the wooden cross and secured with glue to prevent it from slipping. The wire is attached with tape to a stake that will eventually be placed in the ground at the observation site, and the cross is placed on the wire.

In order to calibrate the instrument, one of the pans can be painted a bright color and held outside a car while it is traveling at various speeds. Counting the number of turns per minute at a given speed and dividing that number by a factor of 10 provides an approximation of the velocity in mph of the wind. Care should be taken to calibrate the apparatus on a calm day and when there is no on-coming traffic so as to avoid disturbing currents of air. The students should be cautioned to place the anemometer in a location that is exposed to the wind in all directions. This will ensure that their observations are an accurate indication of true wind speed.

Measurement of Air Pressure

Measurement of the barometric pressure at a particular location can provide valuable data to any class interested in studying weather. However, it is often advantageous for individual students to make these observations at home. This practice presents the expensive prob-

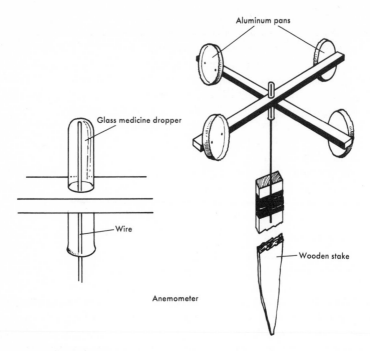

Figure 3-4 Anemometer.

lem of having to provide a relatively large number of instruments to ensure individual observations. A simple, inexpensive barometer can be constructed by students which will provide them with reasonable approximations of air pressure values. Equipment needed to create this device: a milk bottle or any container with an open top and capable of being airtight, a rubber balloon, rubber bands, glue, a soda straw, wooden matches, cardboard, and a protractor (see Figure 3- 5).

The container is warmed by setting it in hot water. While it is still immersed in the water, a portion of the rubber balloon (one thickness) is stretched over its open end and tightly secured with rubber bands. The container is removed from the water and now possesses a partial vacuum that will be maintained, provided the rubber diaphragm is held in place.

A few drops of airplane glue are placed in the center of the rubber, and one end of the soda straw is positioned in the glue. The wooden matchstick is then glued onto the rubber in a position indicated in Figure 3-5. On a piece of cardboard, with the use of a protractor, calibration divisions are marked off. Then it is attached to the bottle.

The rubber diaphragm of the milk bottle will rise and fall with the variations in air pressure. The movement of the diaphragm in turn will cause a corresponding movement of the soda straw. The instrument

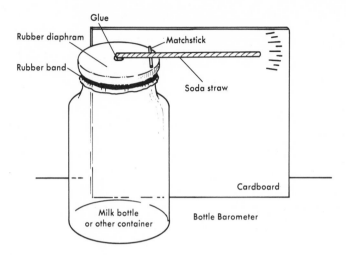

Figure 3-5 Bottle barometer.

can be calibrated by the student using radio or television news broadcasts giving the present area barometric pressure reading.

Although simple in nature, this device does provide each student with his own instrument with which he can make observations of air pressure. Accuracy of each instrument will be determined by the maintenance of its partial vacuum condition. The student can periodically check the accuracy of his instrument with weather reports or with his classmates' readings (providing the observations were made at the same approximate times).

Measurement of Humidity

The hair hygrometer shown in Figure 3-6 is another inexpensive, student-constructed device that can provide each student with the capability of measuring a physical condition of the air, that is, its moisture content.

To construct this apparatus a four-inch broom straw is glued to a one-inch piece of plastic soda straw. A nail is placed into the soda straw and nailed into a wooden block equidistant from both ends. One end of a thoroughly washed and dried strand of human hair (preferrably brunette) approximately 12 inches in length is then glued to the soda straw. After the glue has dried, the straw is twirled so that the free end of the hair is wound around it. The free end of the hair is taped or glued securely to the top of the wooden block in a taut position with the broom straw in a horizontal position. Calibration of the instrument can be accomplished by using an actual classroom

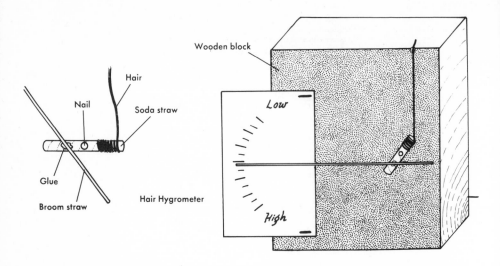

Figure 3-6 Hair hygrometer.

hygrometer and by making calibration divisions on a 3 X 5-inch index card stapled to the wooden block.

As the humidity increases, the hair will absorb moisture and lengthen. This lengthening in turn will cause the straw indicator to lower. When the moisture content of the air decreases, it will have an opposite effect on the apparatus. Although there are minor limitations to a hair hygrometer, this device does prove to be valuable for student observation of this meteorological phenomenon.

Differential Heating of Land and Water

The fundamental cause of movement of air (wind) is a difference in pressure, with air traveling from an area of greater pressure to an area of lower pressure. One of the major causes of these pressure differences is differential heating of earth surfaces. Land and sea breezes are good indicators of this and are caused by the differing heating rates of land and water. This differential heating can be demonstrated by taking two aluminum pie pans and filling one with water and the second with soil. Two thermometers are placed in an upright position in each of the pans equidistant from the surface of both materials, as indicated in Figure 3-7. The thermometers are allowed to come to equilibrium and then their temperatures are recorded. A lamp is then placed 30-40 cm above both pans in a position so that both materials receive equal quantities of light when it is turned on. The students then record the temperature each minute for a period of 10 minutes. After this time, the light is turned off and the students continue to record the temperature at one-minute intervals until another 10 minutes have passed.

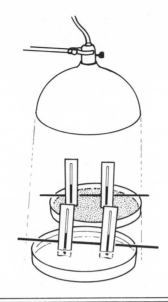

Figure 3-7 Differential heating. (From Earth Science Curriculum Project, *Investigating the Earth* (Boston: Houghton Mifflin Co., 1967, p. 172)).

Student graphs can then be drawn comparing the increases and decreases in temperature of the two materials versus time (see Figure 3-8). From these graphs the students can make interpretations relevant to the relative heating and cooling rates of the materials and their relationship to land and sea breezes as well as other winds.

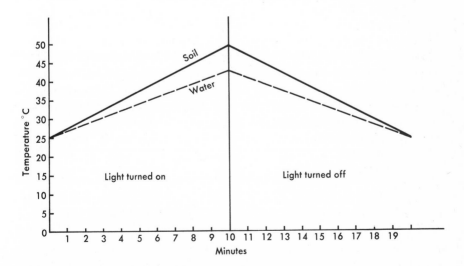

Figure 3-8 Graph showing results of differential heating.

16mm Films

Climatology

"Causes of the Seasons" (color, sd, 11 min, 1962, i-j). Provides an explanation for the seasons through the earth-sun relationship, inclination of solar rays, and revolution of the earth (CF).

"Changing Climates" (color, sd, 11 min, 1957, i-a). Describes studies conducted in Alaskan Glacier Bay area to investigate a possible relationship between changes in the sun's photosphere and the earth's weather cycles (PF).

"Climate and the World We Live In" (color, sd, 13 min, 1957, i-j). Presents the seven factors that determine climates, major types of climates, and how they affect human beings (CF).

"Climates of North America" (color, sd, 17 min, 1962, i-j). Illustrates the variables that determine major climate zones. Provides examples of five climates found in North America (EBEC).

"Earth and the Seasons" (color, sd, 10 min, 1957, i-c). Deals with the various causes of the earth's seasons (A).

"Empire of Windswept Lands, The" (color, sd, 22 min, j-c). Documentary of a research team on the volcanic islands of the Southern French Territories making meteorological observations and other scientific studies (TLI), free.

"Great Winds, Part I: General Circulation" (b/w, sd, 11 min, 1950, j-c). Depicts the world pressure areas, air flow between them, and effects of rotation and the sun's position on the winds (UE&VA).

"Great Winds, Part II: Distribution of Pressure and Winds" (b/w, sd, 11 min, 1950, j-c). Reviews Part I. Describes the development of winds over land and water areas as well as shifts in the pressure and wind belts with the seasons (UE&VA).

"Last Continent, Antarctica, The: Meteorology" (b/w, sd, 29 min, h-a). Describes the role of meteorological research in Antarctica during the IGY (NET:IU).

"Last Continent, Antarctica, The: Studies of the Upper Atmosphere" (b/w, sd, 29 min, 1911, h-a). Deals with the nature and importance of the upper atmospheric studies of the IGY in Antarctica (NET:IU).

"Secrets of the Ice" (color, sd, 27 min, 1961, h-a). Deals with research with glaciers and how they can provide valuable information of past climates. Considers origin of glaciers and solar radiation studies (McGH).

Dynamic Meteorology (Fields of Force and Motion)

"Atmospheric Stability and Instability: Adiabatic Process" (color, sd, 14 min, 1953, h-a). Discusses the various aspects of the adiabatic process including the relationship between temperature and saturation, use of the adiabatic chart, and orographic lifting (UE&VA).

"Atmospheric Stability and Instability: Stability and the Weather" (color, sd, 8 min, 1953, h-a). Describes the relationship between the existing radiosonde recorded lapse rate and the stability of the air. Includes a discussion of the dry and moist adiabatic rates (UE&VA).

"Planetary Circulation of the Atmosphere" (b/w, sd, 25 min, 1967, j-c). Discusses factors that control the basic features of planetary circulation Features of this circulation include the low-latitude easterlies, the mid-latitude westerlies, and the high-speed middle-latitude jet stream (MLA).

"Restless Ocean of Air, The" (color, 20 min, 1969, i-j). Provides explanations for the forces causing movement in the atmosphere (PE).

"What Makes the Wind Blow?" (color, sd, 15 min, 1965, i-h). Using laboratory models and natural demonstrations, the film provides an explanation of the causes of air movements (EBEC).

"Winds Great and Small" (color, sd, 12 min, 1963, i-j). Discusses the factors which produce different varieties of winds including global, local westerlies, sea-level, jet streams, and convection currents (CEF).

Observations and Instruments

"Pressure and Humidity" (color, sd, 10 min, 1965, i-j). Shows the variations in humidity and air pressure, function of instruments designed to measure these quantities, and discusses the formation of clouds and fog (CCAI).

"Research in the Atmosphere" (color, 25 min, 1969, j-h). Documents the various methods used by man to explore the upper regions of the atmosphere from ancient to recent times (NASA), free.

"Temperature and Wind" (color, sd, 8 min, 1965, i-j). Defines weather and illustrates how weather reports are made from observation and measurement of its various constituents (CCAI).

"Tiros, Experimental Weather Satellite" (color, sd, 14 min, 1960, h-a). Traces the history of an experimental weather satellite from preparation to launch (NASA), free.

"Tiros II, Experimental Weather Satellite" (color, sd, 6 min, 1961, h-a). Presents a complete explanation of its function including cloud-cover pictures, taped data, TV cameras used in the photography, and the various subsystems used to calculate earth and atmospheric radiation (NASA), free.

"Weather" (b/w, sd, 10 min, 1956, i-h). Depicts a typical weather bureau station (including instruments), a trip through the stratosphere, and the importance of instruments in forecasting (A).

"Weather Satellites" (color, sd, 15 min, 1965, i-h). Describes the functioning of a weather satellite in photographing the earth and tracing the movement of air masses and violent storms (EBEC).

"Weather Scientists" (color, sd, 13 min, 1960, i-j). Presents a description of the activities of a weather scientist and the instrumentation that is utilized in his work (UE&VA).

"Weathermen of the Sea" (color, sd, 14 min, 1950). Follows the operation of Coast Guard ocean weather station vessels (USCG), free.

"What Will the Weather Be?—Measuring Air Conditions" (color, sd, 11 min, 1968). Points to the work of weather satellites, scientists, and forecasters. Includes a discussion of the recording and communication network used in forecasting (AIMS).

Physical Meteorology (Heat, Optics, Electricity, etc.)

"Air Is for Breathing" (color, sd, 29 min, 1971, j-c). Surveys the major causes of air pollution and the principles that must guide a systematic and effective approach to their control (SOC), free.

"Air Pollution" (color, sd, 20 min, 1971, h-c). Discusses the problem of air pollution, which grows in direct proportion to industrial progress. Includes a definition of air pollution, causes of contamination and its effects (JF).

"Air Pollution: Take a Deep Deadly Breath" (color, sd, 1968). Part I (16 min) illustrates the problems of a person with emphysema. Part II (19 min) describes federal interstate abatements conference between West Virginia and Ohio in attempting to control pollution. Part III (19 min) presents the important role which citizens must play in attempting to fight pollution (HEW), free.

"Atmosphere and Its Circulation (Ocean of Air—Part I)" (b/w, sd, 11 min, 1945, j-a). Deals with the various aspects of the atmosphere including its distribution, composition, variations, and its effect on weather and climate (EBEC).

"Business of Air, This" (color, sd, 30 min, 1966). Discusses air pollution in a large city (St. Louis, Mo.) (HEW), free.

"Fog" (color, sd, 9 min, 1971, c-a). Provides a survey of many views of fog and the phenomena associated with it (unnarrated) (EBEC).

"Formation of Raindrops" (color, sd, 26 min, 1964). Using current experiment, natural and time-lapse photography presents a complete discussion of the processes involved in cloud raindrops and snow formation (AMS).

"Life in a Cubic Foot of Air" (b/w, sd, 11 min, 1958, i-h). Demonstrates that air contains both plant and animal life (CF).

"Missile Meteorology at White Sands" (b/w, sd, 22 min). Reports the operations of the meteorologists at White Sands Missile Range (USAF), free.

"Origins of the Weather, The" (color, sd, 12 min, 1962, i-j). Illustrates, via live photography and animation, the total picture of the wide range of factors that affect the earth's weather and its constituents (EBEC).

"Poisoned Air, The" (color, sd, 50 min, 1966, j-a). Former Secretary of HEW John W. Gardner, industrial representatives, and others discuss air pollution and means of dealing with it (CFI).

"Research in the Atmosphere" (color, sd, 25 min, 1969). Traces the history of man's attempt to explore the upper atmosphere (NASA), free.

"Research by Rockets" (color, sd, 27 min, 1960, i-a). Follows the historical development of rockets, their use as upper atmospheric research tools, and how such research is performed (McGH).

"Rivers in the Sky" (color, sd, 28 min, 1967). Points to the Bureau of Reclamation Program on cloud seeding to induce increased precipitation in various areas of the West (BPR), free.

"Sea Surface Meteorology" (b/w, sd, 24 min, 1967, h-a). Considers the important role that the sea plays in the formation of rain. Depicts an erupting volcano at sea and its role in providing nucleic and charge transfer processed from the sea surface to the atmosphere (UE&VA).

"Solar Radiation I: Sun and Earth" (color, sd, 18 min, 1967). Using animation, considers the energy budget of the earth and such factors that affect it as rotation, atmosphere, cloud cover, and planetary circulation patterns (MLA).

"Story of the Snow Crystal" (color, sd, 18 min, 1963). Uses micro and time-lapse photography to illustrate the formation, and variation in structure of snow crystals. Explains the importance of research on snow crystals in providing information concerning weather forecasting and space exploration (FFI).

"To Set the Record Straight" (color, sd, 29½ min, 1971, h-c). Describes the academic and industrial research programs that are designed to study the effects of lead pollution on public health (EC), free.

"What Makes Clouds?" (color, b/w, sd, 19 min, 1965, i-h). Depicts investigations of the factors that control the formation of clouds; explains that fog and clouds are actually composed of water droplets and that they differ only in their altitude (EBEC).

Synoptic Meteorology (Weather Analysis and Forecasting)

"Aerology (Thunderstorms) Part I" (b/w, sd, 18 min, 1943, h-a). Discusses the formation and structure of two general types of thunderstorms (UE&VA).

"Air Masses and Fronts—Air Masses" (color, sd, 12 min, #TF1-5388a, 1962). Describes the basic concepts of air masses including stability, instability, cloud types, turbulences, and differential heating (USAF), free.

"Air Masses and Fronts—The Cold Front" (color, sd, 9 min, #TF1-4388c, 1962). Outlines the fundamental causes of cold fronts, their appearance, structure, and effects on weather (USAF), free.

"Air Masses and Fronts—Fronts and the Surface Weather Map" (color, sd, 10 min, #TF1-4388b, 1962). Examines the use of surface weather maps in studying the nature of weather phenomena (USAF), free.

"Air Masses and Fronts—The Occluded Front" (color, sd, 9 min, #TF1-5388c, 1962). Presents the fundamental principles of the occluded front and its associated weather patterns (USAF), free.

"Air Masses and Fronts—The Warm Front" (color, sd, 11 min, #TF1-5388d, 1962). Outlines the formation, effects, and patterns of the warm front (USAF), free.

"Air Weather Service of the USAF" (color, sd, 14 min, #SEP 1359, 1966). Describes the nature of the Air Weather Surface and its role in weather forecasting and research (USAF), free.

"Atmospheric Stability and Instability: Existing Temperature Distribution" (color, sd, 14 min, 1953, h-a). Illustrates the relationship of temperature and stability or instability of air to weather patterns (UE&VA).

"Atmospheric Stability and Instability: Thermal Convection" (color, sd, 10 min, 1953, h-a). Relates the changes in weather to the vertical air currents in the atmosphere and their causes (UE&VA).

"Changing the Weather" (color, 29 min, 1970, h-a). A complete view of man's study of clouds and air currents as he attempts to develop weather modification techniques. Includes film footage of successful cloud seeding (NET:IU).

"Cloud Study Time Lapse, Parts I and II" (color, sd, 10 min). Illustrates time-lapse photos of clouds, effects of mountains on cloud development and fronts (MTPS), free.

"Cold Front, The" (color, sd, 9 min, 1962, i-h). Describes the origin, nature and effects of a cold front (FAOC).

"Fronts and Storms" (color, sd, 11 min, 1965, i-j). Explains the concepts of a front and a hurricane (CCAI).

"Fury of the Winds" (color, sd, 25 min, h-c-a). Demonstrates the causes, development, wind patterns, and effects of hurricanes by using hurricane Angela as an example (AISCI).

"Hurricane" (color, sd, 27 min, 1968, j-a). Describes how ESSA advises and alerts area residents about hurricanes (AETNAC), free.

"Hurricane Watch" (b/w, sd, 15 min, 1956, i-h). Presents various methods used in locating, tracking, and preparing for hurricanes (MTPS), free.

"Origin of Weather" (b/w, sd, 26 min, 1959, h-a). Provides a summary of the deficiencies of our meteorological phenomena as well as studies directed at rain and clouds and electrical charges in the atmosphere (CFI).

"Pressure and Humidity" (color, sd, 10 min, 1965, i-j). Shows the variations in humidity and air pressure, function of instruments designed to measure these quantities, and discusses the formation of clouds and fog (CCAI).

"Radar Eyes the Weather, Part A—Fundamentals of Radar Meteorology" (sd, 25 min, #TF1-4344a, 1961). Presents the basic concepts of radar meteorology and factors that affect it. Also illustrates various cloud types and their characteristics (USAF), free.

"Radar Eyes the Weather, Part B—Analysis of Severe Weather" (sd, 21 min, #TF1-5344b, 1961). Builds on the foundation of Part A in observing severe weather. Also discusses, through animation, the life cycle of a thunderstorm (USAF), free.

"Reading Weather Maps" (color, sd, 14 min, 1965, i-j). Traces the preparation of a weather map and the various symbols that are used to describe the weather. Has some discussion concerning the instruments that are used to observe the weather (CF).

"Storm Called Maria" (color, sd, 48 min, j-a). Traces the developmental history of a titanic hurricane and its effects on man (DISNY).

"Texas Tipico—Texas Tornado" (b/w, sd, 11 min, 1957, i-a). Explains the origin of tornadoes and the manner in which they are forecasted by the weather bureau. Also tells how one can protect himself from a tornado (LLA).

"Thunder and Lightning" (b/w, sd, 10 min, 1954, i-j). Discusses thunder and lightning as they are related to static electricity in the atmosphere. Also tells how one may be protected against lightning (McGH).

"Tornado" (color, sd, 15 min, 1968, i-h). Depicts what happens to a town found in the path of a tornado. Illustrates the factors that contribute to the formation of a tornado. Tells of the weather bureau's activity in following a tornado and keeping the public well informed (MTPS), free.

"Unchained Goddess" (color, sd, 57 min, 1955, j-h). Explains the causes of weather, how it is predicted and controlled. Includes scenes of lightning, tornadoes, and hurricanes (BELL), free.

"Warm Front, The" (color, sd, 18 min, 1962, i-h). Illustrates what happens when cold and warm fronts meet, cloud formation, visibility, precipitation, and ceiling conditions (FAOC).

"Weather Research" (b/w, sd, 27 min, 1955, j-h). Traces the work of atmospheric researchers in collecting and analyzing weather data. Presents an airplane flight into a thunderstorm and eye of a hurricane (YA).

"Weather: Understanding Precipitation" (color, sd, 10 min, 1962, j-h). Provides an explanation via photography and animation of dew point, relative humidity, cloud types and precipitation. Illustrates cloud classification based on their origin and altitude (CF).

"Weather: Understanding Storms" (b/w, sd, 11 min, 1965, j-h). Discusses the formation of storms such as tornadoes, hurricanes, dust storms, and blizzards; storm elements of temperature, pressure, and humidity in addition to the function of radar and satellites in studying storms (CF).

"Weather: Why It Changes" (color, sd, 10 min, 1962, j-h). Deals with the cause of weather changes in the U.S. as the result of drifting air masses from the polar and tropical regions. Discusses what occurs when different air masses meet, thus forming fronts (CF).

"When Air Masses Meet" (color, sd, 13 min, 1963, i-j). Illustrates different types of fronts, their formation, movement, and associated weather patterns. Describes high and low pressure areas, warm and cold air masses, and cyclones and anticyclones (CEF).

"Winds That Kill" (sd, 20 min, 1961, i-a). Provides a discussion of the prediction, origin, and effects of hurricanes and tornadoes (USWB), free.

Unclassified

"Above the Horizon" (color, sd, 21 min, 1965, j-c). Uses photography and animation in providing an overall view of the entire field of meteorology, including the status of current research (MLA).

"Because of the Number of Us" (color, sd, 20 min, 1971, j-c). Describes the efforts and accomplishments of an oil company in protecting the environment (SKP), free.

"Inconstant Air, The—Weather and Climate" (color, sd, 27 min, 1961, j-c). Provides a survey of man's attempts throughout history to understand the forces that effect weather and climate changes. Also illustrates various meteorological installations around the world (McGH).

35mm Filmstrips

Climatology

"Climate Regions (color, record, 1967) (LFS).

"Climates of the World" (color, 60 frs, captions, 1964) (W).

"Our Air-Conditioned Earth" (color, 60 frs, captions, 1964) (W).

"Our Changing Weather" (color, 60 frs, captions, 1964) (W).

"Why the Seasons" (color, captions, 1960). Relationship between sun and seasons, solstices, and equinoxes (SVE).

Dynamic Meteorology (Fields of Force and Motion)

"Air in Action" (color, 23 frs, captions, 1952) (ELK).

"Air Migration" (color, 25 frs, captions, 1950) (ELK).

"Atmosphere and Air Pressure" (color, 51 frs, record, 1961) (ELK).

"Atmospheric Currents" (color, 39 frs, record, 1967). Discusses the nature and location of air currents and the problems of weather prediction (EG).

"Ocean of Air We Live In, The" (color, 41 frs, captions, 1961). Discusses the nature of the atmosphere, its motions and observation (PS).

"Why Does the Wind Blow?" (color, 33 frs, captions, 1960). Cause of local and prevailing winds, and jet streams with air photos of hurricanes, tornadoes, and blizzards (SVE).

"Wind and Water Energy" (color, 49 frs, record, 1961) (ELK).

"Winds Around the World" (color, 70 frs, record, 1966). Causes of winds, pressure belts of the earth (SVE).

Observations and Instruments

"How To Forecast the Weather" (color, 65 frs, record, 1966). Making and use of instruments in recording and interpreting weather information (SVE).

"Humidity and How It Affects Us" (color, 70 frs, record, 1966). Humidity—its effects, determination of relative humidity, and measurement (SVE).

"Meteorological Instruments" (color, 41 frs, captions, 1963). Functions and operations of instruments. Factors causing weather, prediction of weather through instruments (PS).

Physical Meteorology (Heat, Optics, Electricity, etc.)

"Air Pollution and You" (color, 46 frs, captions, 1967). Pollution problems, effects of pollution, and various approaches to its control (HEW).

"Atmosphere" (color, 60 frs, captions) (W).

"Atmosphere and Its Interpretation" (color, 64 frs, 1964) (W).

"Canopy of Air" (color, 78 frs, captions, 1955). Shielding effects of the atmosphere (LEP).

"Dust" (color, 42 frs, captions, 1964) (PS).

"Earth's Atmosphere, The" (color, 37 frs, captions, 1961) (HANDY).

"Water and Air" (b/w, 50 frs, captions, 1967). Discusses air and water pollution (NYT).

"Water Conservation Today" (color, 39 frs, 1963) (CEF).

Synoptic Meteorology (Weather Analysis and Forecasting)

"Air Masses and Unusual Weather" (color, 31 frs, record, 1961) (ELK).

"Air Masses and Weather Fronts" (color, 62 frs, record, 1966). Types of fronts with associated weather (SVE).

"Atmospheric Resources" (color, 40 frs, captions) (HM).

"Big Winds—The Destroyers" (color, 41 frs, captions, 1959). Causes of winds, comparison of high- and low-pressure centers, areas of origin of hurricanes and typhoons, and electronic tracking of hurricanes and typhoons (PS).

"Castles in the Sky" (color, 39 frs, captions, 1964) (W).

"Clouds, Rain and Snow" (color, 48 frs, captions, 1959) (SVE).

"Moisture and Precipitation in the Air" (color, 65 frs, record, 1966). Effects of moisture on weather, different types of precipitation (SVE).

"Our Stormy Planet" (color, 60 frs, captions, 1964) (W).

"Storms, Hurricanes and Tornadoes" (color, 42 frs, captions, 1964). Traces the formation of storms including the factors that contribute to their making (PS).

"Studying Everyday Weather" (color, 52 frs, record, 1961) (ELK).

"Weather Changes and Their Causes" (color, 65 frs, record, 1966). Changes in weather phenomena and effects on weather (SVE).

"Weather Folklore" (color, 29 frs, captions, 1959) (EG).

"Weather Fronts and Forecasting" (color, 42 frs, captions, 1957). Air masses; their interactions and effects on weather. Importance of fronts, pressure areas, and their movements (PS).

"Why Does It Rain, Snow, Hail, Sleet?" (color, 39 frs, captions, 1960). Most recent methods of weather analysis (SVE).

"Why Does the Weather Change?" (color, 39 frs, captions, 1960). Description of main air masses affecting the U.S. weather. Depicts the four main fronts and several types of clouds (SVE).

"Wind" (color, 34 frs, captions, 1966). Causes, effects, and measurement of various types of wind (CPC).

"Wind and Rain" (color, 28 frs, record, 1959) (BFA).

8mm Film Loops

Climatology

"Climatology" (color, 3 min, Sup 8, cart, 1970, h-a). Describes the theory behind cloud cover, diurnal heating, planetary circulation, and solar radiation (HR).

"Desert, The" (color, si, 4 min, Sup 8, cart). Shows the major types of plants and animals in each group and how they are adapted to their environment (EG).

"Desert-Physical Factors" (color, 4 min, Sup 8, cart, 1970, j-c). Emphasis is on the temperature variations in the desert and how this affects the environment (E).

"Great Winds—Distribution of Pressure and Winds" (color, sd, Sup 8, cart, 1951, i-h) (UE&VA).

"Great Winds—General Circulation" (color, sd, Sup 8, cart, 1951, i-h) (UE&VA).

"Middle Latitude Deciduous Forest, The" (color, si, 4 min, Sup 8, 1967). Relationship of the plant and animal life to the climate of the region (EG).

"Middle Latitude Grassland, The" (color, si, 4 min, Sup 8, cart, 1967). Relationship of the plant and animal life to the climate of the region (EG).

"Monsoon Lands" (color, si, 1 min, Sup 8, cart, 1967). Describes the climate of Southeast Asia as it is affected by the monsoon winds (UE&VA).

"Movement of the Earth Around the Sun" (color, si, 3½ min, Sup 8, cart). Reasons for variations in the length of day and night throughout the year (UE&VA).

"Pressure Systems" (color, si, 1 min, Sup 8, cart). Pressure systems and associated belts of wind; their distribution and movement with the seasons (UE&VA).

"Savanna, The" (color, si, 4 min, Sup 8, cart). Relationship of the plant and animal life to the climate of the region (EG).

"Seasons—March, The" (color, si, 1½ min, Sup 8, cart). Location of temperature zones during March (EG).

"Seasons—June, The" (color, si, 1½ min, Sup 8, cart). Location of temperature zones during June (UE&VA).

"Seasons—September, The" (color, si, 1½ min, Sup 8, cart). Location of temperature zones during September (UE&VA).

"Taiga, The" (color, si, 4 min, Sup 8, cart). Relationship of the plant and animal life to the climate of the region (EG).

"Tropical Rain Forest, The" (color, si, 4 min, Sup 8, cart). Relationship of the plant and animal life to the climate of the region (EG).

"Tundra, The" (Color, si, 4 min, Sup 8, cart). Relationship of the plant and animal life to the climate of the region (EG).

"Weather and Climate" (color, si, cart, i-j) (CEF).

Dynamic Meteorology (Fields of Force and Motion)

"Air Pressure II: Pressure Box Experiment" (color, si, 4 min, Sup 8, cart, i-a). Demonstration of the flowing of air from an area of high pressure to an area of low pressure (EBEC).

"Atmospheric Circulation, Part I" (color, si, 3–4 min, Sup 8, cart). The concept that the earth is heated less at the pole than the equator is studied by a light beam moving parallel from equator to pole—the spreading of light being obvious to the viewer (HSC).

"Atmospheric Circulation, Part II" (color, si, 3–4 min, Sup 8, cart). Using the University of Chicago Hydro-Lab, shows, in film sequence, the more complex circulation of a fluid in a rotating chamber compared to the similar circulation of earth's atmosphere. Time-lapse color satellite views relate the experiment to true patterns of air currents (HSC).

"Coriolis Effect" (color, si, 3–4 min, Sup 8, cart). Studies the apparent deflection of all objects to the right in the Northern Hemisphere and to the left in the Southern Hemisphere, then relates the principle to satellite views of cloud patterns over both the North and South poles (HSC).

"Major Wind Belts" (color, si, 3 min, Sup 8, cart, 1967) (UE&VA).

"Planetary Circulation" (color, sd, Sup 8, cart, i-h) (UE&VA).

"Why Air Circulates" (color, si, 4 min, Sup 8, cart, i-a) (EBEC).

Observations and Instruments

"Meteorology Station" (color, si, 4 min, Sup 8, cart, 1967) (EBEC).

"Weather Satellites" (color, sd, Sup 8, cart, 1968, i-h) (UE&VA).

"Weather Scientists" (color, sd, Sup 8, cart, 1961, p-j) (UE&VA).

"Weather from Space" (color, si, 3–4 min, Sup 8, cart). Time-lapse views of global weather patterns clearly show cyclonic circulation, prevailing winds, cloud formations, and effects on land and water masses (HSC).

Physical Meteorology (Heat, Optics, Electricity, etc.)

"Above the Horizon" (color, sd, 21 min, Sup 8, cart, 1966, i-a) (UE&VA).

"Air Expansion by Heat" (color, si, 4 min, Sup 8, cart, 1968, i-a). Laboratory experiment illustrating the effect of heating a parcel of air (EBEC).

"Air Pressure I: Change with Altitude" (color, si, 4 min, Sup 8, cart). Experiment depicting the effects of altitude change on air (EBEC).

"Cloud Formation" (color, si, 3–4 min, Sup 8, cart). Using a special chamber, a cloud is created using rapidly changing pressure. Time-lapse photography shows actual cloud formation as it happens in the earth's atmosphere, as viewed from the surface and from space (HSC).

"Condensation Nuclei" (color, si, 4 min, Sup 8, cart). Illustrates the process involved in the formation of water-cloud droplets as the result of certain types of nuclei (EG).

"Evaporation" (color, si, 3 min, Sup 8, cart, 1968). Illustrates several highly saline bodies of water as well as an evaporation experiment (SRA).

"Evaporation and Condensation" (color, si, 3–4 min, Sup 8, cart). The variables—humidity, surface area, wind, and heat—that affect rate of evaporation are studied through time-lapse photography. Also demonstrates the principle of cooling and condensation by re-radiation (HSC).

"Exploring the Upper Atmosphere" (color, sd, 5 min, Sup 8, cart, 1968) (HR).

"Flash Flood" (color, sd, 4 min, Sup 8, cart, 1967). Traces the water from a flash flood in a desert to its disappearance via evaporation and absorption (E).

"Formation of a Cloud: Laboratory Experiment" (color, si, 3 min, Sup 8, cart, i-a). Depicts the importance of nuclei in the atmosphere in the formation of clouds (EBEC).

"Homogenous Nucleation and the Polar Nature of Ice Crystals" (b/w, si, 3½ min, Sup 8, cart). Effects of air expansion on ice crystal growth and electrical fields on crystal orientation (EG).

"Nucleation of Supercooled Water Droplets" (b/w, si, 4 min, Sup 8). Depicts the transformation of supercooled droplets of water into ice through seeding with dry ice (EG).

"Ocean of Air, The" (color, sd, Sup 8, cart, 1961, i-h) (UE&VA).

"Round World and Sun's Rays, The" (color, si, 3½ min, Sup 8, cart). Solar energy from outer space (UE&VA).

"Sea Surface Meteorology" (color, sd, 24 min, Sup 8, cart, h-a) (UE&VA).

"Sun's Energy, The" (color, si, 17 min, Sup 8, cart, 1968, i-j) (CEF).

"Temperature, Pressure, and Wind, Part I" (color, si, 3-4 min, Sup 8, cart). Demonstrates the principle of a barometer. Air exerts pressure and differences in this pressure direct wind flow. Demonstrates that wind blows away from an area of high pressure and toward a low-pressure area (HSC).

"Temperature, Pressure and Wind, Part II" (color, si, 3-4 min, Sup 8, cart). Shows the simple air circulation resulting from three unequally heated areas. Also examines the air circulation resulting from the unequal heating of land and water (HSC).

"Why Is the Sky Blue?" (color, si, 4 min, Sup 8, cart, 1968, i-j) (BFA).

Synoptic Meteorology (Weather Analysis, Forecasting)

"Air Temperature" (color, si, 4 min, Sup 8, cart, 1966) (BFA).

"Clouds (Meteorology Series)" (color, si, 4 min, Sup 8, cart, 1966) (BFA).

"Condensation of Water Vapor" (color, si, 4 min, Sup 8, cart, 1968, i-a). Basic laboratory experiment illustrating the effects of cooling a parcel of air (EBEC).

"Formation of Mist (The Property of Air series)" (color, si, cart) (McGH).

"Fronts" (color, 4 min, Sup 8, cart, 1971, i-j). Animated (McGH).

"Hurricanes" (color, 4 min, Sup 8, cart, 1971, i-j). Animated (McGH).

"Inside the Weather" (color, sd, Sup 8, cart, 1961, i-h) (UE&VA).

"Mountain Storm" (color, si, 4 min, cart, 1967) (ICF).

"Myth, Superstition and Science" (color, si, 13 min, Sup 8, cart, p-h). Discusses various superstitions surrounding weather phenomena in light of scientific thought (IFB).

"Precipitation" (color, si, 4 min, Sup 8, cart, 1968, i-j) (BFA).

"Snow" (b/w, 13 min, Sup 8, cart, 1962, i-c) (BFA).

"Thunderstorms" (color, 4 min, Sup 8, cart, 1971, i-j). Animated (McGH).

"Tornadoes in Nature and the Laboratory" (b/w, si, Sup 8, cart).

Actual tornadoes illustrated, with some features demonstrated by laboratory experiments (EBEC).

"Water Cycle on Land" (color, 4 min, Sup 8, cart, 1970, i-j) (BFA).

"Water Cycle on the Ocean" (color, 4 min, Sup 8, cart, 1970, i-j) (BFA).

"Water Vapor" (color, si, 4 min, Sup 8, cart. 1968, i-j) (BFA).

"Weather: Fronts in a Depression" (color, si, 1½ min, cart) (PPAC).

"Weather Fronts and Precipitation" (color, si, 3–4 min, Sup 8, cart). Animated views show a typical low-pressure center passing over the United States, with its warm and cold fronts and cloud precipitation patterns. A time-lapse satellite-view of a low-pressure center with its associated cloud patterns is studied as the basis for satellite weather prediction (HSC).

"What Makes Weather" (color, si, cart, i-j) (CEF).

"When Air Masses Meet" (color, si, cart, i-j) (CEF).

Overhead Transparencies

Climatology

"Africa—Climate, Vegetation, Yearly Rainfall" (WPC)

"Annual Temperature Cycle in Middle Latitudes" (W)

"Asia—Climate, Vegetation, Yearly Rainfall" (WPC)

"Atmospheric Circulation and the Northern Hemisphere" (K&E)

"Australia and Oceanic—Climate, Vegetation, Yearly Rainfall" (BPC)

"Central America—Climate, Vegetation, Yearly Rainfall" (WPC)

"Climate" (W)

"Climate of Eastern Hemisphere" (JCA)

"Climate of Imaginary Continent" (HM)

"Climate Regions—Great Natural Regions of the United States, Annual Rainfall" (DEP)

"Climate of Western Hemisphere" (JCA)

"Climates" (WPC)

"Climates of the United States" (CV)

"Climatic Graphs" (GMC)

"Climatic Regions" (UTI)

"Earth-Wind Systems" (GMC)

"Economic Geography—Influence of Climate" (WPC)

"Europe—Climate, Vegetation, Yearly Rainfall" (WPC)

"Factors Influencing Climate of North America" (EV)

"Global Air Circulation" (W)

"Global Circulation in Cross Section" (W)

"Global Winds" (IPC)

"Heat Equator, The" (EA-V)

"Isolation and Latitude" (W)

"Latitudinal Patterns of Energy" (CV)

"Middle East—Climate, Vegetation, Rainfall" (WPC)

"Monsoons Are Seasonal Winds" (EA-V)

"Nature and Location of Jet Stream Activity" (EA-V)

"Nature and Location of Jet Stream Activity" (WPC)

"Normal Lapse Rate of Air Temperature" (W)

"North America—Climate, Vegetation, Yearly Rainfall" (World Geography Projecto-Aid Series) (WPC)

"Permafrost Distribution" (W)

"Planetary Winds System" (HM)

"Pressure and Planetary Wind Belts of the Earth" (T)

"Prevailing Surface Winds" (W)

"Prevailing Winds" (UTI)

"Primary Wind Systems" (BPC)

"Russia—Climate, Vegetation, Yearly Rainfall" (WPC)

"Seasons—1" (MPC)

"Seasons of the Earth" (T)

"Seasons of the Year" (UTI)

"South America—Climate, Vegetation, Yearly Rainfall" (WPC)

"Spring, March 21" (BPC)

"Storm Paths" (W)

"Subtropical High Pressure Cells" (W)

"Summer Average Temperature" (UTI)

"Summer, Spring, Fall, or Winter" (MMAMC)

"Water Masses Heat Slowly, Land Masses Heat Rapidly" (BPC)

"Weather Changes with the Seasons, No. 1" (MMAMC)

"Weather Changes with the Seasons, No. 2" (MMAMC)

"Wind Belts" (MPC)

"Wind Belts" (WPC)

"Wind Belts of the Earth" (EA-V)

"Wind Belts of the Earth" (UNC)

"Windbelts—Northern Hemisphere" (CV)

"Windbelts—Northern Hemisphere" (PSC)

"Winds at High Altitude" (W)

"Winter—Average Temperature" (UTI)

"World Average Annual Precipitation" (GMC)

"World Climate Regions" (EA-V)

"World Climate Regions" (GMC)

"World Climates" (DG)

"World Climates Divided into Five Categories" (DG)

"World—Pressure and Winds" (DG)

"World Pressure and Winds—January and July Contrasted" (DG)
"World Rainfall" (HI)
"World Rainfall and Temperature" (HI)
"World Temperature and Precipitation" (DG)
"World Temperature and Precipitation; World Geography" (DG)
"World-Wide Circulation of Air" (MMAMC)
"Zones of Converging and Diverging Air" (HM)

Dynamic Meteorology (Fields of Force and Motion)

"Adiabatic Cooling of Rising Air" (W)
"Causes of Weather" (PS)
"Charged Clouds" (UTI)
"Circulation of Atmosphere If the Earth Did Not Rotate" (EA-V)
"Coriolis Force" (DG)
"Coriolis Force" (W)
"Deflective Force of the Earth's Radiation" (W)
"Does Air Go Up or Down?" (MMAMC)
"How Winds Originate" (T)
"Lapse Rate Graph" (GMC)
"Lowered Air Pressure" (UTI)
"Radiation in the Atmosphere" (EDRECS)
"Rising Air Cools and Loses Moisture" (BPS)
"Rising Air Currents" (UTI)
"Winds Caused by Convention" (MMAMC)

Observations and Instruments

"Aneroid Barometer" (DEP)
"Aneroid Barometer" (MPC)
"Atmospheric Refraction" (CFD)
"Barometer" (WPC)
"Basic Cloud Shapes" (IPC)
"Beaufort Wind Scale" (UTI)
"Cloud Forms" (W)
"Cloud Types" (HI)
"Cloud Types" (MMAMC)
"Cloud Types" (MPC)
"Cloud Types" (T)
"Cloud Types" (W)
"Cloud Types, Part 1" (DG)
"Cloud Types, Part 2" (DG)
"Clouds from Gemini" (IPC)
"Measuring and Recording Weather Elements" (T)
"Mercury Barometers" (MPC)
"Nimbus Photo of USA" (IPC)
"Nimbus Weather Satellite" (IPC)
"Parts of an Aircraft" (T)
"Station Model, The" (MMAMC)
"Temperature Scales" (N)
"Thermometer" (WPC)
"Tiros Weather Satellite" (WPC)
"Torricellian Barometer, The" (DEP)
"Types of Clouds" (T)
"Types of Clouds" (UTI)
"U.S. Space Program—Weather and Cloud Photos" (A series) (IPC)
"Weather Instruments" (CV)
"Weather Instruments" (MMAMC)

"Weather Instruments" (MPC)
"Weather Instruments" (PSC)
"Weather Satellites" (MPC)

"What Might This Thermometer Read?" (MMAMC)
"Wind Barometer Table" (UTI)

Physical Meteorology (Heat, Optics, Electricity, etc.)

"Atmosphere, The" (IPC)
"Atmosphere, The" (MMAMC)
"Atmosphere, The" (MPC)
"Atmosphere of the Earth, The" (MMAMC)
"Atmospheric and Solar Radiation" (W)
"Can You Make a Cloud?" (MMAMC)
"Charged Clouds" (UTI)
"Composition of the Atmosphere" (W)
"Composition of Dry Air by Volume in the Troposphere" (MMAMC)
"Composition of Earth's Atmosphere" (MPC)
"Condensation" (MMAMC)
"Dew Point" (MMAMC)
"Earth's Atmosphere, The" (K&E)
"Earth's Atmosphere, The" (W)
"Energy Budget, The" (HM)
"Evaporation" (BPC)
"Evaporation and Condensation" (MPC)
"Evaporation and Condensation" (W)
"Formation of Lightning" (W)
"Greenhouse Effect, The" (WPC)
"Heat Energy Increases the Motion of a Molecule" (MMAMC)
"Heat and Its Transfer" (MMAMC)
"How Rain Is Formed—Coalescence" (BPC)
"How Snow Is Formed" (BPC)
"Hydrologic Cycle, The" (CV)

"Hydrologic Cycle, The" (K&E)
"Hydrologic Cycle" (UNC)
"Insolation of Earth" (GMC)
"Insolation and Ground Radiation" (W)
"Insolation and Temperature" (CV)
"Layers of the Atmosphere" (CV)
"Layers of the Atmosphere" (PSC)
"Lightning" (PS)
"Melting" (MMAMC)
"Method of Purifying Water" (T)
"Paths of Radiation" (W)
"Precipitation" (MMAMC)
"Precipitation" (MPC)
"Pressure Decreases with Altitude" (W)
"Radiation in the Atmosphere" (WPC)
"Rainbow, The" (CFD)
"Regions of the Atmosphere" (WPC)
"Solar Heating and Greenhouse Principle" (W)
"Some Forms of Precipitation" (W)
"Structure of Air" (PS)
"Structure and Chracteristics of the Atmosphere" (T)
"Sun Helps Us, The" (MMAMC)
"Sun Influences the Temperature of Our Atmosphere, The" (MMAMC)
"Sun Is Our Source of Heat and Light, The" (MMAMC)
"Three States of Water Exist in

the Atmosphere" (BPC)
"Troposphere and Stratosphere"
(W)
"Types of Precipitation"
(MMAMC)
"Water Budget" (HM)
"Water Cycle" (GMC
"Water Cycle" (HM)
"Water Cycle" (JCA)
"Water Cycle, The" (MPC)
"Water Cycle" (T)
"Water Cycle" (WPC)

"Water Cycle—Weather" (IPC)
"What Makes a Cloud?"
(MMAMC)
"What Makes Rain?" (MMAMC)
"What Makes Snowflakes?"
(MMAMC)
"What Warms the Air Outside?"
(MMAMC)
"Why Is It Hot in Summer and
Cold in Winter?" (BPC)
"Wilson Cloud Chamber" (DEP)

Synoptic Meteorology (Weather Analysis and Forecasting)

"Air Currents" (EA-V)
"Air Currents" (WPC)
"Air Currents, Mountains and
Precipitation" (IPC)
"Air Masses" (M)
"Air Masses" (UTI)
"Air Masses of North America"
(W)
"Air Over Land Cools and De-
scends" (BPC)
"Air Pressure" (MMAMC)
"Air Pressure" (MPC)
"Atmospheric Pressure" (T)
"Circulation of Atmosphere"
(HI)
"Circulation—Day and Night"
(CV)
"Circulation—Day and Night"
(PSC)
"Cloud Formation" (MPC)
"Cloud Formations" (IPC)
"Cloud Formations—Weather"
(IPC)
"Clouds" (PS)
"Cold Front" (BPC)
"Cold Front" (EA-V)
"Cold Front" (GMC)
"Cold Front" (IPC)
"Cold Front" (MMAMC).
"Cold Front" (W)

"Cold Front and Its Weather"
(T)
"Cold Fronts" (CV)
"Cold Fronts" (PSC)
"Cold and Warm Fronts" (IPC)
"Contrasts in Land and Water
Heating" (W)
"Convection Circulation in the
Atmosphere" (K&E)
"Convection Currents" (JCA)
"Cross Section of Atmosphere"
(GMC)
"Cumuliform Clouds" (BPC)
"Cumulonimbus Cloud and
Thunderstorm" (W)
"Cyclone" (W)
"Cyclone Movement in the
United States" (CV)
"Daily Cycle of Relative Humidi-
ty and Air Temperature" (W)
"Daily Weather Map" (N)
"Development of Fronts" (H)
"Development of Low Pressure
Areas" (Cyclones) (MMAMC)
"Development of a Middle Lati-
tude Cyclone" (W)
"Earth Science—Weather"
(GMC)
"Frontal Movement" (DG)
"Frontal Movement" (W)

Front East and South" (UNC)
"Warm Air-Cool Air" (BPC)
"Warm Front" (BPC)
"Warm Front" (EA-V)
"Warm Front" (IPC)
"Warm Front" (MMAMC)
"Warm Front" (N)
"Warm Front and Its Weather" (j) (T)
"Warm Fronts" (CV)
"Warm Fronts" (PSC)
"We Dress for Weather" (i-h) (MMAMC)
"We Need Precipitation" (i-h) (MMAMC)
"We Prepare for Weather in Other Ways" (MMAMC)
"Weather Coldfront" (j) (UTI)
"Weather Fronts" (W)
"Weather Information Map" (j-h) (UTI)
"Weather—Land Breeze" (j) (UTI)

"Weather Map" (CV)
"Weather Map" (j-h) (PSC)
"Weather Map, The" (j-h) (T)
"Weather Map Analysis" (CV)
"Weather Map of a Cold Front" (h) (EA-V)
"Weather Map—Fronts" (IPC)
"Weather Map Symbols" (N)
"Weather Maps" (i-h) (DG)
"Weather Maps" (i-j) (MPC)
"Weather Maps" (j-h) (T)
"Weather Maps Tell Us About the Weather" (i-h) (MPC)
"Weather Prediction" (j-h) (MPC)
"Weather—Sea Breeze" (j) (UTI)
"Weather—Warmfront" (j) (UTI)
"Weatherman Tells Us About the Weather, The" (i-h) (MMAMC)
"Wind" (PS)
"Wind—Friend and Foe" (PS)
"Winds, Currents and Explorations" (EBEC)

Unclassified

"Basic Science—Meteorology" (A series) (j-h) (T)

"Earth Science—Meteorology" (A series) (i-h) (DG)

"Earth Science—Meteorology" (A series) (j-h) (HI)

"Earth Science—Meteorology" (A series) (N)

"General Science" (A series) (j-h) (MMAMC)

"General Science—Meteorology" (A series) (T)

"Meteorology" (A series) (h) (EA-V)

"Meteorology" (A series) (PSC)

"Weather" (A series) (BPC)

"Weather" (A series) (IPC)

"Weather" (A series) (MMAMC)

"Weather" (A series) (MPC)

Color Photographs

Key

(1) Climatology
(2) Observations and Instruments
(3) Synoptic Meteorology

Curriculum Color Prints (18″ × 13″)

"Cloud Formations" (CEA), (DG), (IAI), (N), (W)

1. Clouds of Vertical Development, Part I   (3)
2. Clouds of Vertical Development, Part II   (3)
3. High Clouds   (3)
4. Low Clouds   (3)
5. Middle Clouds   (3)
6. Special Cloud Forms   (3)

"Deserts of the World" (CES), (DG), (IAI), (N), (W)

1. Desert Environments and Principles Affecting Their Locations   (1)
2. Desert Pavement   (1)
3. Desert Vegetation   (1)
4. The Polar Deserts: Arctic and Antarctica   (1)
5. The Sandy Desert: The Exception   (1)

"Weather Instruments" (CES), (DG), (IAI), (N), (W)

1. Barometer   (2)
2. Instrument Shelters and Weather Forecasting for Public Safety   (2)
3. Pilot Balloon Observations and Nimbus TV "Pictures"   (2)
4. Precipitation Gauges   (2)
5. Thermometers   (2)
6. Wind Instruments   (2)

"Weather Phenomena" (CES), (DG), (IAI), (N), (W)

1. Dew and Frost   (3)
2. Fog   (3)
3. Rain   (3)
4. Rainbow   (3)
5. Rime Ice   (3)
6. Tornado   (3)

Supplementary Reading Materials

The supplementary reading volumes contained in the following extensive listing are almost exclusively paperbound volumes. Although not all-inclusive, the listings do represent a major portion of the currently available paperback books that should be of interest to both teachers and students. These materials constitute an economical source that is often overlooked. These available paperbacks span all levels of instruction from the junior high school to reference works for the teachers. No attempt has been made to indicate the grade or reading level because many are useful for a wide range of abilities. Prices are subject to fluctuation, but most of these publications are reasonably priced. A brief annotation is included for most titles.

Atkinson, Bruce W. *The Weather Business: Observation, Analysis, Forecasting, and Modification.* Garden City, N.Y.: Doubleday & Co., 1969.

Austin, Mary. *Land of Little Rain.* Garden City, N.Y.: Doubleday & Co., 1961, 171 pp. Description of the semiarid region extending southeast from Yosemite, through Death Valley to the Mojave Desert.

Bates, D. R., *The Earth and Its Atmosphere.* New York: John Wiley & Sons, 1961, 324 pp. Covers knowledge in geophysical sciences including: composition of interior and deep crust of the earth; circulation of the oceans and atmosphere; causes of auroras and magnetic storms; climatology; meteorology; cosmic radiation; and the geomagnetic field of the earth. Also covers the ice ages and the origin of our planet and its probable end.

Battan, Louis J. *Cloud Physics and Cloud Seeding.* Garden City, N.Y.: Doubleday & Co., Anchor Books, 1962, 144 pp. Authoritative account of this field for the general reader.

_____ . *Harvesting the Clouds—Advances in Weather Modification.* Science Study Series. Garden City, N.Y.: Doubleday & Co., Anchor Books, 1969, 168 pp.

_____ . *The Nature of Violent Storms.* Science Study Series, Garden City, N.Y.: Doubleday & Co., Anchor Books, 1961, 158 pp. Discussion of the mechanisms of extratropical cyclones, hurricanes, tornadoes, and so forth, and what modern research is doing toward understanding them.

_____ . *Radar Observes the Weather.* Garden City, N.Y.: Doubleday & Co., Anchor Books, 1962, 153 pp. Introduction to the subject of radar observation of weather for the nonspecialist.

_____ . *The Thunderstorm.* New York: New American Library of World Literature, Signet Service Library, 1964, 128 pp. Interesting, concise, and authoritative presentation on thunderstorms.

_____ . *The Unclean Sky—A Meteorologist Looks at Air Pollution*. Science Studies Series. Garden City, N.Y.: Doubleday & Co., Anchor Books, 1966, 141 pp. Describes how the atmosphere has become a dumping ground, how this has affected the world of man and nature, and what can still be done to improve this worsening situation.

Bentley, W. A., and W. J. Humphreys. *Snow Crystals*. New York: Dover Publications, 1962, 226 pp. Contains over 2,000 photographs of snowflakes. Discusses the technique and problems of photographing snow crystals; classification; crystallography; the science of crystal formation; the nature and causes of ice flowers; windowpane frost; and so on.

Blanchard, Duncan C. *From Raindrops to Volcanoes, Adventures with Sea Surface Meteorology*. Science Study Series. Garden City, N.Y.: Doubleday & Co., Anchor Books, 1967, 180 pp. Describes how meteorology, oceanography, physics, chemistry, and volcanology merge in the study of the raindrop. Gives descriptions of experiments and observations that can be conducted by the reader.

Clausse, Roger, and Leopold Fancy. *The Clouds*. New York: Grove Press, Evergreen Books, 1961.

Craig, Richard A. *The Edge of Space—Exploring the Upper Atmosphere*. Science Study Series. Garden City, N.Y.: Doubleday & Co., Anchor Books, 1968, 150 pp. Presents with clarity the techniques and methods that have been used during the last 50 years to extend our knowledge of the atmosphere from the tropopause to the exosphere.

Defant, Albert. *Ebb and Flow: The Tides of Earth, Air and Water*. Ann Arbor: University of Michigan Press, 1958, 121 pp. Deals with why tides exist, why they work, how they work and what they are.

Edinger, James G. *Watching for the Wind—The Seen and Unseen Influences on Local Weather*. Science Study Series. Garden City, N.Y.: Doubleday & Co., Anchor Books, 1967, 148 pp. Discusses in popular style the author's personal and professional experiences with local weather in California and South America.

Esposito, John C. *Vanishing Air: The Ralph Nader Study Group Report on Air Pollution*. New York: Grossman Publishers, 1970, 328 pp. Startling report that shows that ecological disaster within our lifetime is not beyond the realm of possibility—and yet industry and government show relatively little concern about air pollution.

Flohn, H. *Climate and Weather*. New York: McGraw-Hill Book Co., World University Library, 1969, 253 pp. A general introduction to meteorology covering the main principles of the physics of the atmosphere, aspects of climate and weather, current problems in meteorology, and the controversial subject of climate and weather control.

Hare, F. K. *The Restless Atmosphere* rev. ed. New York: Harper & Row, 1963, 192 pp. An introduction to the field of dynamic climatology in which the author describes the actual day-to-day weather processes involved in the principal types of world climate.

Holmes, David C. *Weather Made Clear*. New York: Sterling Publishing Co., 1965, 128 pp. A survey, with excellent documentation, of the fields of meteorology and climatology. Fine account of the origin of atmosphere. Well illustrated.

Hubert, Lester F., and Paul E. Lehr. *Weather Satellites*. Waltham, Mass.: Blaisdell Publishing Co., 1967, 120 pp. Explains the manner in which weather satellite observations are interpreted and used. Also discusses the history of meteorological satellites, their equipment, data acquisition and reduction, and what we may expect from future weather satellites.

Humphreys, W. J. *Physics of the Air*. New York: Dover Publications, 1964, 676 pp. Covers classical materials and theories in meteorology. Topics include mechanics and thermodynamics of atmosphere, atmospheric optics, atmospheric electricity and auroras, meteorological acoustics, and factors of climate control.

Kimble, George H. T. *Our American Weather*. Bloomington: Indiana University Press, 1961, 322 pp. Analyzes and describes American weather on a monthly basis including regional and statewide weather in detail.

Kuenen, P. H. *Realms of Water: Some Aspects of Its Cycle in Nature*. New York: John Wiley & Sons, 1963, 327 pp. Discusses the importance of water in determining climate and landscape. Considers many aspects of physical geography, meteorology, and oceanography, and many natural phenomena from glaciers to the bottom of the seas, from clouds to subterranean grottoes.

La Chapelle, Edward R. *Field Guide to Snow Crystals*. Seattle: University of Washington Press, 1969.

Landsberg, Helmut E. *Weather and Health—An Introduction to Biometeorology*. Science Study Series. Garden City, N.Y.: Doubleday & Co., Anchor Books, 1969, 168 pp.

Lehr, Paul E., R. Will Burnett, and Herbert S. Zim. *Weather: Air Masses, Clouds, Rainfall, Storms, Weather Maps, Climate*. Golden Nature Guide. New York: Simon and Schuster, 1971, 160 pp. What makes the weather, how it is studied and forecast. Elementary guide to meteorological phenomena and processes with beautiful color illustrations.

Loebsack, Theo. *Our Atmosphere*. New York: New American Library of World Literature, Mentor Book, 1961, 190 pp. Covers subject of earth's atmosphere, the relationship to life on our planet, and speculates about the possibility of life on other planets with associated atmospheres.

Mason, B. J. *Clouds, Rain and Rainmaking*. New York: Cambridge University Press, 1962, 145 pp. Discusses the formation and constitution of clouds and the development of snow, rain, hail, and lightning. Includes some simple experiments.

Miller, A. *Meteorology*, 2nd ed. Merrill Physical Science Series. Columbus, Ohio: Charles E. Merrill Publishing Co., 1971, 154 pp. An introduction to meteorology designed for college nonscience majors. Includes chapters on climate and weather forecasting and modification.

Ohring, George. *Weather on the Planets: What We Know About Their Atmospheres*. Science Study Series. Garden City, N.Y.: Doubleday & Co., Anchor Books, 1966, 146 pp. Describes how meteorologists obtain information about planetary atmospheres and how it is used by earthbound meteorologists and climatologists.

Reiter, Elmar R. *Jet Streams: How Do They Affect Our Weather?* Science Study Series. Garden City, N.Y.: Doubleday & Co., Anchor Books, 1967, 189 pp.

Richardson, Lewis F. *Weather Predictions by Numerical Processes.* New York: Dover Publications, 1965, 236 pp. Shows development of laws of meteorology through mathematical methods.

Rummery, G. R. *The Geosystem.* Brown Foundations of Earth Science Series. Dubuque, Iowa: William C. Brown Co., 1970, 135 pp. Presents the earth as a system in which land, sea, and air are dynamically integrated in a single system through processes by which energy, matter, and momentum are continually exchanged.

Saltzman, Barry, ed. *Selected Papers in the Theory of Thermal Convection: With Special Application to the Earth's Planetary Atmosphere.* New York: Dover Publications, 1962, 461 pp. Describes motions of earth's atmosphere. Twenty-five basic theoretical papers on thermal convection by major scientists, past and present.

Schultz, Gwen. *Glaciers and the Ice Age.* New York: Holt, Rinehart and Winston, 1963, 128 pp. Combines the findings of geology and anthropology to produce the total glacial picture including landforms, geologic processes, atmosphere, oceans, plants, animals, climate, people, and use of land.

Scientific American, eds. *Planet Earth.* New York: Simon and Schuster, 1957, 164 pp. A collection of articles taken from past issues of *Scientific American.* Discusses the origin of the earth, its core and mantle, its crust, the hydrosphere, the atmosphere, and the edge of space.

Spar, Jerome. *Earth, Sea, and Air—A Survey of the Geophysical Sciences,* 2d ed. Reading, Mass.: Addison-Wesley Publishing Co., 1965, 152 pp. Gives the student an overview of man's total natural physical environment.

Spitz, Armand, *Weather,* New York: Bantam Books, 1967, 154 pp. The essential elements of weather—types of clouds, the origin of storms and hurricanes, and the use of weather instruments—are discussed in this basic work.

Whitnah, Donald R. *History of the United States Weather Bureau.* Chicago: University of Illinois Press, 1965, 288 pp. Comprehensive history of the weather bureau, from its birth in 1870 to the present.

Widger, W. K., Jr. *Meteorological Satellites.* New York: Holt, Rinehart and Winston, 1966, 272 pp. Describes the history of meteorological satellites, the various types used at present, use of information from these satellites, and prospects for the future.

Free and Inexpensive Materials

Climatology

"Climate of the United States" (Cat. #A1. 10/a:1824). Forty-six data charts describing the climate of the United States (USGPO), 20¢.

"Climates of the States" (Cat. #C30.71/s). Fifty-one pamphlets describing climates, weather, temperature, and rainfall (USGPO), 10—25¢.

"Climates of the World" Contains a brief description of the main features of the continental climates of the world including: temperature and precipitation maps, monthly and annual temperatures, and precipitation in tabular form (USGPO), 35¢.

"Climates of the World" (A1.10/a:1822). Gives data on mean and extreme temperatures and monthly and yearly precipitation for 387 representative stations throughout the world, exclusive of the United States (USGPO), 10¢.

"Selected Climatic Maps of the United States" (C52.2:C961) (USGPO), 25¢.

"Tornado Statistics" (Pub. #660029). Presentation of statistical incidences and damage of tornadoes throughout 1969 (ESSA), 5¢.

"Worldwide Extremes of Temperature, Precipitation and Pressure" (Pub. #680032). Recorded by continental area (ESSA).

Observations and Instruments

"Aneroid Barometer, The" (C30.2:D26/2). The purpose of this publication is to assist amateur meteorologists and others who own aneroid barometers to obtain an understanding of the operation and use of these instruments (USGPO), 15¢.

"Climatological Observers" (rev. 1962; 76 pp., C30.4:B/962). List of instructions (USGPO), 50¢.

"Cloud Chart" A pictorial presentation of the major cloud types accompanied by a description of their formation and associated weather (one copy per teacher) (SA), free.

"Cloud Folder" Illustrates the different types of clouds with a description of their associated weather phenomena (ESSA), free.

"Clouds" (Cat. #C52.2:C/962). A pictorial presentation of major cloud forms (ESSA), 25¢.

"Hygrometers" (35 pp., Pub. #C13.33:73, 1964). The NBS standard hygrometer (USGPO), free.

"Instructions for Home Weather Casting" Construction of an aneroid barometer and its use in weather forecasting (one copy per teacher) (TIC), free.

"Manual of Marine Meteorological Observations" (Cat. #C30.4:M/964, 1964). Instructions to be used to observe weather at sea (USGPO), $1.50.

"Psychometric Tables" (Cat. #C30.2P95/941). Presents values for vapor pressure, relative humidity, and dew-point temperature (USGPO), 30¢.

"Weather Bureau Spotter's Guide for Identifying and Reporting Severe Local Storms" (Pub. #690013) (ESSA), 25¢.

"Weather Observing" (Cat. #C30.66/2:1.11/2) (USGPO), $1.00.

"Weatherman of the Sea" (Pub. #CG-225). Describes the operation of an oceanic weather station (USGPO).

Physical Meteorology (Heat, Optics, Electricity, etc.)

"Hydrologic Cycle" (Pub. #670003). Presentation of both the land and marine phases of the hydrologic cycle (ESSA), 20¢.

Synoptic Meteorology (Weather Analysis and Forecasting)

"Clouds" (C52.2:C/62). Contains 26 color photographs of various cloud formations and other related information (USGPO), 25¢.

"Evaporation" (28 pp., Pub. #I19.13:1839-m, 1967). Comparison of methods of estimating potential evapotranspiration from climatological data in arid and sub-humid environments (USGPO), 15¢.

"Floods and Flood Warnings" (Pub. #660025). Gives an account of ESSA's observations of the nation's rivers, flood warnings, and safety rules (ESSA), free.

"Frost and the Prevention of Frost Damage" (C30.2F92) (USGPO), 25¢.

"Hurricane—The Greatest Storm on Earth" (Pub. #670055). Includes a description of the incidence, causes, structure, dynamics, and effects of a hurricane, accompanied by a discussion of ESSA's efforts in tracking and warning (ESSA), 65¢.

"Hurricane Information and Atlantic Tracking Chart" (Pub. #680006). Describes hurricanes as well as safety rules, warnings, nomenclature, and names of hurricanes (ESSA), 15¢.

"Hurricane Safety Rules/Storm Surge—Killer from the Sea" (Poster #670007) (ESSA), 65¢.

"Hydrologic Cycle" (Pub. #C52.2:H99, 1967). Importance of water and its sources to human beings. Describes various phases of the cycle, types of precipitation, and work of ESSA (USGPO), 15¢.

"Lightning" (Pub. #C52.2:L/62). Describes lightning and safety rules (USGPO), 15¢.

"National Meteorological Center, The" (Cat. #680023). Describes the work of the center including its data collection, analysis, and forecasting (USGPO).

"Smog and Weather" Brochure describes smog and the role that weather plays in its characteristics and distribution (NCA), free.

"Snowflakes" (Pub. #41). Discusses identification and preservation (ASRC).

"Some Devastating North Atlantic Hurricanes of the 20th Century" (Pub. #680024). Includes storm tracks, deaths, and damage in the U.S. from 1900–1969 (ESSA).

"Thunderstorms, Part II" (rev., 8 pp., Cat. #C30.65:8, 1960). Causes, life cycle, associated phenomena, incidence, and safety rules of thunderstorms (USGPO), 5¢.

"Tornado" Pub. #660028). Describes the causes and effects of tornadoes and ESSA's work in tracking and warning (ESSA), 20¢.

"Tornado Preparedness Planning" (Pub. #680019). Describes community planning against the threat of tornadoes as well as severe thunderstorms (ESSA), 25¢.

"Tornado Safety Rules" (Poster 9" × 11" Pub. #660030) (ESSA), 5¢-$1.50/100.

"Tornado Watch" (Pub#660031). Describes tornado watch and warning system in the context of April 1965's Palm Sunday tornado disaster (ESSA), 5¢.

"Weather Bureau Activities" (15 pp., 1962). Describes the activities of the Weather Bureau (ESSA), free.

"Weather Bureau Marine Weather Services" (Pub. #660003) (ESSA).

"Weather and the Construction Industry" (Pub. #660013). Summary of the effects of weather on construction (ESSA).

"Weather Forecasting" (Cat. #30.2:F76/3, 1960). Fundamental principles of forecasting (USGPO), 25c.

"Weather Maps" (Pub. #C52.11/2). Daily weather maps, weekly series (USGPO), subscription price $4.50/year; 15c/copy.

"What Is This Thing Called Humidity?" Presents various questions and answers concerning humidity (TIC), free.

"Winter Storms" (Pub. #670020). Causes, dangers, terms of watches and warnings, and safety rules surrounding winter storms (ESSA), 15¢.

"Winter Storms" (Cat. C52.2:St/7). Describes conditions accompanying various types of winter storms and provides safety rules (USGPO), 15¢.

Unclassified

"Air Pollution Experiments for Junior and Senior High School Classes" (1969). Nineteen experiments for the science laboratory (APCA), $1.00.

"American Geophysical Union" (publication list) (AGU), free.

"American Meteorological Society" (publication list) (AMS), free.

"British Government" (publication list) (BIS), free.

"Career Opportunities for Meteorologists" Meteorological job opportunities with the weather bureau (ESSA), free.

"Challenge of Meteorology" Opportunities and requirements for a career as a meteorologist (AMS), free.

"Employment Opportunities in Dynamic Meteorology and Applied Mathematics" (Pub. #670023) (ESSA), free.

"Employment Opportunities for High School, Vocational School, Junior College, and Technical School Graduates" (Pub. #680022) (ESSA), free.

"Employment Outlook for Earth Scientists" (Cat. L2.3:1550-29). Geologists, geophysicists, meteorologists, and oceanographers (USGPO), 10¢.

"Environmental Science Services Administration" (publication list) (ESSA), free.

"ESSA—A New Agency" (Pub. #660011). Describes the work and organization of ESSA; contains a publication list (ESSA), free.

"Hurricanes, The Naming of" (Pub. #680021). The what, how, and why of naming both Atlantic and Pacific cyclones (ESSA), free.

"Meteorology" Publication list of the Smithsonian Institution (SI), free.

"Science and Service—Careers in the ESSA Commissioner Officer Corps" (Pub. #660021). Presents the objectives, history, and career opportunities (ESSA), free.

"Threshold ESSA" (Pub. #660022). Discusses the opportunities for a scientific career in ESSA (ESSA), free.

"Weather, Astronomy and Meteorology" Publication lists of Government Printing Office (USGPO), free.

PART...4

Oceanography

Classroom Activities in Oceanography

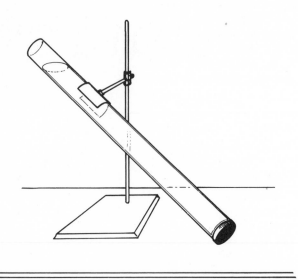

Figure 4-1

The first three classroom activities relating to the topic of oceanography involve the basic apparatus shown in Figure 4-1: a ring stand and accompanying rod, clamp, and plastic cylinder 2½'-3' long, 1½"-3" diameter) stoppered at one end.

Density and Its Relationship to Currents

The relationship between differences in density of water and its circulation can be introduced effectively with an activity involving students working with two factors that influence the water's density.

The activity is best preceded by a brief discussion where the students relate the causes for currents in sea water (namely, temperature and salinity being the chief influences). The students are then given the apparatus shown in Figure 4-1 as well as test tubes, salt, ice, food coloring, thermometer, heat source, stop watch (they may use wristwatches with a second hand), and protractors. With these materials they are asked to investigate the influences of salinity and temperature on density.

The students will try a number of things including varying slope of tube, temperature of water, amount of salt in tube or slurry poured in from the test tube, or varying two or more entities at one time. You are best advised to let them pursue their own interests right through collection of data and conclusions. In the post-laboratory discussion the various groups of students should be asked to present and defend their procedures, data, and conclusions.

This activity invariably leads to a multifaceted discussion that involves not only the influence of salinity and temperature on currents, but also scientific method. One should not be overly concerned with groups who may have followed an inaccurate procedure because they will have learned a great deal that will carry over into future activities.

Turbidity Currents

The investigation of the nature of turbidity currents contains a good deal of relevance to any study of oceanography. An activity contained in the Earth Science Curriculum Project text *Investigating the Earth* (Boston: Houghton Mifflin Publishing Co., 1967) places in the hands of students materials with which they can create models of turbidity currents and thus observe their behavior.

This activity should be preceded by a brief discussion of the effects of these currents; that is, broken oceanic communication cables, coarse sediments on the ocean floor far removed from other such deposits as well as their hypothesized relationship to submarine canyons. Following this discussion, give the students the basic apparatus depicted in Figure 4-1 as well as test tubes and quantities of soil from which they can make slurries of water and soil which will simulate the turbidity current. The students utilize these materials by mixing a number of slurries, pouring them into the cylinder of water, and observing.

In the discussion that follows, the relationship between these models and the real environment should be stressed. In reporting their observations students will come upon a number of related topics such as "turbulent" and "laminar" flow, sedimentation as the current moves down the tube, speed of current versus slope or amount of solid material, and others.

Settling Rates of Sediment

A third topic that can be investigated with the basic apparatus is settling rates of particles in water. In this activity the students can investigate the relationship of average particle size to settling rate.

The students are given (1) the basic cylinder and ringstand—but are asked to set the cylinder in an upright position; (2) sediment separated according to size; (3) stopwatch (wristwatches with second hands may be used); and (4) a meter stick. The students are asked to study the relationship, if any, between particle size and settling rate, to graph their data, and to draw inferences to the natural environment.

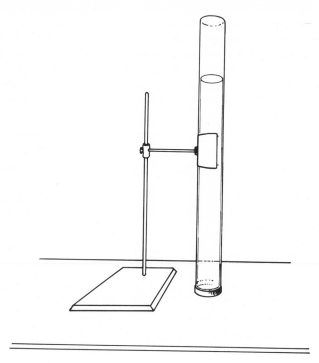

Figure 4-2

In this activity the students will be able to gain first-hand familiarity with the desired concept. The post-activity discussion will not only be directed at student-collected data and conclusions, but will relate this to a wide range of natural phenomena such as deltas, stream loads versus velocity, and other topics. This activity oftentimes provides a valuable springboard to these other areas of earth science.

Water Pollution

Whether one is dealing with salt water or bodies of fresh water, both have the same problem—pollution. Pollution comes in many forms, but one thing is evident: few bodies of water are untouched by it. Many students are quite concerned about this topic but often are not fully aware of the nature or scope of water pollution in their own community. The first step in environmental education is to create an awareness of one's own environment and its pollutants. The most appropriate manner is a field trip to some streams, ponds, or lakes in the vicinity of the school where, in all too many cases, the pollution speaks for itself.

Once this increased awareness is combined with their already established concern, future activities dealing with this topic are usually student initiated. Many of these activities center around studying the water in greater detail and determining the type and source of the pollutants. Other activities may center around taking this data to authorities and urging change. Such activities still fulfill the criteria of students working with science—making observations, collecting data, and drawing conclusions. They do, however, incorporate one added ingredient: that is, *acting*.

Sea Water Density Determination Using the Soda-Straw Hydrometer

In this activity measurements will be taken of the relative densities of sea water, lake or river water, tap water, and distilled water. If sea water is not available, prepare a substitute solution to simulate sea water by making a solution of 96½% water and 3½% regular table salt by weight.

Construct a soda-straw hydrometer to measure specific gravity of the various water samples. The soda-straw hydrometer may be constructed by pushing enough clay in one end of a straw to make it float upright in the test tube of water, with about one-third of the straw's length above the surface when placed in distilled water. Prepare a scale about five centimeters long marked in millimeters. Tape the scale to the soda straw and the hydrometer will be complete.

Because it is pure, distilled water should be used as a standard to compare the densities of other water. Place the now completed hydrometer in a large test tube of distilled water. While the hydrometer is floating freely, note the point on the scale to which the water has risen. In the same manner as with the distilled water, test the other water samples and note the point on the scale to which the water rises. You have measured the relative densities of different water samples using the buoyancy of a liquid as the measure of its density.

In which sample did the hydrometer rise the highest? The lowest? Why? Which sample is the heaviest? The lightest? Sea water, as was probably noted, differs more greatly from the other samples than they differ from each other. What effect would the differing densities of sea water and river water have when a river flows into the ocean?

You might try to quantify your measurements by measuring the length of the hydrometer below the surface in each of the samples and then dividing the length below the surface in distilled water by the length in each of the other samples. This would give you the specific gravity of the sample being compared to distilled water.

Demonstration of Wave Motion

The objective of this activity is to demonstrate wave motion, such as that which occurs on the seas of the earth. Figure 4-3 shows the wave form which travels across water, usually as a result of wind blowing across the surface of the water. Only the crests and troughs of waves travel across the oceans and not the water itself.

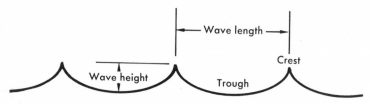

Figure 4-3

To demonstrate this wave motion, tie a knot in the middle of a rope and then fasten one end of the rope to a stationary object, leaving the other end free. Jiggle the rope from the free end while the rope is extended its full length. Waves will pass along the rope toward the stationary end.

Describe the motion of the knot. How does the rope itself move? Can you change wave height and wave length? How? What causes changes in wave height and length in an actual situation on the water?

Using the Stream Table for Oceanographic Studies

The purpose of this activity is to point up the fact that the stream table may be used for oceanographic studies in addition to the other stream-related activities discussed in the physical geology activities section of this Sourcebook. For oceanographic demonstrations, a fairly sizable reservoir of water at one end of the tilted stream table will simulate a marine body of water.

The great variety of activities and investigations that may be conducted using a stream table are limited only by the inventiveness and imagination of the teacher and students.

Waves and wave action may be simulated by using an electric fan or small paddle to generate waves. Model shoreline features can be built of sand and other materials and these can be altered by having the simulated waves act on the shoreline features, which demonstrates how wave erosion and deposition take place in a shoreline environment.

A model shoreline may be built, and subsequently the water level may be raised and lowered to simulate submergence and emergence.

Changes in base level taking place in this type of simulation have far-reaching effects on an entire region, which may also be demonstrated in this activity.

Sedimentation in the ocean and the building of deltaic deposits may also be simulated, in addition to numerous other activities.

16mm Films

Oceanographic Research

"Activities of the U.S. Coast and Geodetic Survey" (color, 22 min, 1953, j-c). Discusses the survey's activities including hydrography, geodesy, photogrammetry, and magnetic observation (USWB), free.

"Atlantic Crossing, The" (b/w, sd, 30 min, 1968, h-c). Reviews the seismic study of the ocean floor from Trinidad to Liberia, which revealed the thickness, altitude and structure of the sediments (TELE).

"Careers in Oceanography" (color, 28 min, 1966, j-a) (MN-10063). Tells of the future research activities and equipment in the laboratory or aboard ship that await an individual who chooses a career in oceanography (USN), free.

"Deep Frontier, The" (color, 25 min, 1967, j-c). Presents recent technological developments in the exploration and study of the ocean (MTPS), free.

"Deep-Sea Drilling Project" (color, sd, 27½ min, 1971, j-a). Illustrates the operations of the deep-sea drilling project to investigate the nature of the oceanic floor (ASF).

"Earth Beneath the Sea, The" (color, 29 min, 1967, i-j). Discusses the procedures used to study the nature and configurations of the ocean floor. Various features are illustrated by use of a precision depth-recorder strip, bottom photographs, bottom sampling with dredge and coring devices, and magnetometer readings. Summarizes how all the various data may be used to formulate a three-dimensional model of the sea bottom (McGH).

"Footprints in the Sea" (color, 26 min, 1966). Using photography, the film presents the most recent deep-sea maneuverable craft being tested and utilized by the Navy such as the sousCoupe, Deep Jeep, Morey, and CURV (USN), free.

"History Layer by Layer" (color, 23 min, 1967, j-c). The film provides an in-depth look into oceanographic research and the benefits that man can derive from such exploration. Gives detailed accounts of sample taking, preparation, and interpretation (McGH).

"Investigation of the Ocean's Bottom" (b/w, 29 min, 1964, j-h). Follows Dr. Harris Stewart, chief oceanographer for the federal government, while he establishes a research project to investigate such movement of sea floor features as the ridges of Cape Cod (NET:IU).

"Last Continent, Antarctica: The Oceanography" (b/w, 29 min, 1958). Describes the Antarctic oceanographic program during IGY. Includes charts and maps illustrating the effects of its waters on weather, tides, and life in the sea. Shows the use of the bathythermograph and nanson bottle in research as well as telling of further research areas and their relation to mankind (NET:IU).

"Man in the Sea" (color, 28 min, 1966, j-a) (MN–10100B). Presents the story of *Sea Lab II*, underwater photography in and outside the lab while submerged (USN), free.

"Marine Sedimentary Research" (b/w, 9 min, 1955, h-a). Depicts the work of geologists investigating the sea floor in the Gulf of Mexico in order to gain knowledge concerning the organisms that live there and their effect on the sediment (MOIL), free.

"Methods and Instruments of Oceanography" (color, sd, 18 min, 1970, j-h). Acquaints the viewer with the basic instruments used in oceanographic research and the manner in which they are employed (JW).

"Mission: Oceanography" (color, 30 min, 1966, h-c) (MN–10145). Presents points of view of oceanography including recent developments and importance to national defense and welfare. Illustrates the work of such research vessels as *Sealab I, Flip, Nomad Buoys*, and *Trieste* (USN), free.

"Oceanographers, Explorers of the Sea" (color, 20 min, 1968, j-h). Illustrates a Caribbean cruise made by geologists looking for various evidence concerning the sea's formation (UE&VA).

"Oceanographers in Polar Regions" (color, 28 min, 1968, j-c) (MN–10301). Deals with oceanographic research in the Arctic and Antarctic (USN), free.

"Oceanographic Predictions Systems" (color, 30 min, 1967, j-c) (MN–10167). Illustrates a variety of approaches followed in the study of oceanography in order to make navigation safer. Points out efforts directed to the forecasting of ice and waves (USN), free.

"Oceanography: Science for Survival" (color, 42 min, 1964) (MN–9835). Illustrates the part the Navy plays in the Interagency Committee on Oceanography and its oceanographic research (USN), free.

"Oceanography: The Study of Oceans" (color, 15 min, 1970, i-j). The film shows oceanographers studying the ocean and such characteristics as island formation, bottom topography, chemical composition, origin of waves, life and rainfall, and sources of food (JF).

"Oceanography: A Voyage to Discovery" (color, 20 min, 1969, i-c). Illustrates the instruments and techniques currently used by oceanographers as they investigate the ocean (UE&VA).

"Probing the Continental Margin" (color, sd, 22½ min, 1971, j-c).

Surveys life and work aboard two ships surveying the Australian continental shelf and slopes (ANIF).

"Project Deep Probe" (color, 28 min, 1969, h-a). Survey of the various techniques that are utilized by geologists to gather evidence to support or refute the theory of continental drift. Provides a somewhat detailed account of the voyage of the *Glomar Challenger* and scientists' interpretations of data gathered from the cruise (NET:IU).

"Project Mohole: Report Number One" (color, 19 min, 1959, j-c). Provides rationale for the project and the selection of the drilling site. Illustrates oceanographic vessels making profiles of the ocean bottom, including coring and gathering of seismic records (EDTS).

"Science of the Sea" (color, 19 min, 1958, j-c). Traces the research of oceanographers as they investigate the geological, chemical, physical, and biological nature of the ocean (IFB).

"Scientist in the Sea" (color, 17 min, 1967, p-h) (MN-10320). Describes the various activities of undersea oceanographers including study of current flow, instrument placement, and observation of corosion effects and sedimentation rates (USN), free.

"Sea Lab I" (color, 28 min, 1965, h-a) (MN-10100). Deals with the Navy's work in studying man's ability to survive and function for prolonged periods of time at a depth of 200 feet (USN), free.

"Ship Explorer Oceanographic Cruise, 1960" (color, 27 min, 1960) (P-1056-30). Depicts 1960 cruise of the Coast and Geodetic Survey's ship *Explorer* and its scientific and oceanographic activities (ESSA), free.

"Station 307" (b/w, 20 min, 1954, j-h). Illustrates how divers from the vessel *Calypso* obtain geological samples from the ocean floor, in search for petroleum in the Persian Gulf (RF).

"Weathermen of the Sea" (color, 14 min, 1950). Tells of the activities of ocean weather station vessels of the Coast Guard by tracing one such vessel through a tour of duty (USCG), free.

"World of Jacques Yves Cousteau" (color, 48 min, 1967, j-c). Traces the daily events of six oceanauts while 328 feet below the Mediterranean for 27 days. Includes studies of the life, turbulence, pollution, and plant growth (photographed with artificial lighting) (EBEC).

Submarine Geology and Shorelines

"Underwater Mining" (color, sd, 28 min, 1971, h-a). A panel discussion revolving around new developments and remaining problems of mining under the sea (SGPO), free.

"Great Barrier Reef" (color, sd, 53 min, 1971, j-a). Describes the geology and ecology of the Great Barrier Reef (NBC).

"Sea Water and the Floor" (color, 17 min, 1970, j-h). Discusses the composition of sea water, variations in its temperature, and composition, sediment load, and nature of the sea floor topography (WI).

"Volcano Surtsey" (color, 26 min, 1966, h-c). Traces the birth and development of a shield volcano in the sea off the coast of Iceland in 1963 (NSNC).

"What's Under the Ocean" (color, 14 min, 1960, i-h). Describes the methods and instruments used by scientists as they study the ocean; that is, skin-diving, bathyscope, and electronic soundings. Illustrates by models the ocean floor topography (FAOC).

Motion of the Sea

"How Level Is Sea Level?" (color, 13 min, 1970, j-h). The film gives the student various information with which he can investigate the question, "How level is sea level?" (EBEC).

"Nature of Sea Water" (color, 28 min, 1967, j-h) (MN–10317). Deals with the major concepts of oceanography including the distribution and circulation of water masses, upwelling, thermocline formation, and several others (USN), free.

"Ocean Currents" (color, 17 min, 1962, j-h). Provides a discussion of tides, winds, and currents and counter currents; their effects on the ocean and weather, as well as how they are affected by the coriolis forces and land forms (McGH).

"Oceanographic Studies Off George's Bank" (color, 15 min, 1958, j-c) (P–1056–25). Reviews the functioning of a current meter, effect of waves on currents, formation of ripple marks on the ocean bottom, and sand migration caused by waves (ESSA), free.

"Tides and Currents" (color, 18 min, 1958, j-a) (P–1056–24). Illustrates the work of the Coast and Geodetic Survey in investigation of these phenomena (ESSA), free.

"Tides of Fundy" (color, 15 min, 1965). Depicts an investigation of those unusual tides and how they affect the life of that particular region of Nova Scotia (CGOC), free.

"Tides of the Ocean" (color, 16 min, 1964, i-h). Discusses the causes of tides including centrifugal force and gravitational attraction of the sun and the moon. Also presents the uses of tides as well as their effects on the activities of man (AF).

"Time Lapse of Antarctica Ice Flows and Tidal Currents" (color, 26 min, 1962, h-c) (MN–10152). Traces the movements of ice flows with currents, cloud formation, and progressive concomitant freezing and thawing of the ice in Newcomb Bay (USN), free.

"Tsunami" (color, 28 min, 1965, h). Points out the dangers of seismic sea waves through a discussion of the Seismic Sea Wave Warning Systems operation (ESSA), free.

"Water Masses of the Ocean" (color, 45 min, 1967, j-a) (MN-10064). Considers the major water masses of the oceans, their locations and movements. Includes circulation patterns, convergences and divergences, seasonal variations of temperature and salinity, and their effects on bottom topography (USN), free.

"Waves Across the Pacific" (color, 30 min, 1967, j-c). Discusses the energy lost by waves, the use of ultrasensitive pressure sensors for recording the passage of storm waves in Antarctica, New Zealand, and Alaska (McGH).

"Waves on Water" (color, 15 min, 1965, i-h). Using experimental laboratory tanks, illustrates the various principles of waves and wave motion on water. Discusses wave refraction, seismic sea waves, and the principal source of their energy (EBEC).

Sea Water—Chemical and Biological Constituents

"Identification of Sea Ice" (color, 12 min, 1953, j-c) (MN-7419B). Demonstrates the criteria used to identify main types of sea ice. Discusses the various stages of the formation of sea ice (USN), free.

"Life in the Sea" (color, 11 min, 1958, p-j). Deals with the plankton (bottom dwellers and free swimmers) and how they capture food, protect themselves, and their relationship to photosynthesis (EBEC).

"Mysteries of the Deep" (color, 24 min, 1961, p-a). Considers a wide variety of deep water marine life and their nutrition, locomotion, reproduction, and protection (DISNY).

"Survival in the Sea: On the Rocks" (color, 29 min, 1958, j-a). Illustrates the flora and fauna of coral reefs and their adaption to this environment, including their protection and food-getting (NET:IU).

"Survival in the Sea: The Life Cycle" (color, 29 min, 1958, j-c). Follows the life cycle of both plant and animal life under the sea. Discusses the importance of plankton, food capture by marine organisms, and food chains of the ocean. Illustrates a wide variety of marine life (NET:IU).

"Survival in the Sea: Where Land and Water Meet" (color, 29 min, 1958, j-c). Points out the large variety of animals that live at the shore of the sea. Tells of their adaptions to this particular type of environment. Uses a wide variety of seashore animals (NET:IU).

Mineral Resources of the Oceans

"Blessing from the Sea" (color, 20 min, 1962, j-h). Traces the importance of phosphate and its geological past, mining, deposition, and processing from the sea (FPC), free.

"The Countdown Under" (b/w, 60 min, 1964, j-c). Considers a number of possible future uses of the seas, such as the harnessing of tidal power, utilization of petroleum resources, diamond mining, and living under the sea (IU).

"Desalting the Seas" (color, 17 min, 1967). Describes the use of nuclear energy in purifying oceanic waters (USAEC), free.

"Minerals from the Sea" (b/w, 14 min, 1953, i-h). Points out the various minerals found in the sea water, their commercial exploration and uses (IOMS), free.

"Oceanography at Work—Diamonds Under the Sea" (color, 25 min, 1965, j-c). Utilization of science in prospecting for diamonds. Illustrates geological mapping of the ocean floor with radar and seismic surveys. Depicts use of underwater television in searching for rock samples and the "rock-eater" being used to recover diamonds (CF).

"Sixth Continent, The" (color, 28 min, 1970, i-a). The film discusses the oceans of the world as untapped resources of mineral, food, and recreation wealth. Also considers the problems of ownership and development which are already a concern to many (McGH).

"Station 307" (b/w, 20 min, 1954, j-h). Illustrates how divers from the vessel *Calypso* obtain geological samples from the ocean floor, in search for petroleum in the Persian Gulf (RF).

General Topics

"Bahamas: Where Limestones Grow Today" (color, 40 min, 1952, h-c). Describes the deposition and formation of such entities as reefs, lime mud, and oolitic sands from limestone reservoirs in the Bahama Islands (MTPS).

"Beach: A River of Sand" (color, 20 min, 1965, i-h). Analyzes currents produced by waves and their effects on the accumulation and depletion of sand in a pattern along the shore (EBEC).

"Drop of Water, A" (color, sd, 14 min, 1971, p-h). The unnarrated film traces the many moods of a river as a drop of water travels from its source as rain to the sea (ABP).

"Galveston Island Barrier Sands" (color, 28 min, 1967, h-c). Traces the development of a barrier island sand body along the south Texas coast. Illustrates the formation process and possible clues for locating similar bodies in ancient rocks (MTPS), free.

"Man Invades the Sea" (b/w, 28 min, 1966, j-h). Provides a summary of recent attempts and achievements in undersea exploration along with individuals expressing problems that may arise in seeking to gain a better understanding of the oceans (McGH).

"Marine Sedimentary Research" (b/w, 9 min, 1955, h-a). Depicts the work of geologists investigating the sea floor in the Gulf of Mexico in order to gain knowledge concerning the organisms that live there and their effect on the sediment (MOIL), free.

"Men at Bay" (color, sd, 26 min, 1970, j-c). Surveys the various ways in which San Francisco Bay is becoming polluted through industrial wastes, sewerage, runoff carrying DDT, and air pollutants (KING).

"Mission: Oceanography" (color, 28 min, 1966, j-a) (MN-19145). Deals with the historical development of the science of oceanography and its importance to the Navy (USN), free.

"No Greater Challenge" (color, sd, 14 min, 1969, j-c). Documents man's past and present need for water and how nuclear energy and the process of desalting can be used to provide not only water but energy, fertilizers, and increased food productions (AEC), free.

"Oceanographer of the Navy (Reports)" (color, 28 min, 1964) (MN-10066). Recent developments in the field (USN), free.

"Oceanographers, Explorers of the Sea" (color, 20 min, 1968, j-h). Illustrates a Caribbean cruise by geologists looking for various evidence concerning the sea's formation (UE&VA).

"Rise and Fall of the Great Lakes, The" (color, sd, 15 min, 1968, j-c). The film, with the aid of music and animation, traces the origin and development of the Great Lakes under the influence of nature and man (McGH).

"Restless Sea, The" (color, 60 min, 1963). Utilizing animation and photography, shows the work of oceanographers while investigating phenomena on the surface of the sea, including waves, tides, and their effects on marine life, and erosion of land; nature of the sea floor, and storms (BELL), free.

"Science of the Sea" (color, 19 min, 1958, j-c). Traces the research of oceanographers as they investigate the geological, chemical, physical, and biological nature of the ocean (IFB).

"Story of the U.S. Lake Survey" (color, 29 min, 1966). Traces the history of lake surveys in the Great Lakes, includes a brief geologic and economic history of the region (USCE), free.

"Torrey Canyon" (b/w, 26 min, 1970, j-a). Surveys the damage caused by the wreck of a giant oil tanker and the implications this tragedy has on the scientific, legal, and social aspects of life (TLF).

"World of Jacques Yves Cousteau" (color, 48 min, 1967, j-c). Traces the daily events of six oceanauts while 328 feet below the Mediterranean for 27 days. Includes studies of the life, turbulence, pollution, and plant growth (photographed with artificial lighting) (EBEC).

35mm Filmstrips

Oceanographic Research

"Career in Oceanography, A" (color, 15 min, 1966, record). Depicts the activities of an oceanographer and characteristics for a career in this field, including the necessary training. Describes employment opportunities, working environment, and the types of research (EBEC).

"Ocean Engineering" (color, 15 min, 1966, record, j-h). Depicts the relationship between engineering and oceanography problems. Discusses research tools, engineering requirements for oceanic study, career opportunities for engineers in oceanography (EBEC)

"Oceanographic Tower" (color, 42 frs, 1962, captions). Shows the nature of the equipment, materials, facilities, and work on an oceanographic tower constructed in shallow water (CER).

Submarine Geology and Shorelines

"Geological Oceanography" (color, 17 min, 1966, record, j-h). Provides an explanation of the continental shelf and slope, deep ocean basins, sea floor topography, oceanic sediments, and other major features (EBEC).

"Landscapes of the Sea" (color, 61 frs, 1962, captions). Illustrates the various topographical and structural features found under the surface of the ocean (LEP).

"Ocean Basins, The" (color, 45 min, 1965, record) (SVE).

Motion of the Sea

"Air–Sea Interaction" (color, 15 min, 1966, record, j-h). Provides a description of the energy and mass exchange between the ocean and atmosphere along with a discussion of the processes involved and importance of salt particles in the exchange across the ocean-air interface (EBEC).

"Currents, Waves, and Tides" (color, 50 frs, 1965, record) (SVE).

"Mighty Currents of the Sea" (color, 15 min, 1966, record, j-c). Depicts the formation and variations in ocean waves (both surface and internal), tides, general circulations and their relationship to water temperature and density (EBEC).

"Ocean Currents" (color, 52 frs, 1967, record). Discusses ocean currents and their relationship to gravity, tides, winds, and other factors (EG).

"Waves, Tides, Currents, and Water" (color, 30 frs, 1966, captions) (CSP).

"Wind and Waves" (color, 42 frs, 1962, captions) (SVE).

Sea Water—Chemical and Biological Constituents

"Biological Oceanography" (color, 15 min, 1966, record, j-h). Illustrates the various important nutrients to be found in the sea. Points out the different ecological systems present in the sea as well as the marine life cycle and the many adaptations that marine life has undergone (EBEC).

"Chemical Oceanography" (color, 15 min, 1966, record, j-h). Describes the composition of sea water and an investigation of effects of trace elements on biochemical and geochemical processes. Discusses composition of marine sediments and effects of atomic wastes (EBEC).

"Life in the Oceans" (color, 41 frs, 1966, captions). Depicts the nature of life at various locations in or on the water (PS).

Mineral Resources of the Oceans

"Marine Resources" (color, 15 min, 1966, record, j). Illustrates the sea as a source area for a wide variety of resources, obstacles to its utilization, problems and potentialities of its desalinization (EBEC).

"Riches from the Sea" (b/w, 34 frs, 1966, with guide). Discusses deep sea diving and living in addition to the various resources of the sea (VEC).

"Wealth in the Ocean" (color, 39 frs, captions). Discusses the various resources to be obtained from the sea (MIS).

General Topics

"Career in Oceanography, A" (color, 15 min, 1966, record). Depicts the activities of an oceanographer and characteristics for a career in this field, including the necessary training. Describes employment opportunities, working environment, and types of research (EBEC).

"Earth and the Sea, The" (color, 3 frs, 1966, captions). General treatment of the origin and nature of the ocean and its water, shores, and bottom (CPC).

"Introduction to Oceanography, An" (color, 15 min, 1966, record, j-h). Presents a general introductory discussion of oceanography and its relationship to the other sciences (EBEC).

"Oceans, The" (color, 30 frs, 1965, p-h). Describes, in simplified fashion, the features and resources of oceans (McGH).

"Sea—La Mer—El Mor, The" (color, 43 frs, 1964). Selected photographs of the oceans and related phenomena (UNESCO).

"Seas About Us, The" (color, 42 frs, 1961, captions). Illustrates the characteristics of the oceans such as its currents, mountains, life, and trenches (PS).

"Study of Oceans" (color, 47 frs, 1965, record) (SVE).

8mm Film Loops

Oceanographic Research

"Bathyscaphe" (color, si, 3 min, 1965). Illustrates the construction of the *Trieste* and the function of its various parts during a typical operation on the ocean bottom (ICF).

Submarine Geology and Shorelines

"Beach I, The: Source of Sand" (color, over 3 min, 1968) (EBEC).

"Beach II, The: Profile Study" (color, over 3 min, 1968) (EBEC).

"Beach IV, The: Formation of a Sand Spit" (color, over 3 min, 1968) (EBEC).

"Beach VI, The: Ocean Shores" (Physical Features) (color, over 3 min, 1968) (EBEC).

"Coastal Waters—Fair Weather" (color, si, 2 min, 1968). Illustrates, through underwater photography, the characteristics of the ocean bottom during calm weather (ICF).

"Deep Ocean Sediments and Turbidity Current" (color, 4 min, Sup 8, cart, 1971, i-j). Animated (McGH).

"Ocean-Basin Topography" (color, 4 min, Sup 8, cart, 1971, i-j). Animated (McGH).

"Ocean Bottoms" (color, si, 4 min, 1965). Shows relief models of the Atlantic and Pacific Basins, isolated seamounts in the Pacific, Tomanche Trench, and the Mid-Atlantic Ridge of the Atlantic (FAOC).

"Ocean Circulation: Depth" (color, 4 min, Sup 8, 1969). Film shows through demonstration the idealized vertical circulation in the oceans caused by temperature differences (HSC).

"Ocean Circulation: Surface" (color, 4 min, Sup 8, 1969). The film reveals how surface ocean currents are set in motion by wind and modified by earth rotation and continental barriers (HSC).

"Ocean Currents" (color, 4 min, Sup 8, cart, 1971, i-j). Animated (McGH).

"Seashore, The" (color, si, 3 min, 1968). Shows the different types of wave movements and shore features (SRA).

Motion of the Sea

"Beaches III, The: Longshore Transport" (color, over 3 min, 1968) (EBEC).

"Beaches V, The: Water Waves" (color, over 3 min) (EBEC).

"Beaches VII, The: Origin of Water Waves" (color, over 3 min) (EBEC).

"Coastal Water—Stormy Weather" (color, si, 2 min, 1968). Depicts disturbances that occur beneath the surface of the sea during a heavy storm. Shows erosion, "dust" storms, and other changes to the ocean and its flora and fauna (DCI).

"Ocean Density Currents" (color, si, 3½ min, 1967). Experiments illustrating the effects that temperature, salinity, and turbidity have on ocean currents (E).

"Ocean Temperature" (color, 4 min, Sup 8, 1969). Reveals how water masses of different temperature settle into distinct layers of different depth (HSC).

"Ocean Tides" (color, 4 min, Sup 8, 1969). The position of the earth, sun, and moon is studied in relation to the cause of tides (HSC).

"Ocean Waves" (color, 4 min, Sup 8, 1969). Wave-tank demonstrations reveal the orbital motion of waves (HSC).

"Seashore, The" (color, si, 3 min, 1968). Shows different types of wave movement and shore features (SRA).

"Turbidity Currents" (color, si, 3 min, 1968). Laboratory experiments illustrating the characteristics of turbidity currents by use of a long, narrow tank, plastic beads, and dye (SRA).

"Waves" (color, si, 3 min, 1968). Compares wave activity in a demonstration tank to aerial views of actual river and ocean waves (SRA).

"Wind Set-Up on Lakes" (color, 4 min, Sup 8, cart, 1970, i-j). Effect of wind blowing across a lake in the production of waves and increased water levels (BFA).

Sea Water—Chemical and Biological Constituents

"Coastal Waters—At Night" (color, si, 3 min, 1968). Presents the characteristic activity or inactivity of many animals of the ocean during the night with the dangers they encounter from their natural enemies (DCI).

General Topics

"Evolution of a Lake" (color, si, 4 min, 1969). Describes (through aerial views and animation) the gradual changes that occur to a glacial lake as it is filled in and overgrown by vegetation (EBEC).

"Oceans and Sea" (color, si, 5 min, 1967). Illustrates the various locations and names of the major bodies of water found on the earth. Draws a comparison between the water and land masses that cover the earth (EBEC).

"Water Bodies" (color, si, 4 min, 1968). Compares a relief map to corresponding bodies of water such as an ocean, river, lake, bay, and sound (EMI).

Overhead Transparencies

Oceanographic Research
"Echo Sounding" (DG)

"Mapping the Ocean Floor with Sonar" (W)

Submarine Geology and Shorelines
"At the Edge of the Ocean—Project Mohole" (W)

"Atlantic Ocean Floor, The" (W)

"Beaches and Beach Cycles" (DG)

"Configuration of the Ocean Floor" (HI)

"Coral Reef" (DG)

"Coral Reef Development" (W)

"Deeps and Trenches—Mid-Ocean Ridge" (W)

"Earthquake Zones and Volcanoes" (DG)

"Fracture Zones" (DG)

"Guyots—Table Mounts" (DG)

"Magnetism of the Sea Floor" (DG)

"Ocean Floor" (WPC)

"Ocean Floor, The" (UTI)

"Oceanic Ridge—Rise System" (DG)

"Oceanographic Features" (DG)

"Oceans and Ocean Currents" (HI)

"Profile of the Ocean Floor" (N)

"Submarine Canyons" (DG)

"World Structural Patterns" (HI)

Motion of the Sea
"Air–Sea Interaction" (W)

"How Ocean Currents Are Formed" (N)

"Internal Waves" (DG)

"Ocean Currents" (DG)

"Ocean Currents" (N)

"Ocean Currents" (UTI)

"Ocean Currents" (WPC)

"Ocean Currents of the World" (EA-V)

"Rip Currents" (DG)

"Seismic Sea Waves—Tidal Waves" (DG)

"Tides" (MPC)

"Tides" (N)

"Tides, The" (HI)

"Turbidity Currents" (DG)

"Upwelling" (DG)

"Warm and Cold Ocean Currents" (N)

"Waves-Deep Water" (DG)

"Waves—Shallow Water" (DG)

Sea Water—Chemical and Biological Constituents
"Coral Reef" (DG)

"Coral Reef Development" (W)

"Life in the Sea" (DG)

"Life Zones and Food Cycles" (W)

"Ocean Chemicals, No. 1" (WPC)

"Ocean Chemicals, No. 2" (WPC)
"Ocean Temperature and Pressure" (WPC)

"Salinity in the Sea" (DG)
"Temperature in the Sea" (DG)

General Topics

"Air–Sea Interaction" (W)
"At the Edge of the Ocean—Project Mohole" (W)
"Earth Science—Oceanography" (HI)
"Earth Science—Oceanography" (W)
"Earth Science—Oceanography 1" (DG)
"Earth Science—Oceanography 2" (DG)

"Four Main Oceans" (UTI)
"How Deep Is the Ocean?" (MMAMC)
"Hydrologic Cycle" (HI)
"Oceanograph Series" (HI)
"Oceanographic Features" (DG)
"Oceans" (MPC)
"Oceans and Ocean Currents" (HI)
"Water Cycle" (UNC)
"Water Masses" (DG)

Color Photographs

Curriculum Color Prints (18″ x 13″)

"Life in the Sea I" (CES), (DG), (IAI), (N), (W)

1. Coelenterates
2. Echinoderms
3. Plants
4. Protozoa
5. Sponges
6. Worms

"Life in the Sea II" (CES), (DG), (IAI), (N), (W)

1. Crustaceans
2. Fish
3. Mammals
4. Mollusks
5. Reptiles
6. Sea Birds

"Ocean Laboratory" (CES) (Titles available upon request)
"Ocean Meteorology" (CES), (DG), (IAI), (N), (W)

1. Fronts
2. Hurricanes
3. Sea Breezes
4. Sea Fog
5. Tropical Marine Atmosphere
6. Winds Over the Sea

"The Sea" (CES), (IAI)

1. Currents in the Sea
2. Islands in the Sea

3. Salinity of the Sea
4. Sea Temperature
5. Shores of the Sea
6. Waves in the Sea

"Sediments of the Sea Floor" (CES), (DG), (IAI), (N), (W)

1. Biogenous Sediments
2. Hydrogenous Sediments
3. Pelagic Clay
4. Sediment Distribution
5. Sediment Sampling
6. Terrigenous Sediments

"Tools of Oceanography" (CES), (DG), (IAI), (N), (W)

1. Computers
2. Flip, An Oceanographic Buoy
3. Oceanographic Instruments
4. Scuba
5. Submersibles
6. Surface Research Vessels

"Topography of the Sea Floor" (CES), (DG), (IAI), (N), (W)

1. Continental Margin
2. Echo Sounding
3. Mid-ocean Mountains
4. Seamounts
5. Submarine Canyons
6. Trenches

Supplementary Reading Materials

The supplementary reading materials contained in this section are not all-inclusive, but they do represent a major portion of currently available paperback books of interest to teachers and students. They constitute an economical source that is often overlooked and span all levels of instruction from the junior high school to reference works for the teacher. No attempt has been made to indicate the grade or reading level because many are useful for a wide range of abilities. Prices are subject to fluctuation, but most of these publications are reasonably priced. A brief annotation is included for most titles.

Abbott, R. Tucker. *How to Know the American Marine Shells.* New York: New American Library of World Literature, 1961, 222 pp. Field guide for beginners, which includes drawings, descriptions, color photographs, and a brief introduction to the life and classification of mollusks.

Bascom, Willard. *Waves and Beaches: The Dynamics of the Ocean.* Science Study Series. Garden City, N.Y.: Doubleday & Co., 1964, 267 pp. Readable, authoritative account of the interaction between sea and land. A section is devoted to man's attempt to defend against the relentless onslaught of the sea by construction of shoreline structures. Illustrated throughout with line drawings and photographs.

Behrman, A. S. *Water Is Everybody's Business: The Chemistry of Water Purification.* Chemistry in Action Series. Garden City, N.Y.: Doubleday & Co., Anchor Books, 1968, 229 pp. Presents a broad and useful picture of water supply and water purification. Discusses basic principles in sufficient detail to give the reader a good working knowledge of the subject. Includes chapters on water supply, fluoridation of water, desalting the ocean, and the future.

Carlisle, Norman. *Riches of the Sea: the New Science of Oceanology.* New York: Bantam Books, 1970, 136 pp. This introductory work unfolds an entire panorama covering the new science of oceanology. Well illustrated.

Carson, Rachel. *The Edge of the Sea.* New York: New American Library of World Literature, 1959, 238 pp. Describes inhabitants of three typical tidal environments: rocky shore, sand beach, and coral coast. Relates tides, waves, and currents with ecology.

_____ . *The Sea Around Us.* New York: New American Library of World Literature, 1950, 169 pp. History of the sea from its earliest beginnings to later discoveries, including: geography, life forms, man's heritage of the sea, ocean currents, tides, winds, oceanographic mapping, and origin of the oceans.

Chorley, Richard J., ed. *Water, Earth, and Man: A Synthesis of Hydrology, Geomorphology, and Socio-economic Geography*. London: Methuen, and New York: Barnes & Noble, 1969.

Clancy, Edward P. *The Tides: Pulse of the Earth*. Science Study Series. Garden City, N.Y.: Doubleday & Co., 1968.

Clarke, Arthur S. *The Challenge of the Sea*. New York: Holt, Rinehart and Winston, 1960, 167 pp. The geology, geography, and history of the oceans discussed in dramatic style. Includes information about the resources of the sea, its marine life, and methods of exploration.

Coker, R. E. *This Great and Wide Sea: An Introduction to Oceanography and Marine Biology*. New York: Harper & Row, 1962, 325 pp. Comprehensive introduction to the science of the sea including discussion of conversion of salt water to fresh water and the use of the sea as a source of food.

Cousteau, J. Y., and James Dugan. *The Living Sea*. New York: Pocket Books, 1964, 241 pp. Study of developments in sea exploration, containing the adventures and discoveries of the world's most famous undersea explorer.

Cowen, Robert C. *Frontiers of the Sea*. New York: Bantam Books, 1960, 312 pp. Examines the origins and shifting patterns of the sea, the creatures that inhabit its depths, and the development of the science of oceanography.

Daniel, Hawthorne, and Francis Minot. *Inexhaustable Sea*. New York: Collier Books, 1961, 192 pp. Forecasts the continuing growth of the world's population and the resulting insufficiency of food produced from the soil. Explains how this need may be filled from the resources of ocean life.

Darwin, Charles. *The Voyage of the Beagle*, annotated, with an Introduction by Leonard Engel. Garden City, N.Y.: Doubleday & Co., 1962, 534 pp.

Davis, Kenneth S., and John Arthur Day. *Water: The Mirror of Science*. Science Study Series. Garden City, N.Y.: Doubleday & Co., 1961, 195 pp.

Defant, Albert. *Ebb and Flow: The Tides of Earth, Air and Water*. Ann Arbor: University of Michigan Press, 1958, 121 pp. Deals with why tides exist, why they work, how they work and what they are.

Friedmann, Wolfgang. *The Future of the Oceans*. New York: George Braziller, 1971, 128 pp. Presents the ocean as a great source of wealth. Discusses our potential to exploit the abundant minerals contained in the oceans, as well as the fish—one of the world's most important foods—in the waters above. Technology also reveals ways of using the seas and the sea floors for military and strategic purposes. The question of who controls the oceans is raised as one of the most complicated international legal problems.

Gross, M. G. *Oceanography*, 2d ed. Merrill Physical Science Series. Columbus, Ohio: Charles E. Merrill Publishing Co., 1971, 150 pp. An introduction to oceanography. Includes chapters on the ocean floor, deep-sea sediment, ocean currents, waves and tides, and the coastal area.

Hoyt, John H. *Field Guide to Beaches*. ESCP Pamphlet Series PS-7. Boston: Houghton Mifflin Co., 1971, 46 pp.

Kuenen, P. H. *Realms of Water: Some Aspects of Its Cycle in Nature*. New York: John Wiley & Sons, 1963, 327 pp. Discusses the importance of water determining the climate and landscape. Considers many aspects of physical geography, meteorology, and oceanography, and many natural phenomena from glaciers to the depths of the seas, and from clouds to subterranean grottoes.

Long, John L. *New Worlds of Oceanography.* New York: Pyramid Publications, 1965, 221 pp. Account of the scientific assault on the sea; its history, resources, and particularly its future.

Marx, Wesley. *The Frail Ocean.* New York: Ballantine Books, 1967, 248 pp.

Meinzer, Oscar E. *Hydrology.* New York: Dover Publications, 1957, 723 pp. Symposium on hydrology prepared for the National Research Council. Information on precipitation, evaporation, transpiration, snow, glaciers, lakes, infiltration, soil moisture, ground water, runoff, drought, physical changes produced by water, hydrology of limestone terrains, and other subjects.

Olson, Ralph E. *A Geography of Water.* Brown Foundations of Geography Series. Dubuque, Iowa: William C. Brown Co., 1970, 132 pp. Contains chapters on water in the oceans, rivers, lakes, in the atmosphere, ground water, and the management of water.

Peterson, Mendel. *History Under the Sea: A Handbook for Underwater Exploration.* Washington, D.C.: The Smithsonian Institution, 1965, 108 pp. Written for amateur divers in an attempt to prevent needless destruction by providing instructions for recovering, preserving, and identifying various objects they might find on the ocean floor.

Pickard, G. L. *Descriptive Physical Oceanography.* Elmsford, N.Y.: Pergamon Press, 1963, 200 pp. Discusses ocean dimensions, shapes, bottom materials, physical properties of seawater, typical distributions of water characteristics in the oceans, salt water, salt and heat budgets of the oceans, circulation of water masses, instruments, and future work.

Rummery, G. R. *The Geosystem.* Brown Foundations of Earth Science Series. Dubuque, Iowa: William C. Brown Co., 1970, 135 pp. Presents the earth as a system in which land, sea, and air are dynamically integrated in a single system through processes by which energy, matter, and momentum are continually exchanged.

Schultz, Gwen. *Glaciers and the Ice Age.* New York: Holt, Rinehart and Winston, 1963, 128 pp. Combines the findings of geology and anthropology to produce the total glacial picture including landforms, geologic processes, atmosphere, oceans, plants, animals, climate, people, and use of land.

Scientific American, eds. *The Ocean.* San Francisco: W. H. Freeman and Co., 1969, 140 pp. Contains 10 chapters which originally appeared as articles in the Sept. 1969 issue of *Scientific American.*

_____. *Planet Earth.* New York: Simon and Schuster, 1957, 164 pp. Collection of 14 articles taken from past issues of *Scientific American.* Discusses the origin of the earth, its core and mantle, its crust, the hydrosphere, the atmosphere, and the edge of space.

Spar, Jerome. *Earth, Sea, and Air—A Survey of the Geophysical* Sciences, 2d ed. Reading, Mass.: Addison-Wesley Publishing Co., 1965, 152 pp. Gives the student an overview of man's total natural physical environment.

Stephens, William M. *Science Beneath the Sea.* Science Survey Series. New York: G. P. Putman's Sons, 1966, 224 pp. Presents oceanography today and in the beginning, rivers in the sea, waves and tides, the floor of the sea, the building of islands, life in the sea, sounds under the sea, mining and farming the sea, and man's invasion of the sea.

Turekian, K. K. *Oceans.* Foundations of Earth Science Series. Englewood Cliffs, N.J.: Prentice-Hall, 1968, 128 pp. Offers an integrated approach to the study of oceans with special emphasis on the chemistry and geology of ocean basins. The physics and chemistry of ocean water and oceanic circulation processes are assessed in light of recent research using trace elements and radioactive tracers.

Yasso, Warren E. *Oceanography: A Study of Inner Space.* New York: Holt, Rinehart and Winston, 1965, 176 pp. Emphasizes the significance of the oceans to weather and climate, food production, mineral resources, and waste disposal, in addition to presenting information on oceanography in general.

Yonge, C. M. *Sea Shore.* New York: Atheneum Publishers, 1963, 352 pp. Natural history of the seashore with all its variety of plants and animals.

Zim, Herbert S., and R. Tucker Abbott. *Sea Shells of the World.* New York: Golden Press, 1962, 160 pp. Guide for collecting the attractive and better-known species.

Free and Inexpensive Materials

Oceanographic Research

"Atom and the Ocean, The" (50 pp., 1958). Illustrated booklet describing how nuclear energy can be utilized in studying the oceans of the world in order to develop more productive fisheries, accurate long-range weather forecasting, control over hurricanes and typhoons, and pollution control (USAEC), free.

"Drift Bottles" (4 pp.). Use of drift bottles and other drift apparatus in investigating the oceans (USC&GS), free.

"International Ice Patrol" (24 pp.). Describes the work of the Coast Guard Ice Patrol; includes: ocean currents, sea ice, icebergs, and other oceanographic phenomena (USC&GS), free.

"Marine Sciences Research" (18 pp., March 1966). (USAEC), free.

"Nuclear Energy for Desalting" (50 pp., May 1967). Discusses the history, development, purpose, benefits, and future of desalinization of sea water with the use of nuclear energy (USAEC), free.

"Ocean Science Program of the U.S. Navy" (1967). (NODO), free.

"Opportunities in Oceanography" (33 pp.). Illustrates various aspects of oceanography and the many career opportunities available in the field (ICOO), free.

"Photomapping the Ocean Floor" (4 pp.). Depicts procedures used by oceanographers and photogrammetrists as they survey the ocean floor (USC&GS), free.

"Undersea Vehicles for Oceanography" (Pamphlet No. 18, 1965, 81 pp.). (ICOO), 65¢.

"USC. & GSS Discoverer" (OSS-02) (Pub. #PI-66001). Illustrates a new research vessel, her oceanographic capabilities, and role in oceanographic research (USGPO), 25¢.

"USC & GSS Oceanographer" (05501) (Pub. #PI-660001). Depicts the characteristics, capabilities, and role of this new ESSA oceanographic research vessel (USGPO), 20¢.

Submarine Geology and Shorelines

"Atlantic Continental Margin, The" (Color; Pub. #1-45). Chart, 3 sheets showing area from Nova Scotia to Key West (USGPO), 50¢.

"Coastline of the United States" (1 p.). Illustrates the normal and tidal shorelines of the various states and territories (USC&GS), free.

"Submarine Topography, DeSota Canyon to Great Bahama Bank" (Color; Pub. #1-475). (USGPO), $1.00.

Motion of the Sea

"Significant Aspects of the Tides" (6 pp.). Describes the formation types, and prediction of tides and tidal waves (USC&GS), free.

"Tidal Currents" (6 pp.). Describes the types of tidal and other ocean currents (USC&GS), free.

"Tsunami Watch and Warning" (Color; Pub. #660026). Depicts ESSA's Pacific tsunami watching and warning service including terminology and safety rules (ESSA), free.

Sea Water—Chemical and Biological Constituents

"Nuclear Energy for Desalting" (50 pp., May 1967). Discusses the history, development, purposes, benefits, and future of desalinization of sea water with the use of nuclear energy (USAEC), free.

"Study of Water Quality, A" (46 pp., 1968). By C. E. Renn. Discusses the problems solutions, and methods of testing water quality (LCPC), free.

"Water of the World" (20 pp.). Illustrates the sources and amounts of the water supply including glaciers, lakes, oceans, rivers, and underground water. Also discusses the World Hydrologic Survey (USGS), free.

"What Is Water?" (9 pp.). Chemical and physical properties of water (USGS). free.

"Why Is the Ocean Salty?" (11 pp.). Discussion of the origin of oceans, nature of the salts, and variations in salinity (USGS), free.

General Topics

"A Reader's Guide to Oceanography" (13 pp., 1965). A guide that is revised periodically (WHOI), free.

"Atoms, Nature, and Man" (57 pp., 1968). Describes environmental studies that have been conducted with the aid of the atom since 1945 (USAEC), free.

"Films on Oceanography" (Pub. #C-4, 1966) (NODO), 75¢.

"Glossary of Oceanographic Terms" (2d ed.; Pub. #Sp.-35), (NODO).

"Limnology" (40 pp., 1969). By W. H. Amos. Introduction to the study of the fresh water environment (LCPC), free.

"Ocean Science Program of the U.S. Navy" (1967). (NODO), free.

"Ocean Study Kit" Teachers Kit, $4.20, Student Kit, (NODO), $1.60.

"Oceanographic Curriculum for High Schools" (Outline P-81, 1968). (NODO), free.

"Oceanography Index" By Cohen. Cumulative index of articles to be found in *The Science Teacher* (NSTA), 25¢.

"Oceanography Material Sources" (6 pp.). List of educational materials including articles, pamphlets, and references dealing with oceanography (NAS/NRC), free.

"Oceanography News Stories" (8 pp.). Composite list of references dealing with oceanographic news stories and feature magazine articles (NAS/NRC), free.

"Oceanography—The Ten Years Ahead" (58 pp.). Outlines the "Long Range National Oceanographic Plan (1963-1972)."

Utilizes tables, charts, and written descriptions of the national goals, capabilities, systems, and surveys of services (ICOO), free.

"Opportunities in Oceanography" (33 pp.). Illustrates the various aspects of oceanography and the many career opportunities available in the field (ICOO), free.

"Our Environment Battles Water Pollution" (32 pp., 1969). By C. E. Renn. Describes changes that go on when water is polluted (LCPC), free.

"Preparation for Oceanography" (S100), free.

"Questions About the Ocean" (Pub. #D-2032, Oct. 2, 1968). (USGPO), 55¢.

"Standard Time Zone Chart of the World" (21st ed., October 1968; U.S. Oceanographic Office Chart #5192; Pub. #D-208, 22, 5192). Shows the 12 international standard time zones (USGPO), $1.00.

"University Curriculum in Oceanography" Composite list of the institutions, courses, faculty, and degrees offered in the marine sciences (ICOO), free.

"Uses of the Seas" Provides recommendations resulting from a May 1968 meeting held to discuss various aspects of the United States involvement in the science of oceanography, including governmental organization, law, and strategy surrounding the use of the seas (TAA), free.

"Water of the World" (20 pp.). Illustrates the sources and amounts of the water supply including glaciers, lakes, oceans, rivers, and underground water. Also discusses the World Hydrologic Survey (USGS), free.

"Your Future in Oceanography with the U.S. Oceanographic Office" (USCSC), free.

PART...5

Historical Geology

Classroom Activities

Classification of Fossils

If you live in an area that has fossiliferous rocks containing invertebrate fossil remains, such as brachiopods, an interesting and quite meaningful activity deals with their collection and gross classification by the students. If time and facilities allow, have your students collect a significant number of specimens that will provide at least 20-30 fossils per student group. If the fossils are quite abundant in your particular area, then a small slab of rock may contain a suitable number for study. In the event that fossils are nonexistent in your area then a sufficient number may be purchased from a supply company, or plastic replicas can be obtained in the same manner.

After the fossils have been assembled, have the students classify the fossils into groups based on the criteria that they determine important. After the students have grouped the fossils, a discussion between each group can take place in which the students discuss and defend their rationale for grouping, importance of classification, and the relationship of their activity to that of a paleontologist.

Fossil Casts and Molds

Quite often it is difficult for some students to distinguish between a mold and a cast of a fossil and their relationship to the original life form. This problem can be solved with the use of individual fossils, brachiopods, for example, or recent clam and snail shells, or even objects such as pencils, paper-clips, and numerous other objects sturdy enough to leave an impression in modeling clay.

Have your students take the object, press it into the clay to form the mold of the object. Experience has shown that a much more distinct impression is formed if you first coat the object lightly with regular cooking oil before pressing it into the clay.

To make a cast of an object, a mixture of plaster of paris is poured into the mold and allowed to dry. When the mold is removed, each student will have a cast of the original object as well as a mold. Make sure that the mold is lightly coated with the oil to prevent the plaster of paris from sticking to the mold as it dries.

A post-activity discussion may relate the procedures of the students to what takes place in the environment when a fossil mold or cast is made in sediment and preserved in rock. Interest in the activity is heightened if actual fossil molds and casts are made available during the course of the discussion or at least pictures are used.

One follow-up activity to this exercise is to have your students prepare casts and molds of objects, exchange them, and try to interpret the nature of the original object. A number of variations and interesting interpretations arise, which result in a very good model requiring observation, inference, and other scientific processes.

Interpretation of Footprints

An interesting and yet quite simple activity that may be used with students with a wide range of abilities and grade levels involves interpretation of a series of footprints drawn on a blackboard or mimeographed on a sheet of paper.

The initial set of footprints should represent some activity such as a predator stalking its prey, catching it, and then leaving the scene thus causing the disappearance of the prey's track. The students are presented with the picture (shown in Figure 5-1) and asked to interpret what events are represented by the tracks.

A lively discussion usually follows when the students are asked to give their interpretations and to defend them. During the discussion, attention should be drawn to the correlation between this exercise and actual footprints preserved in ancient rock and the work of paleontologists who attempt to decipher the nature of ancient animals and events from them. Interest in the discussion is often heightened through the use of actual preserved footprints or pictures of them.

Figure 5-1

A successful follow-up activity involves the students in constructing their own puzzles, exchanging them, and making interpretations of each other's materials. This activity generates interest and interaction among the students as well as creating a good model of fossil evidence preserved in rock.

Model of Geologic Time

The concept of the immensity of geologic time is often a difficult one for many students to grasp. But a number of activities can help to make the abstraction more concrete. One activity involves the use of adding-machine tape and a geologic time chart with the duration, in years, of the various eras, periods, and epochs. After the students are given the materials, each group is asked to devise some scale with which they can represent geologic time. Because of the activities and the ensuing discussion, a better grasp of the concept of geologic time usually results.

Other methods of putting the concept of geologic time in more concrete terms include making a comparison between duration of time and (1) a calendar year and (2) the distance from New York to California and (3) the height of the Empire State Building. Another variation which often increases student interest and lends to the concreteness of the model is to add various geologic and paleontological events such as appearance of life, extinction of dinosaurs, and appearance of man to the original time scale.

Amber Preservation

Modes of fossil preservation are varied in nature and prove to be interesting to a wide number of students. One of these forms of preservation involved ancient insects being trapped and encased in pine resin. As the substance hardened into amber, the insect remains were protected from decay by this air-tight chamber and were preserved. The entrapment is often a complete one with the entire animal, including its delicate external structures, being preserved inside the amber.

Students can duplicate this amber preservation by locating a small dead insect, placing it on a hard surface, such as a microscope slide or jar cover, and dropping a small drop of clear nail polish or airplane cement on it. The preserving material is allowed to dry for several minutes, then succeeding drops are added until the insect is completely encased in the substance.

This activity entails little class time and can even be performed at home. Because the preservation of insects in amber is still going on today, the students can often find conifer trees and observe the preservation of modern-day insects in much the same manner as insects were preserved millions of years ago.

Reconstruction of Animals from Skeletal Remains

Some paleontologists are more concerned with the study of ancient

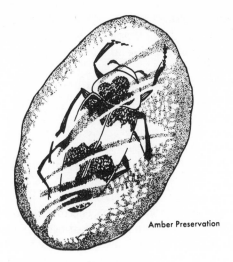

Amber Preservation

Figure 5–2 Amber preservation.

vertebrate than invertebrate life. Toward this end these geologists are continually searching for preserved bones and bone fragments from these higher forms of ancient life. Students are often quite interested in the manner in which these skeletons are assembled by the vertebrate paleontologist in his attempts to reconstruct the physical nature of the animal.

Individual students or entire class groups can be involved in such an activity through the use of chicken or turkey skeletons. Whole animals (complete with legs and head) can be obtained from a local farmer or poultry wholesaler. The animal is plucked of feathers, if necessary, and then placed in a kettle of water and boiled until all of the flesh has fallen away from the skeleton. The bones are then removed and soaked in hot soapy water for approximately 30 minutes to ensure that all flesh has been removed from the surface of the bones. The bones are then removed from the water and allowed to dry.

The problem presented to the students is that "they have found these bones of a now extinct animal and have the task of reconstructing its skeletal remains." The students are provided with airplane cement and wire to help them with this task. The activity can prove to be time consuming, and a teacher might well prefer to have students do this activity at home or after school. In any case, the activity proves to be of great interest to the students, and they carry this interest over into other areas of paleontological study as well.

Radioactive Decay

The use of radioactive decay in the earth sciences has proven to be a very valuable asset to the scientist. The concept of radioactive decay can be introduced into the classroom with the use of a geiger counter and a naturally radioactive mineral such as carnotite or even sands that contain the mineral.

A geiger counter can usually be obtained from the high school physics department, or one can be borrowed for educational purposes from your local Civil Defense organization. The radioactive mineral is available from a wide number of suppliers (see the list of Earth Science Suppliers in Part I of this book).

First, establish an imaginary situation where your students are told that they are prospecting for uranium and that there is a uranium "deposit" somewhere in the classroom. The class is divided up into groups of four or five and each succeeding group is sent out of the room while the "deposit" (the mineral or container of sand) is hidden. The group then is asked to find the uranium with the use of the geiger counter. This procedure proves much more interesting and enjoyable to the students than a simple teacher demonstration and greatly enhances the post-activity discussion relevant to radioactivity and its uses in the earth sciences.

Half-Life of Radioactive Substances

An activity that can be used to depict half-life and one which builds on the experiences and interest created in the preceding activity dealing with radioactivity, involves the creation of a statistical model approximating radioactive decay and half-life.

Each group of two or three students is given a shoebox, 100 pennies, and graph paper. The students place the pennies in the shoebox, all with the same sides up. The box is then closed and given a hard shake. The box is then opened and all the pennies that have turned over are removed and counted. The procedure is repeated until there are no more pennies left in the box. The students then construct a graph consisting of the number of shakes versus the number of flipped coins.

Student graphs will approximate that shown in Figure 5-3. Although their graphs will terminate at a point, they do represent a model of radioactive decay and resulting half-life. A more accurate graph can be made by combining the data from all the class groups and taking averages of pennies removed after each shaking. However, one should be cautious in extending this model beyond its capabilities. In this model (1) the "nuclei" (pennies) do not change randomly or without the use of external energy and (2) the nuclei do not remain but are removed. These two phenomena are in direct opposition to what actually occurs in nature. Even with these limitations the activity proves to be an interesting one for the students and allows them to gain increased knowledge about an important concept in geology.

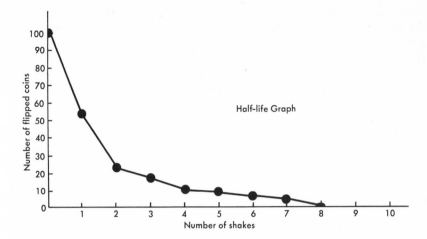

Figure 5-3 Half-life graph.

Preservation Through Carbonization

Still another form of fossil preservation, which can be demonstrated by students, involves that of carbonization. This type of fossilization is most common for the preserved remains of ancient plants. Carbonized plant remains are very useful to paleontologists in that even delicate structures of the plant are often preserved by the deposition of thin films of carbon that takes place as the plant material slowly decays in the sediments in which it is encased.

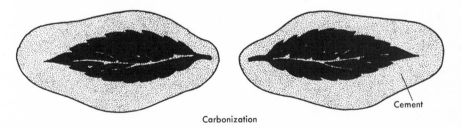

Carbonization

Figure 5-4 Carbonization.

Carbonization can be replicated by the students at home by taking a leaf (preferably large) and embedding it in approximately one inch of ready-mix cement in a disposable aluminum pie plate or even aluminum foil. The material is then placed in a hot oven and baked for about two hours. When the material is removed from the oven and cooled, it can be opened by striking it sharply with a hammer on its thin edge. The carbon impression of the leaf will be visible on both halves of the cement and can be made even more distinct with the use of clear nail polish or thin oil. The specimens produced as the result of this activity prove very useful as stimuli for further discussion on fossil preservation and the importance of these remains in interpreting geologic history.

16mm Films

Vertebrate Paleontology

"Age of Dinosaurs, The" (b/w, sd, 30 min, i-h). Follows the history of the vertebrates during the Mesozoic and Triassic eras (NET-IU).

"Dinosaur in the Wall" (color, sd, 9 min, i-h). Illustrates the Dinosaur National Monument, formation of the dinosaur quarry, age of the dinosaurs, a theory concerning their extinction, and pictures the environment of the Paleozoic era (NET-IU).

"Dinosaurs" (color, sd, 28 min, 1961, h-c). Follows the complete history of the dinosaur including a consideration of the question of their success or failure as a life form (McGH).

"Dinosaurs: The Age of the Terrible Lizard" (color, sd, 11 min, 1970, i-j) Illustrates the characteristics, types, habits, and behavior of dinosaurs and their place in geologic history (AIMS).

"Dragon of Komodo, The" (color, sd, 19 min, 1969, p-a). Presents a pictorial view of this remnant from the Mesozoic era (McGH).

"Prehistoric Animals of the Tar Pits" (color, sd, 14 min, 1957, i-h). Follows the identification and assemblage of skeletons taken from the Rancho LaBrea tar pits (FAOC).

Origin and Evolution of Life

"Animals of Prehistoric America" (color, sd, 15 min, 1959, i-j). Discusses how the evolution of ancient life is interpreted from the fossil evidence (McGH).

"Beginning and Development of Life, The" (color, sd, 15 min, 1969, i-j). The film traces evolution from one-celled organisms through the development of the more complex organs found in higher forms of life (McGH).

"Darwin and the Theory of Evolution" (color, sd, 14 min, 1967). Describes how Darwin formulated the theory of Natural Selection based on his observations in South America and his experiments in England (CF).

"Dr. Leakey and the Dawn of Man" (color, sd, 28 min, 1967, i-c). Illustrates the work of Dr. and Mrs. Leakey and the making of a significant find marking a major breakthrough in the theory of the Age of Man (AETNAC).

"Earth Science—Parade of Ancient Life" (color, sd, 15 min, 1964, i-h). Traces the evolution of life from the Paleozoic to the Cenozoic Era with the use of museum displays (IU).

"Extinction: A Lesson from the Past" (color, sd, 13 min, 1971, i-j). Describes the work of paleontologists and the origin and development of prehistoric life forms through geologic time (JF).

"In the Beginning" (color, sd, 29 min, 1963). Origin of the earth, and its life on the Great Plains (MLA).

"Natural Selection" (color, sd, 16 min, 1963, h-c). Uses modern examples of plants and animals to illustrate well-known and studied examples of natural selection (EBEC).

"Rise of Mammals, The" (color, sd, 12 min, 1969, i-j). The film depicts evolutionary changes that have taken place in mammals during the geologic past including size, mobility, brain dimensions, body temperature, and hair. These changes, in turn, have allowed the mammals to adapt and survive in a changing environment (McGH).

"Voyage of *Beagle*, Charles Darwin, The" (b/w, sd, 30 min, j-h). Traces Darwin's life through the details of famous voyage (NET-IU).

Paleoecology

"World Before Man, The" (color, sd, 11 min, j-h). Outlines the five eras of geologic time complete with each era's surface topography and life forms (CF).

Geological Time

"Geological History of the Grand Canyon Country" (color, sd, 11 min, 1961, i-h). Tells how the sedimentary strata of the Grand Canyon reflects some five eras of geological time and how they can reflect the ancient environments of which they are the product (ABP).

"Journey into Time" (b/w, sd, 14 min, 1958). Illustrates the origin of the earth and its development. Depicts a full range of fossil life (protozoans, trilobites, and others) through the ancient forms of man (SEF).

"Long Time Intervals" (color, sd, 25 min, 1959, h-c). Points out the importance of extensive periods of time and the use of radioactive dating in measuring the earth's age (MLA).

"Measuring Geologic Time" (b/w, sd, 27 min, 1960, h-c). Describes the use of the basic stratigraphic laws such as superposition, original horizontality, assemblages and sequences, and others in attempting to create an absolute scale of time. Explains the major methods of radioactive dating (UOT).

"Nuclear Radiation in Earth Studies" (color, sd, 15 min, 1961, h). Discusses the process of radioactive decay, how it is measured, and how carbon 14 is utilized to date fossils (CEF).

"Reflections on Time" (color, sd, 22 min, 1969, j-c). Deals with the subjective aspects of our awareness of time, measurement of time, and geologic time.

General Topics

"Animals of the Ice Ages" (color, sd, 16 min, 1960, j-c). Traces the excavation, identification, and restoration of ice age animal bones (NF).

"Coming of Man, The" (color, sd, 13 min, 1969, i-j). Traces the evolution of man living the last 50 million years of geologic history. Includes studies of Australopithecus, Peking man, Neanderthal and Cro-Magnon man (McGH).

"Dinosaur Age, The" (color, sd, 15 min, 1958, i-c). Traces the activities of paleontologists as they discover, recover, transport, and reconstruct a typical Paleozoic skeleton. Illustrates other models of Paleozoic era (FAOC).

"Dinosaur Hunting Today" (color, sd, 12 min, 1964). Describes the outstanding fossil preservation evidenced in the "Badlands" of Alberta, Canada. Traces a paleontological trip that ends with the discovery of a portion of a prehistoric animal. Illustrated with the various displays in the Brumheller Museum (NFBOC).

"Early Land Plants" (color, 28 min, 1961, h-c). Discusses the evolution of land plants through the gymnosperms through the use of specimens and models. Provides examples of how specimens are prepared for study (McGH).

"Fossil Story, The" (color, sd, 19 min, 1953, i-h). Describes the importance of fossils in providing evidence of prehistoric life. Uses the Grand Canyon, LaBrea tar pits, and the Petrified Forest to illustrate their relationship to gem stones, iron, and oil (SOC).

"Geological History of Grand Canyon Country" (color, 11 min, 1961, j-c). Traces the history of this region in five separate parts with the use of cross sections, photographs, and reference to present-day processes (ABP).

"In the Beginning—Grand Canyon Story" (color, sd, 28 min, 1954). Presents the concept of the Grand Canyon's formation by the Colorado River as revealed by its rock layers (HMP).

"Mister Peal's Dinosaur" (b/w, sd, 26 min, 1953, i-h). Tells the story of Charles W. Peal who opened the first National History Museum and how he reconstructed a mastodon skeleton for display in it (EIDDN).

"Parade of Ancient Life" (color, sd, 15 min, 1964, i-h). Illustrates the work of a paleontologist, geographical areas where fossils may be located, use of fossil remains in interpreting the history of the earth, and an imaginary journey through the three most recent eras of geological time (IU).

35mm Filmstrips

Vertebrate Paleontology

"Dinosaurs" (33 frs, color, 1960) (SVE).

"Dinosaurs—Giant Reptiles of the Past" (39 frs, color, captions, 1961). Traces the geologic history of dinosaurs, the discovery of their fossil remains and the possible effects of geologic changes on the reptiles (PS).

"Reptiles Inherit the Earth" (67 frs, color) (LEP).

"Rise of the Dinosaurs, The" (50 frs, color, captions, 1953) (W).

"Evolution Today" (81 frs, color, captions, 1960). Describes current findings and hypotheses concerning the origin and development of life including an emphasis on man's place in the schema (LEP).

"Fossils and Organic Change" (47 frs, color, sd, with guide, 1960) (EBEC).

"How Life Began" (rev. ed). (32 frs, color, captions, 1959) (ELK)

"Man from the Dim Past" (39 frs, color, captions, 1958). Follows the history of man from Pithecanthropus erectus to Cro-magnon man with present-day examples of stone age man (PS).

Paleoecology

"Age of Dinosaurs, The" (32 frs, color, with guide, 1968). Illustrates the discovery, excavation, reconstruction, and utilization of fossils to interpret the environment of dinosaurs and their relationship with later animals (IFB).

"Age of Mammals" (75 frs, color, captions, 1955). Evolution of mammals in North America through the six epochs of the Cenozoic Era (LEP).

"Coming of Reptiles, The" (50 frs, color, captions, 1953) (W).

"Fossils and Their Prehistoric Environments" (47 frs, color, sd, with guide, 1960) (EBEC).

"Life of the Cenozoic Era" (53 frs, color, with guide, 1965). Describes the life of the Cenozoic with emphasis on man (W).

"Life of the Lower Paleozoic Era" (53 frs, color, with guide, 1965). Presents a survey of the life forms of the Paleozoic Era (W).

"Life of Mesozoic Era" (53 frs, color, with guide, 1965). Presents a survey of the life forms of the Mesozoic Era (W).

"Life of the Upper Paleozoic Era" (53 frs, color, with guide 1965). Presents a survey of the life forms of the upper Paleozoic Era (W).

"Triumph of the Dinosaurs, The" (50 frs, color, captions, 1953) (W).

Geological Time

"Fossils and Relative Ages of Rocks" (47 frs, color, sd, with guide, 1960) (EBEC).

General Topics

"Animals of Long Ago" (rev. ed.) (34 frs, color, 1959) (ELK).

"Collecting and Interpreting Fossils" (47 frs, color, sd, with guide, 1960) (EBEC).

"Discovering Fossils" (50 frs, color, 1953) (W).

"Fossils—Key to Past" (47 frs, color, with guide). How fossils are used to date rocks and to indicate prehistoric environments (W).

"How Fossils Are Formed" (47 frs, color, sd, with guide, 1960) (EBEC).

"Nature of the Fossils" (53 frs, color, with guide, 1965). Describes how formed and where and how found (W).

"Rocks and Fossils" (32 frs, color, with guide, 1968). Illustrates the formation of rocks and fossils and their uses in dating and in reconstructing past geological and paleontological events (IFB).

"South American Fossils" (78 frs, color, captions, 1960). Tells of Darwin's theory of a land bridge between North and South America during the Pleistocene time and its effects on evolutionary change in the various species (LEP).

"Story Fossils Tell, The" (41 frs. color, captions, 1957). Surveys the formation of fossils, their locations, geologic time periods, and the evolution of the horse (PS).

8mm Film Loops

Vertebrate Paleontology

"Animals of the Tar Pits" (color, si, 3 1/2 min, Sup 8, cart). Illustrates, with pictures and models, the trapping of a large variety of extinct Pleistocene animals (FAOC).

"Archaeopteryx, The" (color, si, cart, 1968). (PPAC).

"Dinosaur Age, The" (color, sd, 15 min, Sup 8, cart, 1958, i-a). Traces the activities of a paleontologist in finding, exposing, transporting, and reconstructing fossil remains of the dinosaur age (BFA).

"Dinosaurs" (color, si, 3 1/2 min, Sup 8, cart, 1965). Illustrates, with models in natural settings, the brontosaurus, stegosaurus, trachodon and tyrannosaurus (FAOC).

"Dinosaurs—Meat Eaters" (color, si, 3 min, Sup 8, cart, 1967). Traces a representative food chain involving meat-eating dinosaurs (E).

"Dinosaurs—Plant Eaters" (color, si, 4 min, Sup 8, cart, 1967). Depicts, by animation, some of the plant-eating dinosaurs (E).

Geological Time

"Changing Continents" (color, si, 3 1/2, Sup 8, cart, 1965). Presents one hypothesis, based on both geological and paleontological evidence, concerning the appearance of continents and seas on the earth (PPAC).

General Topics

"Fossils: Part I, Collecting in Ancient Fossil Beds" (color, Sup 8, cart, 1970). Removal of dinosaur remains from strata (HSC).

"Fossils: Part II, Collecting and Restoration of Fossil Skeletons" (color, si, Sup 8, cart, 1970) (HSC).

"Fossils" (b/w, sd, 14 min, Sup 8, cart). Follows the development of the scientific view of fossils and the evolution of life (AEF).

"Fossil Interpretation" (color, sd, 10 min, Sup 8, cart, 1956, i-j). Discusses how fossils can provide us with evidence as to the earth's changing surface and life forms (BFA).

"Fossils" (color, 4 min, Sup 8, cart, 1970, i-h). Depicts fossils which provide indications of evolutionary trends (HR).

"Fossils Are Interesting" (color, sd, 10 min, Sup 8, cart, 1956, i-j). Discusses how fossils can provide us with evidence as to the earth's changing surface and life forms (BFA).

"Paleontologists at Work" (color, si, 3 1/2 min, Sup 8, cart, 1965). Follows a fossilized flipper of a Cretaceous marine reptile from its discovery to its final display in a museum (FAOC).

"Rocks That Reveal the Past" (color, sd, 12 min, Sup 8, cart, 1962, i-a) (BFA).

"What Are Fossils?" (color, sd, 6 min, Sup 8, cart, i-a) (AL).

Overhead Transparencies

Invertebrate Paleontology

"Fossils—Invertebrate" (WPC)
"Phylum Brachiopoda" (W)
"Prehistoric Arthropods" (PSC)

"Prehistoric Plant Life" (MPC)
"Subphylum Agnatha" (W)
"Subphylum Trilobita" (W)

Vertebrate Paleontology

"Fossils—Vertebrate, No. 1" (WPC)
"Fossils—Vertebrate, No. 2" (WPC)
"Prehistoric Amphibians" (PSC)
"Prehistoric Birds" (PSC)
"Prehistoric Fish" (PSC)

"Prehistoric Flying Reptiles" (PSC)
"Prehistoric Mammals Part 1" (PSC)
"Prehistoric Reptiles" (PSC)
"Prehistoric Reptiles—Dinosaurs" (PSC)

Origin and Evolution of Life

"Origin of Living Matter, The—Abiogenesis" (PSC)

"Origin of Living Matter, The—Biogenesis" (PSC)

Paleoecology

"Cambrian Period" (WPC)
"Cretaceous Period" (WPC)
"Devonian Period" (WPC)
"How North America Has Changed, Part 1" (W)
"How North America Has Changed, Part 2" (W)
"Jurassic Period" (WPC)
"Mississippian Period" (WPC)
"North America During Cambrian Period" (EA-V)
"North America During Cretaceous Period" (EA-V)
"North America During Devonian Period" (EA-V)
"North America During Miocene Period" (EA-V)
"North America During Ordovic-

ian Period" (EA-V)
"North America During Pennsylvania Period" (EA-V)
"North America During Permian Period" (EA-V)
"North America During Silurian Period" (EA-V)
"North America During Triassic Period" (EA-V)
"Old Stone Age" (WPC)
"Ordovician Period" (WPC)
"Pennsylvanian Period" (WPC)
"Permian Period" (WPC)
"Quaternary Period" (WPC)
"Silurian Period" (WPC)
"Tertiary Period" (WPC)
"Triassic Period" (WPC)

Geological Time

"Carbon-14 Dating" (UTI)

"Correlation by Means of Guide Fossils" (EA-V)

"Geologic Time, 1" (DG)

"Geologic Time, 2" (DG)

"Geologic Time Periods" (PSC)

"Geologic Time Scale" (WPC)

"Geologic Time Scale—Earth" (WPC)

"Geologic Time Table" (WPC)

"Mississippian Period" (WPC)

"Modern Earth Science—Geological Development of North America" (EA-V)

"Origin of the Earth, The" (PSC)

"Uranium Decay Dating" (UTI)

General Topics

"Fossil Formation" (MPC)

"How to Collect and Prepare Fossils" (PSC)

"How the Past Explains the Present" (PSC)

"Index of Fossils Contained in Rocks" (EA-V)

"Paleontology" (a series) (PSC)

"Past Explains the Present, The" (CV)

"Reading the History of Rocks" (WPC)

"Reconstructing Geologic History" (EA-V)

"Record in Rocks" (MPC)

"Types of Fossil Preservations" (EA-V)

"What Are Fossils?" (PSC)

"Where Fossils Are Found" (PSC)

Color Photographs

Key
(1) Origin and Evolution of Life
(2) Paleoecology
(3) Geological Time
(4) General Topics

Curriculum Color Prints (18" x 13")
"Cenozoic Era" (CES), (EG), (IAI), (N), (W)

1. The Tertiary Period (2)
2. The Quaternary Period (2)
3. Cenozoic Life: Part I (2)
4. Cenozoic Life: Part II (2)
5. Development of the
   Horse (1)
6. Development of·Man (1)

"Life: Present and Past" (CES), (DG), (IAI), (N), (W)

1. The Ways in Which Fossils
   Are Formed (4)
2. How Fossils Are Named (4)
3. The Uses of Fossils (1)
4. The Parade of Life: Part I (1)
5. The Parade of Life: Part
   II (1)
6. The Parade of Life: Part
   III (1)

"Mesozoic, The" (CES), (DG), (IAI), (N), (W)

1. The Triassic Period (2)
2. The Jurassic Period: Part
   I (2)
3. The Jurassic Period: Part
   II (2)
4. The Cretaceous Period: Part
   I (2)
5. The Cretaceous Period: Part
   II (2)

6. The Family Tree of the Dinosaurs (2)

"Precambrian and Paleozoic Eras, The" (CES), (DG), (IAI), (N), (W)

1. The Precambrian and the
Cambrian Periods (2)
2. The Ordovician Period (2)
3. The Silurian Period (2)
4. The Devonian Period (2)
5. The Mississippian and Pennsylvanian Periods (2)
6. The Permian Period (2)

"Record in the Rocks, The" (CES), (DG), (IAI), (N), (W)

1. Reading the Record (4)
2. The Geologic Time Scale (3)
3. Measuring Geologic Time (3)
4. The Origin of the Earth (1)
5. Fossils: Keys to Life of the
Past (4)
6. Paleontology: The Study of
Fossils (4)

Supplementary Reading Materials

The supplementary reading materials are not all-inclusive, but they do represent a major portion of currently available paperback books of interest to both teachers and students. They constitute an economical source that is often overlooked and span all levels of instruction from the junior high school to reference works for the teacher. No attempt has been made to indicate the grade or reading level because many are useful for a wide range of abilities. Prices are subject to fluctuation, but most of these publications are reasonably priced. A brief annotation is included for most titles.

Adams, Frank Dawson. *The Birth and Development of the Geological Sciences.* New York: Dover Publications, 1954, 506 pp. Traces the history of the geological sciences, from Greek and Roman times through Middle Ages, Renaissance, and modern era up to the twentieth century. Analyzes in detail ideas of such men as William Smith, Agricola, Geikie, Hutton, Werner, Aristotle, Becher, Cuvier, etc. Re-creates birth of modern mineralogy, metals and their ores, mountains and earthquakes, springs and rivers.

Adler, Irving. *How Life Began.* New York: New American Library of World Literature, 1959, 128 pp. Elementary introduction to organic chemistry and biochemistry, including a glimpse of cytology, evolution, and earth science. Concerned with the nature of life as well as the origin of life.

Anfinsen, Christian B. *Molecular Basis of Evolution.* New York: John Wiley & Sons, 1964, 228 pp. Discusses problems that are intellectually fascinating and also of vital importance to anyone who cares about the future of mankind and organisms on our planet.

Asimov, Isaac. *The Wellsprings of Life.* New York: New American Library of World Literature, 1962, 224 pp. Discusses questions of how, when, and why life began in the oceans and traveled to land. Traces evolutionary theories from Genesis, through Darwin, to Mendel's findings on genetics.

Beerbower, James R. *Field Guide to Fossils.* ESCP Pamphlet Series PS-4. Boston: Houghton Mifflin Co., 1971.

Bell, P. R. *Darwin's Biological Work.* New York: John Wiley & Sons, 1965, 342 pp. A collection of essays demonstrating the breadth of Darwin's interests and his ability as a biologist. Embodies original work, using Darwin's theories as points of departure. Shows how Darwin anticipated current concepts in biology.

Berry, W. B. N. *Growth of a Prehistoric Time Scale—Based on Organic Evolution.* San Francisco: W. H. Freeman and Co., 1968, 158 pp. History of the development of the geologic time scale.

Blume, Harold F. *Time's Arrow and Evolution.* New York: Harper & Row, 1962,

224 pp. Considers properties of life, nucleic acids, history and structure of the earth, irreversibility, and direction in evolution. Speculates on possible origins of living systems.

Cain, A. J. *Animal Species and Their Evolution*. New York: Harper & Row, 1960, 190 pp. Survey of evolution and taxonomy. Discusses methods of classification, naming, and biological definition of a species.

Clark, D. L. *Fossils, Paleontology and Evolution*. Dubuque, Iowa: William C. Brown Co., 1968, 130 pp. Introduction to life of the past for students of earth science. Presents a survey of fossils, their study, and what their interpretation means in the context of earth history.

Croneis, C. G., and W. C. Krumbein. *Down to Earth: An Introduction to Geology*. Chicago: University of Chicago Press, 1961, 499 pp. Interesting, lively, and occasionally humorous introduction to geology which explains man's origin, his place in nature, and the interrelationships between geology, physics, biology, and mathmatics.

Curtis, Brian. *Life Story of the Fish*. New York: Dover Publications, 1961, 285 pp. Presents information about the structure and habits of fish. Covers the evolution of fish, taking into account body covering, framework, the senses and the nervous system, the air bladder, internal organs, and reproduction and growth.

Darwin, Charles. *The Origin of Species*. New York: Collier Books, 1962, 512 pp. Scientific classic that presents a cumulative statement of theory of evolution. Includes historical sketches and statements indicating importance of Darwin's work. Explains survival of the fittest in the author's own words.

_____. *Structure and Distribution of Coral Reefs*. Berkley: University of California Press, 1962, 256 pp. Presents Darwin's impression of the puzzling symmetry of coral islands with their massive foundations made up of coral, and his fascination with the problem of their origin and the fact that the coral animals live only at restricted depths. This leads to Darwin's theory that mid--ocean reefs have grown up as underlying volcanic islands subsided beneath the sea.

_____. *The Voyage of the Beagle*, annotated with an Introduction by Leonard Engel, Garden City, N.Y.: Doubleday & Co., 1962, 534 pp. Complete journal of trip Darwin took around the world before publishing his theory of evolution.

de Beer, Sir Gavin. *Charles Darwin*. Garden City, N.Y.: Doubleday & Co., 1965, 296 pp. Concentrates primarily on Darwin's scientific contributions and provides a brilliant synthesis showing how Darwin's theory of natural selection ties in with molecular biology and genetics. Describes the many facets of Darwin's monumental career, his authorship of *The Origin of Species*, and his later reflective years.

Delevoryas, Theodore. *Plant Diversification* New York: Holt, Rinehart and Winston, 1965, 144 pp. Survey of the evolution of form and function in the plant kingdom outlining and tracing some of the major changes through time. Includes: the evolution of the plant body from simplest unicells to more elaborate forms; evolution of reproductive mechanisms; migration of plants from water to land; increasing specialization in response to the land environment;

evolution of the seed habit in plants; and evolutionary trends within the flowering plant.

Dellenbaugh, Frederick S. *A Canyon Voyage*. New Haven, Conn.: Yale University Press, 1962, 277 pp. Account of Powell's second expedition down the Colorado River. Covers journey down the river, over the comparatively unknown high plateaus of Utah, and discovery of the Escalante River and the Henry Mountains.

Dobzhansky, Theodosius. *Evolution, Genetics and Man*. New York: John Wiley & Sons, 1963, 398 pp. Presents evolution as a dynamic process in which we are involved today and tomorrow as well as in the living past.

Dowdeswell, W. H. *Mechanism of Evolution*. New York: Harper & Row, 1960, 115 pp. Presents evolution as an active process that can be studied to some extent experimentally. Introduces practical suggestions from experience of the author as research worker, field naturalist, and teacher.

Eicher, D. L. *Geologic Time*. Foundations of Earth Science Series. Englewood Cliffs, N.J.: Prentice-Hall, 1968, 150 pp. Relates geologic time to rocks. Shows how the concept of geologic time developed, how geologic time is measured, and how events are interpreted within it.

Eiseley, Loren. *Darwin's Century: Evolution and the Men Who Discovered It*. Garden City, N.Y.: Doubleday & Co., Anchor Books, 1961, 378 pp. Presents a definitive account of how the concepts of evolution came about in the nineteenth century, what its components were, and why it so deeply affected man's views of himself. Covers Darwin's career, creative achievements, and impact of his work. Includes achievements and discoveries of men in different fields of science who paved the way for him. Extensive discussion of ways in which Darwin's work has been challenged, improved upon, and occasionally refuted.

_____. *The Immense Journey*. New York: Random House, 1958, 210 pp. Unusual blend of scientific knowledge and imaginative vision tell the story of the evolution of man. Reveals life's endless mysteries in the author's own experiences, departing from their immediacy into meditations on the long past, wandering with nature through the byways of time, and then returning to the present.

Faul, Henry. *Ages of Rocks, Planets, and Stars*. New York: McGraw-Hill, 1966, 109 pp. Deals with the measurements of geological and astrophysical time. Emphasizes principles rather than techniques and applications. A clear and concise, yet comprehensive book.

Fenton, Carroll Lane, and Mildred Adams Fenton. *Giants of Geology*. New York: Dolphin Books, 1952, 318 pp. Traces development of geology from ancient Greece to modern times by means of a series of biographical sketches of history's outstanding geologists.

Freeman, Tom. *Field Guide to Layered Rocks*. ESCP Pamphlet Series PS-3. Boston: Honghton Mifflin Co., 1971, 46 pp.

Gamow, George. *A Planet Called Earth*. New York: Bantam Books, 1963, 256 pp. Presents theories on the evolution of the solar system and the successive reformations of the earth's surface. Includes origin and evolution of life.

Geike, Archibald. *Founders of Geology*. New York: Dover Publications, 1962,

486 pp. Survey of the work of the major figures of the period in which the main foundations of modern geology were laid—the latter half of the eighteenth century to the first half of the nineteenth century. Covers Palissy, Demarest, Lehmann, Werner, Hutton, Playfair, Hall, Cuvier, Lyell, Darwin, Agassiz, and others.

Goodrich, Edwin S. *Studies on the Structure and Development of Vertebrates* (2 vols.) New York: Dover Publications, 1958, 857 pp. Deals with the various systems of vertebrates. Detailed information on the morphology of the head region, the relationships between lungs and fish bladders, and reptilian and mammalian ear structure.

Grabau, Amadeus W. *Principles of Stratigraphy* (2 vols.). New York: Dover Publications, 1960, 1185 pp. Classic work of twentieth-century geology originally published in 1924. Brings together facts and principles that lie at the foundation of our attempts to interpret the history of the earth from records left in the rocks.

Greene, John C. *Darwin and the Modern World View*. New York: The New American Library of World Literature, 1963, 126 pp. Considers the effect of Darwin's theory on the Christian doctrine of creation; explains current trends in biology and anthropology; and offers a new understanding of the vital relation between science and religion.

Guyenot, Emile. *Origin of Species*. New York: Walker & Co., 1965, 148 pp. Comprehensive survey of what is known about evolution.

Harbaugh, J. W. *Stratigraphy and Geologic Time*. Dubuque, Iowa: William C. Brown Co., 1968, 113 pp. An introduction to stratigraphy and geologic time. Discusses the methods of dating and correlating the rocks of the earth. Includes chapters on the geologic time scale, sedimentary facies, and radiometric age-dating.

Harper, Dorothy. *Isotopes in Action*. Elmsford, N.Y.: Pergamon Press, 1963, 172 pp. Traces the development of atomic theory from ancient to present times and tells how isotopes are used in geology as well as in historical and archaeological research, industry and agriculture.

Hotton, Nicholas. *Dinosaurs*. New York: Pyramid Publications, 1963, 192 pp. Discusses the questions of how dinosaurs lived and why their extinction occurred. Traces history, habits, environment, and problems of dinosaurs. Contains a section on where dinosaur remains can be located.

Huxley, Julian. *Evolution: the Modern Synthesis*. New York: John Wiley & Sons, 1964, 653 pp. Discusses aspects of evolution and suggests future evolutionary trends.

Huxley, Thomas H. *Man's Place in Nature*. Ann Arbor: University of Michigan Press, 1959, 190 pp. Discusses the natural history of the manlike apes, relationship of man to lower animals, and fossil remains of man.

Koenigswald, G. H. R. von. *The Evolution of Man*. Ann Arbor: University of Michigan Press, 1962, 160 pp. Traces evolution of man through geologic time beginning with early vertebrates. The anthropoid apes, the *Australopithecus* discoveries, Neanderthal man, and the origins of Homo sapiens are covered. Human evolution is followed through to the development of culture.

Kottlowski, Frank E. *Measuring Stratigraphic Sections*. New York: Holt, Rinehart and Winston, 1965, 253 pp. Discusses the chief purpose in measuring sections, then stresses their application to stratigraphy, subsurface correlation, structural geology, and sampling problems. Covers the methods and instruments used in section measuring as well as the types of field problems generally encountered.

Kurten, Bjorn. *The Age of the Dinosaurs*. New York: McGraw-Hill Book Co., 1968, 255 pp. Discusses how prehistoric reptiles are to be studied in their environment, and how the Mesozoic era is viewed within earth history.

Laporte, L. F. *Ancient Environments*. Foundations of Earth Science Series. Englewood Cliffs, N.J.: Prentice-Hall, 1968, 128 pp. Provides an introduction to the principles for recognition and interpretation of the ancient environments of animals and plants throughout geologic time. Outlines the ways in which fossils and their enclosing sedimentary rock matrix can be analyzed for reconstructing the environments in which fossils lived and sediments formed.

Mann, Wilfred B., and S. B. Garfinkel. *Radioactivity and Its Measurement*. Princeton, N.J.: D. Van Nostrand Co., 1965, 160 pp. Covers the early history of the discovery of radioactivity, briefly reviews the properties of nuclear radiations, and describes methods available for their measurement.

Matthews, W. H. *Fossils: An Introduction to Prehistoric Life*. New York: Barnes & Noble, 1962, 337 pp. Introduction to the study of fossils written primarily as a handbook for collectors. Contains sections on fossil collecting as a hobby, the geologic time scale, evolution of life, fossil man, and summary of the major divisions of organisms.

Montagu, Ashley. *Man: His First Million Years*. New York: New American Library of World Literature, 1962, 21 pp. An enlightening picture of man's evolution from his earliest preprimate form to his present stage of development. An introduction to the science of anthropology, showing from where man came and the direction in which he is heading.

McAlester, A. L. *The History of Life*. Foundations of Earth Science Series. Englewood Cliffs. N.J.: Prentice-Hall, 1968, 151 pp. Presents an overall survey of the development and evolution of life on earth. Emphasizes the necessity of treating both geological and biological evidence. Testimony of the fossil record is emphasized as essential background for life history, stressing pertinent aspects of genetics, physiology, and biochemistry.

Olson, Everett C. *Evolution of Life*. New York: New American Library of World Literature, 1965, 299 pp. Comprehensive account of evolution, and the ethical, moral, and cultural dilemmas posed for mankind by the theory of evolution.

Oparin, A. I. *Life: Its Nature*. New York: Academic Press, 1961, 207 pp. Discusses the nature, origin, and evolution of life.

_____. *Origin of Life*. New York: Dover Publications, 1953, 270 pp. English translation of Russian text originally published in 1938. First modern statement of theory of gradual evolution of life from nitrocarbon compounds. Includes evaluation of Oparin's theory in light of later research.

Palmer, E. Laurence. *Fossils.* Boston: D. C. Heath and Co., 1965, 144 pp. Introduction to paleontology. Discusses what fossils are, where they can be found, their collection and storage. Provides guide to over 200 fossil species. Relates fossils to understanding of age of earth and evolution.

Powell, John Wesley. *Exploration of the Colorado River and Its Canyons—Canyons of the Colorado.* New York: Dover Publications, 1961, 399 pp. Unabridged republication of the work first published in 1895 under the title *Canyons of the Colorado.* Fascinating account of Major Powell's expedition with a party of ten to explore the last great unmapped and unknown part of the U.S.—the Colorado River.

Rensch, Bernhard. *Evolution Above the Species Level.* New York: John Wiley & Sons, 1965, 436 pp. Describes broader aspects of organic evolution.

Rhodes, F. H. T. *Evolution of Life.* Baltimore: Penguin Books, 1962, 302 pp. Describes emergence and evolution of life. Evidence from study in geology and paleontology form much of the basis for chapters concerned with reptiles, plants, birds, and ancient man.

_____, Paul R. Shaffer and Herbert S. Zim. *Fossils.* New York: Golden Press, 1962, 160 pp. Guide to prehistoric life. Surveys life of the past, era by era. Systematic survey of typical invertebrate fossil groups. Discussion of some common groups of vertebrate fossils and some common fossil plants.

Romer, A. S. *Man and the Vertebrates* (2 Vols.). Baltimore: Penguin Books, 1954, 437 pp. Traces the history of vertebrates through four hundred million years to modern man. Vol. I is concerned primarily with evolution from primitive fish to modern man. Vol. II is mainly about human origins and evolution, races, embryology, anatomy, and physiology.

Schmitt, Waldo L. *Crustaceans.* Ann Arbor: University of Michigan Press, 1965, 204 pp. Lively and informative introduction to the natural history of the crustaceans, intended for the general reader.

Simpson, George Gaylord. *Horses.* Garden City, N.Y.: Doubleday & Co., 1961, 323 pp. Presents lineage of horse over past sixty million years. Case history of evolution. Fascinating discussion of both ancient and modern breeds.

_____. *Life of the Past.* New Haven, Conn.: Yale University Press, 1961, 198 pp. Introduction to work and aims of paleontology and manner in which workers in this discipline obtain results.

_____. *The Major Features of Evolution.* New York: Simon and Schuster, Clarion, 1967. Integrates paleontological data with the information from genetics to synthesize general principles about the course of evolution and the causal factors that underlie evolutionary change.

_____. *Meaning of Evolution.* New Haven, Conn.: Yale University Press, 1960, 364 pp. Attempts to convey an understanding of forces acting on and through life. Emphasizes principles of evolution and human meaning of evolution.

Smith, Homer W. *From Fish to Philosopher.* Garden City, N.Y.: Doubleday & Co., 1959, 304 pp. Describes evolution of man with emphasis on how the kidney enables man's prehistoric ancestors to regulate their own internal environment and emerge from the sea.

Smith, J. Maynard. *Theory of Evolution.* Baltimore: Penguin Books, 1958, 314 pp. Explains causes of evolution using processes of variation, selection, and inheritance in plants and animals. Summary of ideas and concepts particularly in fields of paleontology and embryology.

Stirton, Robert Arthur. *Time, Life and Man.* New York: John Wiley & Sons, 1963, 558 pp. Informative introduction to paleontology. Includes condensed, but excellent, classification of both plant and animal life.

Viorst, Judith. *The Changing Earth.* New York: Bantam Books, 1967, 244 pp. Rocks and minerals, the process of erosion, and the geological history of the earth are among topics covered. Many photographs and linecuts.

Wallace, Bruce. *Chromosomes, Giant Molecules and Evolution.* New York: W. W. Norton & Co., 1966, 202 pp. Gives evidence for evolution contributed by studies of genetics and molecular biology.

_____ , and Adrian Srb. *Adaptation,* 2d ed. Englewood Cliffs, N.J.: Prentice-Hall, 128 pp. Traces phenomenon of adaption of living things to their changing environments and describes the evolution of natural populations.

Walters, Max and David Briggs, *Plant Variation and Evolution,* New York: Mc-Graw-Hill, 1969, 256 pp. Discusses processes of plant evolution and distribution.

Woods, Henry. *Paleontology-Invertebrate,* 8th ed. Cambridge, Mass.: Cambridge University Press, 1961 477 pp. Gives a short account of each invertebrate group. General zoological features with a more detailed description of the hard parts of the animals; classification and the characteristics of important genera, with remarks on the affinities of some forms; and the geological range.

Zim, Herbert S., R. Will Burnett, and Harvey I. Fisher. *Zoology.* New York: Golden Press, 1958, 160 pp. Written on an elementary but informative level. Covers animal life of the past and living world. Topics include: lower animals, animals with jointed legs, animals with backbones, maintaining the race, and animals and their environments.

Free and Inexpensive Materials

Vertebrate Paleontology

"Fossil Mammals of Florida" (74 pp.). Illustrates the prehistoric mammals of Florida with accompanying description of each (FSG), free.

"Mammoths and Mastodons—Ice Age Elephants of New York" (31 pp., Educational Leaflet 13). Discusses fossils, fossil preservation, and geologic time scale. Emphasis is placed on fossil Ice Age elephants found in the state (NYSMSS), free.

Paleoecology

"Oldest Forest and the Naples Tree, The" (NYSMSS), free.

Geological Time

"Fossils: Numbers on the Pages of Time" (4 pp.). Discusses the nature of fossils and shows a variety of common forms to be found in Indiana (IGS), free.

"Geologic Time" (20 pp.). Brochure describes the use of relative and absolute time scales to determine the age of the earth (USGS), free.

General Topics

"Field Book of Pennsylvanian Plant Fossils of Illinois" (35 pp., Educational Series 6). Describes formation, occurrence, collection, and common forms of Pennsylvanian plant fossils (ISGS), free.

"Fossil Collecting Areas in Iowa" (2 pp.). Composite list of fossil-collecting areas, description of the fossil types, and the rocks where they are located (IOGS), free.

"Guide for Beginning Fossil Hunters" (39 pp., Educational Series 4). Explains the nature of fossils and fossilization and describes some common Illinois fossils (ISGS), free.

"Guide to Fossils" (32 pp.). Describes the nature of fossils and common forms to be found in Michigan (MGSD), free.

"Pennsylvania Teachers Fossil Set" A collection of six fossils that are found in the rocks of Pennsylvania (PTGS), free.

"West Virginia Fossil Localities" (2 pp.). (WVGS), free.

PART...6

Physical Geology

Classroom Activities

Model Volcano

A classical activity, which can be used as a demonstration, laboratory investigation, or extra curricular activity, involves creating a model of a volcanic eruption utilizing the chemical, ammonium dichromate. The activity can be quite simplified from the traditional method commonly reported and recommended. The only materials necessary for the activity are the chemical and an asbestos pad large enough to cover an area at least 4 times that encompassed by the base of the pile of dichromate placed on it.

Place a quantity of the chemical, in granular form, on the asbestos (caution should be taken to keep the amount of chemical small enough to keep within the recommended limits) and ignite it with a wooden splinter. The students merely observe the chemical as it gradually is consumed as more and more of it is oxidized. This activity presents a somewhat realistic picture of a volcano eruption and the formation of a cinder cone. It may be done twice—once with the room lights turned off and a second time with them on (to show the building of the cone).

This activity always proves to create a good deal of student interest in the topic of volcanology as well as to provide a number of points from which further related activities or discussions can follow.

Stream Table Study

A number of concepts in physical geology can be investigated through the study of streams in the natural environment. Many times, however, it is not logistically possible to visit a local stream for these first-hand observations. One can create a model of a stream in the classroom and thereby provide the students ample opportunities to study such features as deltas, erosion, meandering, and other phenomena commonly related to streams.

A wide variety of stream tables are available from suppliers of earth science materials and many may be within the science budget of your school. If, however, your budget is not sufficient to accommodate such an expense, then you can make one by fabricating a plastic or aluminum trough (the wider the better) with hoses connected to the water supply and a small aquarium or plastic dishpan to represent a lake or sea into which the stream would be emptying.

Earthquake Record

During most earth science courses the topic of earthquakes usually arises. More often than not the students are told about the characteristic distribution of this phenomenon or shown pictures of a world map illustrating the "ring of fire." An activity, which involves the students in collecting and recording data, entails the use of "Epicenter Cards" distributed by the U.S. Coast and Geodetic Survey. These cards contain a list of the earthquakes that have occurred throughout the world during a series of days or weeks of time. Each quake is identified as to its date and time of occurrence (GMT), exact location of its epicenter, depth, and magnitude.

The students, using the information on the cards and a world map, can plot the various earthquakes as to location and magnitude. Sufficient numbers of earthquakes occur each day so that a relatively short period of time (1-2 weeks) is needed to be able to draw conclusions as to distribution of quakes in areas of crustal unrest.

This activity, like others, has the advantage of centering around data that is recorded and interpreted by the students themselves, and thus they develop their own realization of the devised concept, but at the same time use other questions dealing with related topics.

Field Trip

There can not be enough emphasis placed on the wide range of benefits that accrue through any type of experience with the natural environment. Often there are a number of geologic phenomena in close proximity, even in the case of an urban school. These excursions into the environment need not take the entire day, but merely a period or two of time.

Going into the environment, however, does not automatically ensure student interest and relevancy to the curriculum. Students will not develop the capacity to observe or gain an interest in their environment by being told about everything present. The students will gain much greater interest from even the most brief excursion if they are allowed to investigate the phenomena on their own. This open-endedness will allow the student to seek out that which interests him and to question those aspects he does not understand. These questions will provide the basis for subject matter discussions that are relevant to the local environment and the phenomena it exhibits.

Geologic Features of the National Parks

The National Park System of the United States encompasses areas that have tremendous geologic value to the student of the earth sciences, in addition to being areas of recreation and magnificent scenery. Students frequently have traveled to these areas or may plan to do so, and therefore activities relating to these areas may be very meaningful. The National Park Service has also established a network of "Environmental Study Areas" where natural and cultural values of park areas are interpreted through environmental education programs in nearby schools. Activities can be developed that bring in both the geologic and environmental aspects of the park areas.

Suggested Activities.
1. Map activity. Have the students shade in the National Park areas on a map of the United States and label these areas; and, in addition, label all of the states. Also indicate National Monuments and other "National" areas of geologic significance.
2. Make up a list of selected National Parks and have the students write a brief description of the geologic features for which each park is noted.
3. Have students report on National Park Service areas that they have visited or anticipate visiting in the near future.
4. If you are located near an "Environmental Study Area," try to become involved in this program.

REFERENCES

Matthews, III, William H. *A Guide to the National Parks: Their Landscape and Geology* (2 Vols.) (Vol. I: *The Western Parks*; Vol. II: *The Eastern Parks*). Garden City, N.Y.: Doubleday & Co., Natural History Press, 1968.

National Educational Association, *Man and His Environment: An Introduction to Using Environmental Study Areas*. Washington, D.C.: National Education Association, 1970, 56 pp.

Determination of Specific Gravity of Minerals

The *specific gravity* of a mineral is the ratio between the weight of the mineral and the weight of an equal volume of water. The purpose of determining specific gravity in this investigation is (1) to demonstrate the technique by which specific gravity is determined and (2) to use the determined values as an aide in identification of minerals. In addition, the determination is an application of Archimedes' Principle, which may be stated as follows: A body totally or partially immersed in a fluid is buoyed up by a force equal to the weight of the fluid displaced. The weight of the water displaced is equal to the weight of the mineral in air minus its weight in water. The volume of water displaced is equal to the volume of the mineral. Specific gravity may be computed from the following relation:

$$\text{Sp. Gr.} = \frac{\text{wt. of mineral in air}}{\text{wt. of equal volume of water}} = \frac{\text{wt. of mineral in air}}{\text{wt. of min. in air} - \text{wt. of min. in water}}$$

Select several common minerals such as quartz, galena, calcite, feldspar, fluorite, or barite. The minerals selected should be relatively free of impurities. You will also need a beaker partially filled with water, some fine wire to tie around the mineral specimen when weighing, and apparatus for doing the weighing. The weighing apparatus may be a simple balance of the type shown in Figure 6-1, along with a set of weights. A simple beam balance of this type could be constructed by students in a relatively short time as a project. A simple spring scale, of the type shown in Figure 6-2, would also be adequate.

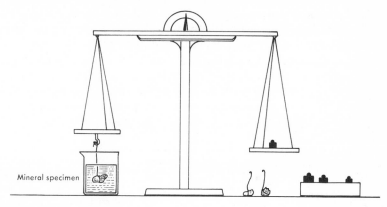

Mineral specimen

Figure 6-1 Beam balance.

To make specific gravity determinations, first the mineral should be weighted carefully in air and the weight recorded. Next, the same specimen is reweighed while suspended in water, making sure that the specimen is fully immersed and that it does not touch the sides or bottom of the beaker. Once both weights are known, you can solve for Sp. Gr. according to the formula given.

Repeat the determination operation using several different minerals. The obtained results should be compared with those given in a textbook or furnished by the teacher, and along with other mineral properties may be used to identify the mineral. A number of questions could be raised after the determinations are made, including: What are the possible sources of error? Why do different minerals have different

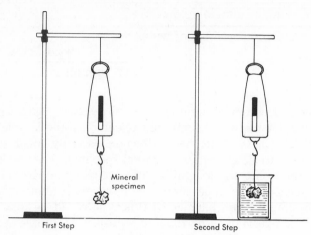

First Step   Second Step

Figure 6-2 Spring scale.

specific gravities? What problems would arise in trying to determine the specific gravity of halite using this method?

Specific gravity is one of the most valuable scientific methods used in identifying minerals. It is a property that may be of help in identification in the field where one does not customarily have a weighing apparatus. With a little practice one can handle mineral specimens and judge whether their specific gravity is high, medium, or low.

Growing Crystals from an Aqueous Solution

Crystal growing is an activity that may be conducted by students as the basis for studying crystallography as well as for development of scientific skills. The activity fits in as a natural outgrowth of the study of minerals; and although the crystals grown will not be minerals, they will be real crystal forms that represent different crystal systems. Observation of the development of crystals from tiny nuclei allows the student to see the variety of characteristics displayed by crystals of substances. The activity is generally best suited for a relatively long-term project.

The growing of crystals of soluble salts from water solutions of several different salts is relatively easy. Among these salts are: copper sulfate ($CuSO_4 \cdot 5H_2O$), deep azure blue color, triclinic crystal system; potassium alum or "Alum" ($KAl(SO_4)_2 \cdot 12H_2O$), colorless octahedrons, isometric crystal system; and "Rochelle Salt" ($KNaC_4H_4O_6 \cdot 4H_2O$), colorless, orthorhombic crystal system.

Several important factors influence the development of crystals grown from water solutions: temperature of the solution, rate of evaporation, impurities in the solution, and shape of the crystallizing vessel.

Several different methods may be employed to grow crystals. They may be grown on the bottom of a flat-bottomed dish or they may be grown by suspending a seed crystal by a thread in a jar containing the solution. The seed crystal may be suspended in a supersaturated solution in a sealed jar thereby allowing excess salt to crystallize on the seed, or the seed crystal may be suspended in an unsealed jar containing a saturated solution that is permitted to evaporate slowly with excess salt crystallizing on the seed. Your students may find that experimentation with different methods is a valuable experience.

The first step in growing crystals is to prepare a solution that is saturated at the temperature at which the crystals will be growing. This may be done by letting the solution evaporate slowly or by heating the solution and dissolving as much of the salt as possible and then cooling the solution to room temperature.

The next step is to let crystals start to grow on the bottom of a flat-bottomed dish or to prepare the seed crystals for suspending in the saturated solution. In the later case after seed crystals have been prepared, they must then be suspended in the solution.

Next, allow the crystals to grow to desired size. Fairly constant temperatures are important in growing crystals, because change in temperature will change the degree of saturation or supersaturation. It is a good idea to grow crystals in a place where the crystals will not be disturbed during growth.

REFERENCE

Holden, Alan, and Phyllis Singer. *Crystals and Crystal Growing*. Science Study Series. Garden City, N.Y.: Doubleday & Co., 1960, 320 pp.

Growth of Crystals from a Molten Substance

Many common minerals crystallize from a *melt* (molten rock or magma) at very high temperatures, so it is difficult to observe their crystal growth directly. However, you can simulate the crystallization of magma in the laboratory by using a substance that has a low melting point which will crystallize at room temperature. Although certainly different than a magma certain principles of crystallization are demonstrated by using a low temperature melt that pertain generally to a magma. Two substances that are particularly suitable are "salol" and "thymol." Normal laboratory precautions should be taken when handling these chemicals, because they may cause irritation to the skin and eyes.

Salol (phenyl salicylate), which has a melting point of 43°C., is obtainable at a drugstore. To watch crystals grow from molten salol, put 25 grams of salol in a tightly closed bottle, and melt it by standing the bottle in hot water. Then let it cool. Little crystals of salol will form in the molten material, and you may watch them get bigger until eventually the salol has all crystallized into a solid mass.

Crystalline thymol may be placed in a petri dish on a hot plate at low heat and allowed to melt. You may heat several dishes of thymol at the same time and then allow them to crystallize under different conditions. Allow one dish to cool slowly at room temperature where it will not be disturbed. Set one petri dish on top of an ice cube and allow it to cool more rapidly. You may melt one dish of thymol and then transfer the petri dish to the stage of a microscope, add several "seed" crystals to the melt, and observe the growth of crystals under the microscope.

Ask your students to respond to the following inquiries:

1. Describe the manner of crystal growth in each different situation.
2. Does salol or thymol have the lower melting point?
3. What effect does the rate of cooling have on crystal size?
4., What role do "seed" crystals play in starting crystal growth?
5. Sketch the crystalline aggregates that developed under each of the different sets of conditions.

16mm Films

Earth Materials and Economic Geology

"All You Have to Do Is Dig" (color, sd, 19 min, 1970, j-a). A description of opal prospecting and mining in Australia (ANIB).

"Challenge of the Arctic" (color, sd, 26 1/2 min, 1969, j-a). Lowell Thomas reports on the Alaska oil operations (ARC), free.

"Coal, a Source of Energy" (color, 15 min, 1967, i-j). Shows the formation of coal, surface and subsurface coal mining, and the uses of coal (McGH).

"Coal Mining the Consol Way" (color, sd, 20 min, 1967, j-a). Description of the modern coal mining industry, sharing both conventional and continuous mining cycles used in underground mines (CCC), free.

"Copper Mining" (color, 14 min, 1960, i-h). Follows copper ore from open-pit mining to transportation, smelting, and refining into pure metal (BFA).

"Crystals" (color, 25 min, 1958, j-c). Discusses the formation and growth, shape, and basic nature of crystals as viewed through a microscope (MLA).

"Crystals, Jewels of Time" (b/w, 30 min, i-h). Origin, characteristics, and identification of common crystal forms of quartz, mica, garnet, and others (NET:IU).

"Crystals and Their Structures" (b/w, 22 min, 1962, j-c). Demonstrates the relationship of the external features of crystals to cleavage planes and shows how given crystals effect x-ray to produce diffraction patterns (NET:IU).

"Diamond Mining in East Africa" (color, 9 min, 1969, p-c). Traces the mining of diamonds from the original deposits through the processing of the mineral (F).

"Earth Reveals, The" (color, 20 min, 1963). Traces the exploration and mining of minerals in Australia (ANIB).

"Earth Science: Minerals and Rocks" (color, 17 min, 1968, j-h). Discusses the identification and classification of rocks and minerals based on their characteristics. Follows the growth of minerals and their related rocks (IU).

"Earth, the Resources in Its Crust" (color, 11 min, 1960). Illustrates the organic and mineral resources of the earth, their mining, processing, use, and conservation (CF).

"Horizons Deep, Horizons Wide" (color, 22 1/2 min, 1970, j-a). Surveys the petroleum industry and the challenges and demands it faces in the years ahead. Ranges from Alaska to Cape Kennedy and includes career opportunities in the industry (API), free.

"Lead Matrix, The" (color, 28 min, 1967, i-h). Presents an explanation of the history, uses, location, processing, atomic structure, and characteristics of lead (USNAC), free.

"Metals and Ores" (color, 10 min, i-h). Describes the geologic formation of metals, open-pit and underground mining, and the extraction and processing of ores (DOUG).

"Minerals Challenge, The" (color, 27 min, 1970, j-a). Documents the country's need for fuels, metals, and other minerals and how these needs are being met with modern day technology. Depicts mining (surface and subsurface) for metals, nonmetals, coal, oil, and gas (USBM), free.

"North Slope—Alaska" (color, sd, 19 min, 1965, j-a). Shows how an oil company explores for oil (BPNA), free.

"Pipeline to Japan" (color, sd, 25 1/2 min, 1970, j-a). Shows how natural gas produced in Alaska is processed into a liquid form, then transported by specially designed ships to Japan (MOC), free.

"Riches of the Earth" (Revised) (color, sd, 17 min, 1966, j-h). Animated film showing how Canada's underground resources took shape through geological ages (McGH).

"Rocks and Minerals: How We Identify Them" (color, b/w, 13 1/2 min, 1971, i-j). Describes how one can identify rocks and minerals using their physical properties (CF).

"Rocks That Form on the Earth's Surface" (color, 16 min, 1964, i-h). Illustrates the formation and composition of sedimentary rocks (EBEC).

"Rocks That Originate Underground" (color, 23 min, 1966, i-h). Origin and common characteristics, including factors controlling the internal structure of igneous and metamorphic rocks (EBEC).

Igneous Activity

"Aetna" (color, sd, 11 min, 1970, j-h). An unnarrated study, using close-up photography and extreme slow-motion filming, of an eruption of Mt. Aetna on the island of Sicily (AEF).

"Case History of a Volcano" (color, 30 min, 1966, j-c). Illustrates the work of an investigator as he designs and constructs instruments to study the events that precede a volcanic eruption. Pictures eruptions of a volcano on Hawaii (NET:IU).

"Crater Lake Story, The" (rev. ed.), (color, 16 min, 1967, p-h). Presents the formation of the caldera, including related geological phenomena associated with its origin (TSP).

"Discovery: Heat, Blacksmith of the Earth" (b/w, 30 min, 1956, i-h). Illustrates volcanism and formation of igneous rocks and igneous structures (NET:IU).

"Earth The: Volcanoes" (color, b/w, sd, 11 min, 1969, j-h). Surveys the origin of volcanic activity, types of activity, volcanic shapes and topographic features commonly associated with volcanoes (CF).

"Eruption of Kilauea, 1959–60" (color, 28 min, 1960, j-c). Illustrates, through filmed sequences, the eruption of the Hawaiian volcano (USGS), free.

"Fire Mountain" (color, sd, 9 min, 1971, i-h). Unnarrated film of the August, 1969, eruption of Kilauea, containing both close-up and telephoto views of lava flows (EBEC).

"Geology of Zuni Salt Lake Maar, The" (color, 15 min, j-c). Illustrates the geological history of the volcanic-produced cinder cones and crater located in this western New Mexico site (DFL), free.

"Geysers and Hot Springs" (color, 11 min, 1951, i-h). Hydrothermal activity and features of Yellowstone National Park (BARR).

"Heartbeat of a Volcano" (color, 21 min, 1971, j-a). Presents a case study of the volcano Kilauea in Hawaii during a rare major eruptive cycle (EBEC).

"Igneous Rocks" (color, 20 min, 1965, i-h). Presents an introductory discussion of magma, crystallization, classification of igneous rocks, and illustrates exposures of igneous rocks in nature (MLA).

"Lava and the River" (color, 20 min, 1959, i-c). Discusses the origin of the Columbia River Plateau, the life forms that were trapped by the numerous flows, and the effects of glaciation on the area (MM).

"Lava Flows" (color, si, 1965). Illustrates the characteristics of basaltic and pahoehoe lava flows (FAOC).

"Past Is a Prelude, The" (color, sd, 13 min, 1971, j-h). Studies active and recently active volcanoes to determine factors that contribute to their formation. Also discusses other sources of the earth's mountains (UE&VA).

"Succession on Lava" (color or b/w, 14 min, 1970, j-h). The film illustrates the aftermath of a volcanic eruption and examines the difficulties overcome by the various life forms that reappear on the lava flow (EBEC).

"Volcano Surtsey" (color, 26 min, 1966, j-c). Follows the volcanic eruption of Volcano Surtsey off the coast of Iceland on November 14, 1963, and the subsequent month of volcanic activity. Also discusses the nature and development of a shield cone (NSNC).

Crustal Rock Deformation and the Earth's Interior

"Alaska Earthquake, 1964, The" (color, sd, 1966, 22 min, j-a). The film focuses on the Good Friday Alaska quake of 1964, with the causes, damage and suggestions for alleviation of much of the destruction included (USGS), free.

"An Approach to the Prediction of Earthquakes" (color, sd, 39 min, 1969, j-a). Illustrates the study of earthquakes by seismologists and how data collected from their research has led to a better understanding of this phenomena (AEF).

"Birth and Death of Mountains" (color, 12 min, 1961, j-h). Depicts both the constructive and destructive geologic forces acting on the earth Discusses the classification of some of the world's better-known mountains and mountain ranges (FAOC).

"Continents Adrift" (color, 15 min, 1971, j-c). The film traces the nature and development of the continental drift theory from 1915 to 1970. Includes discussions of magnetic north, paleo-magnetic analysis, deep sea drilling, sea floor spreading, oceanic ridges and plate tectonics (AEF).

"Diastrophism, What Moved the Mountains, What Shaped the Seas?" (color, 19 1/2 min, 1970, p-h). Provides a survey of the forces (crustal movements, earthquakes, and the effects of water) which influence the earth's surface (UE&VA).

"Drifting of the Continents, The" (color, sd, 50 min, 1971, j-a). A survey of the theories of continental drift, sea floor spreading, and plate tectonics (TLF).

"Earth, The—Its Structure" (color, 11 min, 1960). Explains the gas-cloud hypothesis of the earth's formation, the nature of its core and crust (CF).

"Earthquake" (color, 15 min, 1966, j-c). Depicts the origin and effects of earthquakes (FAOC).

"Earthquakes—Lesson of a Disaster" (color, sd, 13 min, 1971, j-c). A case study of two recent earthquakes—one in Turkey and the other in California. Surveys the recording and analysis of energy waves, damage, and finally the questions about the effectiveness of present earthquake emergency planning (EBEC).

"Faults and Folds, Part I" (b/w, 27 min, 1960, h-c). Demonstrates footwalls, hanging walls, normal faults, reverse faults, strike-slip faults, and monoclines through the use of blocks, sandbox experiments, and clay experiments (UOT).

"Faults and Folds, Part II" (b/w, 29 min, 1960, h-c). Discusses strike, dip, standard structural map symbols, and relationship between faults and folds (UOT).

"Hidden Earth, The" (color, 27 min, 1960, j-c). Follows the development of the science of seismology, instruments used in the study of the earth's interior, significance of volcanism and earthquakes, and theories concerning the solar system (McGH).

"How Solid Is Rock?" (color, 22 min, 1968, j-h). Compares the movement of air and water to that of rock. Discusses the response of rock to high pressure and temperature (EBEC).

"Not So Solid Earth, The" (color, 25 min, 1971, c-a). Provides an overall view of the theories of continental drift, plate tectonics, and sea floor spreading through the use of diagrams, models, and live photography (TLF).

"Trembling Earth, The" (color, 30 min, 1968, h-a). The film presents an indepth survey of the work of seismologists as they study earthquakes. The film includes views of a seismic laboratory and the 1964 Alaskan earthquake (NET:IU).

"Why Do We Still Have Mountains?" (color, 20 min, 1965, i-h). Shows the interaction of the processes of mountain building and those of weathering and erosion. Indicates present-day measurements of uplift and its effects in the geologic future (EBEC).

Surficial Geologic Processes

"Barrier Beach" (color, si, 20 min, 1971, j-h). This film, using time-lapse photography, studies the changes in a barrier beach over a period of a year (ACI).

"Beach: A River of Sand" (color, 20 min 1965, j-c). Illustrates varieties of ocean shorelines, the nature and the behavior of sand along many of the shores as they are affected by waves (EBEC).

"Birth of Land" (color, sd, 16 min, 1970, i-h). The film shows the processes of erosion, sedimentation, volcanism, uplift and submergence as they contributed to the formation of the islands of Japan (AEF).

"Birth of a River" (color, 12 min, 1963, h). Describes the water table, its relationship to a watershed, and the origin of a river (TSP).

"Birthplace of Icebergs, The" (b/w, 11 min, 1941, i-j). Follows the activities of Father Hubbard as he investigated glaciers and icebergs in Alaska. Discusses his theory concerning the rise of icebergs (TCF).

"Caverns and Geysers" (color, 15 min, i-h). Discusses ground water; the water table, movement of ground water, and the relationship of bodies of water; caverns, their structural formations; and geysers to ground water (FAOC).

"Century's Greatest Flood, No. 1" (b/w, 11 min, 1965). Illustrates the effects of the flooding of the Mississippi River system in the Midwest in April 1965 (EMERY).

"Continental Glaciers" (color, 13 min, 1955, j-c). Illustrates the mechanisms involved in maintenance and movement of a continental glacier and the nature of various glacial deposits (OSU).

"Downslope Movement" (b/w, 27 min, 1960, h-c). Illustrates, with clay models, various characteristics and features produced by movement of materials under the influence of gravity. Discusses cause and prevention of such movements (UOT).

"Drop of Water, A" (color, 14 min, 1971, h-c). Provides an overall survey of the features of a river as its water goes to the ocean (ABP).

"Dust Bowl, The" (b/w, 23 min, h-c). Shows the Dust Bowl area before and after the dust storms of the 1930s. Stresses the work of conservationists and the outlook of residents toward the future (McGH).

"The Earth: Action of Rivers" (color, 11 min, 1969, j-h). The film explores the relationship between the action of rivers and the formation of certain topographic features such as canyons, alluvial fans, terraces, channels, sandbars, delta and flood plains (CF).

"The Earth: Coastlines" (color, 11 min, 1969, j-h). Investigates the forces that create different coastline features (CF).

"Erosion—Leveling the Land" (color, 14 min, 1964, i-h). Studies the nature and effects of weathering, erosion, and deposition of earth materials (EBEC).

"Evidence for the Ice Age" (color, 19 min, 1965, i-h). Shows deposits and other geologic features that provide evidence for the existence of glacial ice in the past (EBEC).

"Geology of Yellowstone" (color, sd, 16 min, 1967, j-a). Concentrates on the thermal activity of the National Park, with geysers, hot springs, paint pots, fumaroles, and the formation of travertine terraces among some of the topics discussed (McGH).

"Glaciation" (color, sd, 11 min, 1965, j-c). Traces the development and movements of glacial ice and the common erosional and depositional features of continental glaciation (McGH).

"Great Lakes and How They Were Formed" (color, 11 min, 1951, i-h). Traces the development of the Great Lakes to their present-day drainage and topographical changes still occurring (EBEC).

"Ground Water" (b/w, 26 min, h-c). Discusses porosity, permeability, artesian systems, different varieties of aquifers, and karst topography (UOT).

"Ground Water—The Hidden Reservoir" (color, 19 min, 1971, j-a). Provides a summary of such concepts as origins of ground water, permeability, aquifer, water table, springs, artesian wells, temperature, geyser, hard water, cavern formation, and ground water protection (WI).

"Hard Water" (color, 9 min, 1970, i-j). Traces the processes which act on rainwater to make its hardness increase (BFA).

"Mountain Glaciers" (color, sd, 19 min, 1966, h-c). Illustrates mountain glaciers including their many depositional and erosional processes and features (OSU).

"New Jersey Shoreline, The" (color, 18 min, 1971, j-h). The film outlines the crises that have developed during the past century, along with some typical solutions that are being attempted in order to rebuild beaches and prevent further erosion (EF).

"River Characteristics" (b/w, 27 min, 1960, h-c). Explains the tributary systems; effects of width, depth, velocity, and quantity on a river; meanders and flash flood; importance of ground water (UOT).

"Rock Weathering—Origin of Soils" (b/w, 26 min, 1960, h-c). Mechanical and chemical weathering, development of soil, soil zones, and profiles of different soils (UOT).

"Sand—The Desert in Motion" (color, 11 min, 1969, i-h). The film provides an overall survey of the desert region, with particular emphasis on the sand (BFA).

"Stalactites and Stalagmites—Subterranean Sculpture" (color, 11 min, 1969, j-h). Discusses the nature and causes of underground formations resulting from the action of ground water (BFA).

"Story of Two Creeks, The" (color, sd, 1970, j-c). Describes and interprets the glacial geology of the Two Creeks' forest bed on the west shore of Lake Michigan, in Wisconsin (UOW).

"Time Changes the Land" (color, 23 min, 1963). Describes the effect of geological forces throughout time on the Zion-Brice region of southern Utah (BFA).

"Water Below, The" (b/w, si, 30 min, 1964). Discusses the origin of coves, sinkholes, geysers, and hot springs (MTPS), free.

"Ways of Water, The" (color, sd, 13 min, 1971, i-j). Provides an opportunity for one to see the various stages of the water cycle in a natural setting—unnarrated (EBEC).

"Weathering" (b/w, 12 min, 1961). Depicts, via animation, the formation of rocks as well as their destruction by agents of weathering (DOUG).

"What Happens at the Front of a Glacier" (color, sd, 15 min, 1972, h-c). This film, using time-lapse photography and sequence photographs, summarizes the four-year investigation of the Athabasca Glacier, Alberta. Includes rates of retreat, changing conditions of ice, and the formation of morainal ridges (EBEC).

"Winter Geyser" (color, sd, 7 min, 1966, p-j). Shows scenes of nature in the geyser country, Yellowstone National Park (PYRF).

"Work of the Wind and Running Water" (color, sd, 19 min 1970, j-h). Explains and illustrates the processes involved in the geologic work of the wind and the principal landforms that result. The second portion of the film deals with the geologic work of running water (JW).

Measurement and Mapping

"Earth, The" (b/w, 16 min, j-c). Discusses latitude and longitude—their positions and significance in determining locations on the earth (NORWOOD), free.

"Phase One: Prince Charles Mountains" (color, sd, 22 min, 1970, h-a). Documents the work of a research team as they conduct a topographical and geological survey of the Prince Charles Mountains in Antarctica (ANIB).

"Understanding Topographic Maps" (color, sd, 14 min 1970, j). Explains how a topographic map is made and what it illustrates (JW).

"What's Inside the Earth" (color, 14 min, 1959, i-h). Summarizes man's findings concerning the nature of the earth's interior, using a variety of methods and instruments. Illustrates the nature of the various regions of the earth (FAOC).

Environmental Geology

"Atom Underground" (color, sd, 20 min, 1969, h-c). Describes the use of the explosive power of the atom to recover valuable natural resources beneath the surface of the earth (USAEC), free.

"Before the Mountain Was Moved" (color, sd, 58 min, 1971, j-a). Depicts the progress (although quite slow) of community action in organizing the citizens of a town to publicize the destruction of their community and its resources by strip-mining operations (McGH).

"Beyond the Pack Ice" (color, sd, 18 min, 1969, j-a). Illustrates the work of Australian Antarctic research teams and the conditions they operate under as they study environmental aspects of the continent (ANIB).

"Bitter and the Sweet, The" (color, sd, 29 1/2 min, 1971, h c). Discusses all aspects of desalting technology and the status of commercial desalting in the Western Hemisphere (USAEC), free.

"Desalting the Seas" (color, sd, 17 min, 1967, j-c). Describes the various methods of purifying saline waters through the use of nuclear energy and resulting in the production of large amounts of electric power at the same time (USAEC), free.

"Disaster, 1906" (b/w, 29 min, 1961). Describes San Francisco before and after the April 18, 1906 earthquake (SEF).

"Endless Chain" (color, sd, 28 min, 1971, j-a). Tells the story of an ecological study on the isolated desert steppe of southeastern Wash ington State; aimed at helping man learn how to live with his delicate, complex environment (USAEC), free.

"Glen Canyon" (color, sd, 1965, 30 min, i-a). Portrays the "drowning" of Glen Canyon of the Colorado River as the result of damming that portion of the river (ASF).

"Isotopes in Environmental Control" (color, sd, 14 min, 1971, h-c). Shows some of the ways radioactive atoms are being used to help man preserve and restore his environment (USAEC), free.

"Mud" (color, sd, 20 min, 1968, j-a). The film illustrates problems that develop from improper or inadequate control of urban development. Provides a series of case histories demonstrating the detrimental results of urban erosion and sedimentation (NACD).

"No Turning Back" (color, sd, 27 1/2 min, 1971, j-a). A visit to some of the men involved in AEC-supported ecology studies at laboratories and sites across the country (USAEC), free.

"Northwest Passage" (color, sd, 27 min, 1970, j-a). Documents the initial voyage of the oil tanker *Manhattan* going through the Arctic passage (McGH).

"Nuclear Power and the Environment" (color, sd, 14 min, 1970, j-c). Discusses the problems that stem from growing demands for power and the care that is taken in studying and controlling effects of nuclear and fossil-fueled power plants on the environment (USAEC), free.

"Project Salt Vault" (color, sd, 11 min, 1969, j-c). Deals with the feasibility of permanent disposal of high-level radioactive wastes in vacated salt mines in Kansas (USAEC), free.

"Prudhoe Bay or Bust" (color, sd, 30 min, 1971, h-c). Documentary tracing the development and environmental, social and economic

implications of a proposed 800-mile hot oil pipeline from the Bay
through Alaska (NET:IU).

"Ravaged Land" (color, sd, 15 min, 1971, j-c). Describes the problem
of strip-mining, concentrating on the Appalachian states. It shows
the enormity of the economic, social and ecological problems
created by strip-mining and provides constructive suggestions for
future actions (JW).

"San Francisco: The City That Waits to Die" (color, sd, 57 min, 1971
h-a). Provides an overall view of the danger that nature possesses in
the form of earthquakes to the San Francisco area and man's attempts to ignore and/or alleviate the threat (TLF).

"Tomorrow Is Maybe" (color, sd, 60 min, 1971, j-a). Scenes of Yellowstone National Park, Pikes Peak, Mesa Verde, and Arches National Monument are compared with scenes sharing environmental
problems confronting cities and suburbs while the film explores
man's relationship to his environment (NET:IU).

"Torrey Canyon" (b/w, sd, 26 min, 1970, j-a). Depicts the March,
1967, wreck of the giant tanker *Torrey Canyon* of Sicily, the attempts to clean the beaches, rescue efforts trying to save animal life
of the area, and the divergent viewpoints of shipping experts and
scientists about the legal and social consequences of the tragedy
(TLF).

"Untroubled Waters" (color, sd, 21 1/2 min, 1971, j-a). Illustrates
how little disturbance there has been in Loch Long, Scotland, since
the deep water terminal at Finnart was established in 1969 for oil
tankers, and compares it to Valdez, Alaska (BPNA), free.

"Waste Disposal by Hydraulic Fracturing" (color, sd, 11 min, 1966,
j-c). Depicts the development of a process for the disposal of inter-
mediate-level radioactive wastes in underground bedded shale formations. Shows actual injection with animation illustrating what happens to the material once injected (USAEC), free.

General Topics and Regional Studies

"Alaska—The Great Land" (color, sd, 27 1/2 min, 1971, j-a). Examines
Alaska as it is today and surveys its history, from Bering's discovery
in 1741 to the discovery of oil close to the Arctic shore (BPNA),
free.

"Antarctica—Coldest Continent" (color, 14 min, 1968, i-h). Discusses
the fundamental geological, geographical, and biological aspects of
Antarctica (AIMS).

"Arctic: Islands of the Frozen Sea, The" (b/w, 30 min, j-c). Illustrates
the geography, climate, flora, and fauna of the Queen Elizabeth

Islands. Discusses the misconceptions about the Arctic and hypotheses about its origin and development (EBEC).

"Blueprint for Discovery" (color, 28 min, j-c). Tells of the Mohole Project off the coast of Mexico to investigate Mohorovicic Discontinuity (NAS), free.

"Canadian Rockies, The" (color, 11 min, j-h). Depicts the Canadian Rockies with emphasis on the flora and fauna, glaciers, peaks, rivers, and lakes (BFA).

"Cascade Mountains, The" (color, 20 min, i-h). Shows the geological aspects of the Cascades including their geologic formations, glaciers, and features that allow the interpretation of its past (MM).

"Columbia River, The" (color, 11 min, 1966, i-h). Follows the path of the river from its source region to the Pacific Ocean, and the nature and use of the dams constructed along its route (CF).

"Death Valley—Ancient and Modern" (color, 20 min, 1962). Describes the historic, geologic, and scenic nature of the valley (BFA).

"Earth in Change, the Earth's Crust" (color, 16 min, 1961, i-h). Describes the effects of earthquakes, sedimentation, volcanism, erosion, and folding on the earth's surface. Discusses the interpretation of the geologic past from the crust of the earth (EBEC).

"Earth in Evolution, The" (color, 11 min, 1961, i-j). Illustrates two hypotheses that attempt to account for the development of the earth and how the various constructive and destructive forces leave their marks on the earth's crust (AEF).

"Face of Britain, The" (color, sd, 20 min, 1971, j-c). Aerial survey of the wide variety of landforms that are found in the British Isles (IFB).

"Four Seasons of Yellowstone" (color, sd, 30 min, 1968, i-a). Narrated by Lowell Thomas, the film features the spectacular scenery of Yellowstone National Park (COC), free.

"Geological Influences on Local Plant Distribution" (color, 17 min, 1958, h-c). Describes the relationship between soil conditions and geologic terrain to the types of plants to be found in the driftless area of southwestern Wisconsin (UOI).

"Geology of the Grand Canyon Country" (color, 17 min, 1967, i-j). Relates erosion, deposition, volcanism, and seismic activity to the nature of the Grand Canyon. Describes the use of fossil evidence to interpret the history of the canyon (BFA).

"Last Continent, Antarctica: The Glaciology" (b/w, 29 min, j-h). Tells of the nature of the Antarctica glaciological investigations carried out on the ice cap (NET:IU).

"Last Continent, Antarctica: The Seismology" (b/w, 29 min, h-c). Discusses the seismological research conducted on the continent during the IGY (NET:IU).

"Niagara Frontier" (color, sd, 20 min, 1968, j-a). Features the Falls and swift-running waters of the Niagara River (ASF).

"Rapids of the Colorado" (color, sd, 15 min, 1970, i-a). A documentary of a river trip by boat down the rapids of the Colorado River (PYRF).

"Teton Trails" (color, sd, 22 min, i-a). Scenic and wildlife beauties of Jackson Hole and Grand Teton National Park (SOCC), free.

"When the Astronaut Speaks" (color, 20 min, 1968, j-c). Describes the field work of a geologist and how the procedures may be used to collect meaningful data on the lunar surface (DFL), free.

35mm Filmstrips

Earth Materials and Economic Geology

"Changing Ores into Metals" (47 frs, color, 1955). Follows the refining of various metals from their ores (PS).

"Coal: a Fossil Fuel" (42 frs, color, 1963). Follows the geological development of coal, its mining, processing, and uses (PS).

"Coal Mining" (29 frs, color, 1952) (EG).

"Common Minerals" (45 frs, color, 1962) (SVE).

"Conservation of Minerals, The" (38 frs, color, 1958). Importance and need for their conservation (EG).

"Using Our Minerals Wisely" (44 frs, color, 1961). Results of use, misuse, and rehabilitation of minerals (EBEC).

"Crystallization" (30 frs, color, 1964) (EBEC).

"Crystals and Their Deformation" (26 frs, color, with script, 1961) (EBEC).

"Crystals and Their Properties" (44 frs, color, 1963). Production of crystals in the laboratory, crystal systems, crystal structures, and properties correlated with type of bonding (PS).

"Desert Rocks and Minerals" (30 frs, color, 1955) (BFA).

"Desert Soil, Sand and Stone" (30 frs, color, with record, 1960). Close-ups of alkali deposits and a variety of minerals (BFA).

"Digging for the Earth's Treasures" (30 frs, color, 1955). Mining and importance of minerals (PS).

"Exploring the Rocks Around Us" (30 frs, color, 1956). Nature, formation, identification, and use of sedimentary rocks (SC).

"Gold Mining" (44 frs, b/w, 1951). Compares lode and placer gold and procedures followed in the placer-gold mining (BFA).

"Gypsum Dunes, The" (60 frs, color, with record, 1966) (SVE).

"How Rocks Are Formed" (50 frs, color, 1952) (McGH).

"Mineral Resources" (2d rev. ed.) (35 frs, color, 1960) (ELK).

"Mineral Riches of America" (33 frs, color, 1956). Follows a variety of minerals from their mining to finished product, also discusses their conservation (SC).

"Minerals, How They Are Identified" (41 frs, color, 1962). Shows diagnostic properties of some common minerals and various laboratory procedures used to identify minerals (PS).

"Minerals in the Soil" (59 frs, b/w, 1956) (EBEC).

"Packing of Atoms in Crystals" (27 frs, color, 1961) (EBEC).

"Rocks and Minerals, Part I" (57 frs, color, with record, 1967). Origin, properties, identification tests, location, and uses of rock-forming minerals, ores, and gem stones (EG).

"Rocks and Minerals, Part II" (61 frs, color, with record, 1967). Formation and identification of rocks, nature of the earth's crust and geologic time (EG).

Igneous Activity

"Active Volcanoes" (36 frs, color, 1964). Actual photographs of volcanic eruptions (S).

"Earth's Surface and Earthquakes and Volcanoes" (49 frs, color, 1961) (McGH).

"Earthquakes and Volcanoes" (49 frs, color, with record, 1967). Elastic Rebound theory of earthquakes and the course and nature of volcanoes (EG).

"Extinct Volcanoes" (40 frs, color, 1964) (S).

"How Rocks Are Formed" (50 frs, color, 1952) (McGH).

"Igneous Rocks" (41 frs, color, 1964) (S).

"Story of Mountains, The" (40 frs, color, 1961). Development and modifications of volcanic, dome, and block mountains with a demonstration of folding, using clay (PS).

"Volcanic Cinder Cone, The" (60 frs, color, with record, 1966) (SVE).

"Volcanic Origin and Growth" (32 frs, b/w) (BFA).

"Volcanism" (41 frs, color, 1961) (G).

"Volcanoes and Earthquakes" (40 frs, color, 1962) (SVE).

"Volcanoes and Birth of the Islands" (35 frs, color, with record, 1957) (C).

"Volcanoes, Geysers and Hot Springs" (rev. ed.) (43 frs, color, 1959) (ELK).

Crustal Rock Deformation and the Earth's Interior

"Diastrophism" (41 frs, color, 1966). Evidence of diastrophism and theories accounting for movement of the crust of the earth (PS).

"Earth's Crust, The" (43 frs, color, 1962) (SVE).

"Earth's Surface and Earthquakes and Volcanoes" (49 frs, color, 1961) (McGH).

"Earthquakes and Volcanoes" (49 frs, color, with record, 1967). Elastic Rebound theory of earthquakes and the course and nature of volcanoes (EG).

"Mountain Building" (59 frs, color, with record, 1967). Process of mountain building and various stages in the life cycle of a mountain range (EG).

"Mountains" (46 frs, color, 1962) (SVE).

"Story of Mountains, The" (40 frs, color, 1961). Development and modifications of volcanic, dome, and block mountains with a demonstration of folding, using clay (PS).

"Work of Internal Forces" (50 frs, color, 1965) (SVE).

Surficial Geologic Processes

"Changing Surface of the Earth, The" (55 frs, color, 1953). Nature of the geological processes which change the earth's surface (McGH).

"Desert Soil, Sand, Stone" (30+ frs, color, record, 1960). Close-ups of alkali deposits and a variety of mineral (BFA).

"Evolution of a Butte" (65 frs, color, 1966). Development of a butte through the action of geologic processes (SVE).

"Factors in the Evolution of Landscapes" (67 frs, color, with record, 1966) (SVE).

"Glacial Valley, The" (63 frs, color, record, 1966). Development of this type of valley (SVE).

"Glaciation" (54 frs, color, with record, 1967). Hypotheses concerning the ice age and the effects of glaciation on the earth's surface (EG).

"Glacier and Rocky Mountain National Parks" (38 frs, color, 1960) (EG).

"Ice Age, The" (42 frs, color, 1965). Development and effects of the ice age (PS).

"Ice-Carved Mountains" (rev. ed.) (44 frs, color, 1954) (ELK).

"Life Cycle of Rivers, The" (42 frs, color, 1965). Factors that influence a river's life cycle (PS).

"Limestone Canyon, The" (58 frs, color, with record, 1966) (SVE).

"Underground Water" (43 frs, color, 1962) (SVE).

"Work of Ground Water" (47 frs, color, 1965) (SVE).

"Work of Running Water" (47 frs, color, 1965) (SVE).

"Work of Snow and Ice" (48 frs, color, 1965) (SVE).

Measurement and Mapping

"Antarctic, The" (60 frs, color, 1962). Describes the value of the continent for earthquake and geologic history studies as well as for establishing satellite control stations (LEP).

"Introducing the Topographic Map" (58 frs, color, 1965). Describes how physical features are represented on a topographical map (BOW).

Environmental Geology

"Conservation of Minerals, The" (38 frs, color, 1958). Importance and need for their conservation (EG).

"Using Our Minerals Wisely" (44 frs, color, 1961). Results of use, misuse, and rehabilitation of minerals (EBEC).

"Mineral Conservation Today" (52 frs, color, with record, 1963) (SVE).

General Topics and Regional Studies

"About Our Earth" (rev. ed.) (27 frs, color, 1959). Origin and nature of the earth depicted by paintings and close-up photography (ELK).

"Antarctic, The" (60 frs, color, 1962). Describes the value of the continent for earthquake and geological history studies as well as for establishing satellite control stations (LEP).

"Glacier and Rocky Mountain National Parks" (38 frs, color, 1960) (EG).

"Mesa Verde National Park" (50 frs, color, 1954) (H).

"Yellowstone National Park" (57 frs, color, 1966) (SVE).

"Yosemite" (50 frs, color, 1954) (H).

"Zion and Bryce Canyon" (51 frs, color, 1954) (H).

8mm Film Loops

Earth Materials and Economic Geology

"Bead Test, The" (color, si, 4 min, 1968, i-h). Physical test for the determination of the principal elements in a mineral (BFA).

"Copper Mining" (color, 14 min, 1960, i-h). Open-pit mining and smelting of the ore (BFA).

"Crystal Formation" (color, si, 1968). Deals with the investigation illustrating an alum-solution crystallizing (SRA).

"Crystal Growth" (color, 3 min, Sup 8, cart, 1970, h-c). The film uses time-lapse photography to reveal the nature of crystal growth (HR).

"Flame Test, The" (color, si, 4 min, 1968, i-h). Describes the procedure of a flame test to determine the principal element in a substance (BFA).

"Formation of Oil" (color, si, 2 min, 1968). Location of oil in the world and the aspects of oil formation (GEFL).

"Formation of Oil" (color, si, 4 min, 1968, h-c). Methods and seismographic equipment used to search for oil (ICF).

"Mineral Composition of Granite, The" (color, si, 4 min, 1968, i-h). Illustrates the basic minerals of granite and the elements that in turn constitute the minerals. Points out the significance of different combinations of elements in minerals (BFA).

"Origin of Rocks, The" (color, sd, 7 min, 1968, i-j). Presents the formation and location of the three major classes of rocks (AL).

"Preparing Thin Sections" (color, si). Illustrates techniques of slide preparation (SRA).

"Silicate Minerals" (color, si, 4 min, 1968, i-h). Atomic structure and characteristics (BFA).

"Thin Sections" (color, si, 1968). Procedures for photographic examination of thin sections. Illustrates a number of rocks (SRA).

Igneous Activity

"Birth of an Island" (color, si, 4 min, 1967, i-h). Illustrates the formation of Surtsey by volcanic eruption (BFA).

"Dike, A" (color, si, 5 min, 1967, i-j). Presents the three classes of rocks as well as an igneous dike (EBEC).

"How Geysers Work" (color, si, 3 min, 1965, i-h). Describes the origin and traces events prior to and following an eruption (BFA).

"Igneous Process" (color, 4 min, Sup 8, cart, 1971, i-j). Animated (McGH).

"Lava Flows" (color, si, 4 min, 1965, i-h). Depicts the nature of Aa and Pahoehoe lavas and what happens when they reach the sea (PPAC).

"Mud Pots, Hot Springs and Geysers" (color, si, 1968). Depicts these features in Yellowstone National Park. Illustrates cause of geysers (SRA).

"Volcanic Eruptions" (color, si, 1968). Follows the various features of the eruption of the Kilauea volcano (SRA).

"Volcanoes: Part I, Eruption of Volcano and Lava Flows (Extrusive Formation)." (color, si, 4 min, 1970, i-c). This film includes films taken inside the crater of an active volcano. Extensive lava flows and cinder cones are also shown. The geographic extent of active and extinct volcanoes encircling the Pacific Ocean in a "ring of fire" is explained (HSC).

"Volcanoes: Part II, Volcanic Necks, Sills and Dikes (Intrusive Formation)." In this film, the subsurface development of sills and dikes is explained with diagrams and close-up photography. A large sill exposed in a 13,000-foot peak illustrates the gigantic scale on which intrusive activity takes place (HSC).

"Volcanoes" (color, si, 3 min, 1965, i-c). Traces the development of a volcano (ICF).

"Volcanoes and Laccoliths" (color, si, 4 min, 1967). Compares intrusive and extrusive igneous rock and relates both types to magma (EBEC).

Crustal Rock Deformation and the Earth's Interior

"Alaskan Earthquake, The, 1964" (color, 20 min, 1964). Discusses the causes, location of earthquake zones, and effects of the earthquake (USNAC).

"Dome and Volcanic Mountains" (color, silent, 3 min, 1965, i-h). Formation of volcanic dome mountains by both intrusive and extrusive activity, and the weathering of the dome (BFA).

"Earthquake Mechanism" (color, si, 4 min, 1966 i-h). Causes of the majority of earthquakes (BFA).

"Earthquakes" (color, si, 1968). Elastic Rebound theory, and quake and tidal damage (SRA).

"Earth Structures" (color, 3 min, Sup 8, cart, 1968, i-h). Surveys the origin and nature of mountains, including the folding and faulting of rocks (EBF).

"Fault Block Mountains: Part I, Dynamics of Formation and Structure" (color, si, 4 min, 1970, i-c). The dynamics of fault block mountain formation are shown with a working model. Faults several yards in length are shown in road cuts and one fault that extends for a score of miles is shown from the air. Alluvial fans and bahadas are also shown (HSC).

"Fault Block Mountains: Part II, Origin of Associated Land Forms" An escarpment, rift valley, and mountain remnant typical of fault block mountain regions are shown. A small scale graben in a road cut introduces the concept of the graben valley, which is further explained with a clay model and aerial shots of two large graben valleys (HSC).

"Folded Mountains" (color, si, 3 min, 1965, i-h). Deformation of horizontal strata into folds, with weathering and erosional effects on the folds (FAOC).

"Folded Mountains: Part I, Formation of Anticlines and Synclines" (color, si, 4 min, 1970, i-c). Explains how the forces of lateral pressure have folded once horizontal beds of sedimentary rock to form parallel mountain ranges. Aerial and ground photography depict synclines and anticlines, valleys and ridges. Clues to the existence of vast underground coal deposits are provided by outcropping of coal seams (HSC).

"Folded Mountains: Part II, Erosion and Drainage Systems" The effects of erosion in folded mountain regions are shown by the formation of anticlinal and synclinal valleys and ridges. Trellis drainage patterns, characteristic of folded mountains are shown. Meandering streams are shown flowing through fertile valleys (HSC).

"Folding and Faulting" (color, si, 1968). Demonstration of the cause of folding and faulting, including examples of each (SRA).

"Forces That Build Land" (color, si, 5 min, 1965, i-j). Shows the forces of folding and faulting (AL).

"Mountain Building" (color, 4 min, Sup 8, cart, 1971, i-j). Animated (McGH).

"Mountains and Plateaus" (color, sil, 5 min, 1967, i-j). Distinguishes between mountains, plateaus, and plains (EBEC).

"Offset Along Faults" (color, si, 3 min, 1966, i-h). Creation of faults and the resulting offsets (BFA).

"San Francisco Earthquake, The" (b/w, si, 4 min, 1967, i-j). Effects of the earthquake of 1906 (CF).

"Seismic Prospecting" (color, si, 1968). Procedures of a seismic shot and results of such an explosion underground (SRA).

"Structural Processes: Faults" (color, si, 3 min, 1967, h-c). Examples of four major classes of faults (E).

"Structure of the Earth" (color, si, 3 min, 1965, i-h). Depicts the layers of the earth and the relationship between the Moho and surface relief (FAOC).

"Tectonic Movements" (color, si, 4 min, 1967). Products of crystal deformation (EBEC).

Surficial Geologic Processes

"Alluvial Fan and Lake Delta" (color, si, 3 min, 1967, p-c). Illustrates the development of an alluvial fan and lake delta by stream deposition (E).

"Alluvial Fans" (color, si, 4 min, 1969). Pictures the development of an alluvial fan with its accompanying partical sorting and layering (HSC).

"Antarctica" (color, si, 3 min, 1967, p-c). Depicts the topography of Antarctica as well as the formation of icebergs from glacial ice (E).

"Arctic Icefloes" (color, si, 5 min, 1965, i-c). Traces a glaciological expedition encountering icefloes (ICF).

"Arctic Thaw, Part I" (color, si, 4 min, 1966, i-h). Illustrates the results of snow melting on snow fields and glaciers (ICF).

"Arctic Thaw, Part II" (color, si, 4 min, 1966, i-h). Shows the results of a frozen river breaking up (ICF).

"Baymouth Bar Formation on Coastline of Submergence" (color, si, j-h) (SRA).

"Beach Development" (color, silent, j-h) (SRA).

"Beach Formation and Elevated Beaches" (color, si, 3 min, 1967, j-c). Describes the development of a normal and an elevated beach (E).

"Canyon Lands: Part I, Erosion and Deposition in an Arid Region" (color, si, 4 min, 1970, i-c). Deals with formation of a canyon produced by the gradual down-cutting of a river through horizontal sedimentary beds that have been uplifted through geologic time. Pinnacles and arches represent residual formations. Shows how boulders are ground into pebbles, cobbles, sand, and silt (HSC).

"Canyon Lands: Part II, The Cycle of a Plateau—Youth, Maturity, Old Age". The wind as an erosive and depositional agent is shown.

Wind-produced, cross-bedded sandstone formations are eventually uplifted to form a plateau. Meanwhile, a river gradually cuts the formation to form broader and broader canyons. The final stage depicts a flat plain with mesas and buttes as the only remnants of the original plateau (HSC).

"Cavern Formations" (color, si, 4 min, 1965, i-h). Shows a cavern including a wide variety of formations produced by dripping water (FAOC).

"Coastal Processes" (color, 4 min, Sup 8, cart, 1971, i-j). Animated (MGH).

"Coastlines I & II" (color, Sup 8, cart) (HSC).

"Cross-Channel Flow in Rivers" (color, 4 min, Sup 8, cart, 1970, i-j) (BFA).

"Debris Flows" (color, si, 1968). Debris flows and alluvial fans formed in a stream table (SRA).

"Deltas" (color, si, 1968). Delta formation of the Colorado and Mississippi rivers (SRA).

"Desert Sculpture" (color, si, 1968). Shows how ridges and mesas and other desert erosional features are produced (SRA).

"Development of Shorelines" (color, si, 4 min, 1969). Overhead and side views of a stream table demonstration depicting the development of sea cliffs, wave-cut terraces and other shoreline features (HSC).

"Dry Channel and Flood Flow in Rivers" (color, 4 min, Sup 8, cart, 1970, i-j). Relates the water in a river to the level of the water table (BFA).

"Erosion" (color, si, 4 min, 1968, p-j) (BFA).

"Erosion and Denudation in Desert Regions" (color, si, 1968) (PPAC).

"Evolution of a Lake" (color, si, 4 min, 1967, i-j). Traces the history of a glacial lake (EBEC).

"Flash Flood" (color, si, 4 min, 1967, p-c). Illustrates the development of a flash flood in a desert (ICF).

"Flatland Rivers and Canyons" (color, si, 1968). Describes various features such as sandbars, meandering, goosenecks, and others present in some flatland rivers of the U.S. (SRA).

"Flow in Meandering Rivers" (color, 4 min, Sup 8, cart, 1970, i-j). Describes the process by which river banks and river channels are eroded through the action of irregularities in banks and cross currents (BFA).

"Folded Mountains, Part II, Erosion and Drainage Systems" (color, si, 1970, i-c). The effects of erosion in folded mountains are shown by the formation of anticlinal and synclinal valleys and ridges. Trellis drainage patterns, characteristic of folded mountains, are shown. Meandering streams are shown flowing through fertile valleys (HSC).

"Glacial Movement" (color, si, 3 1/2 min, 1965, i-h). Time-lapse photography of the movement, cause of movement, and calving when a glacier reaches the sea (PPAC).

"Glaciation" (color, 4 min, Sup 8, cart, 1971, i-j). Animated (McGH).

"Glaciers: Part I, Alpine and Valley Glaciers" (color, si, 1970, i-c). Former extent of alpine glaciation contrasted with conditions today is shown on the model. Aerial and ground photography depicts glacial features including ice falls, crevasses, and moraines. A party of mountaineers is shown climbing a glacier. Icebergs are seen forming at the toe of the glacier (HSC).

"Glaciers: Part II, Erosion and Deposition". Large-scale residual effects of glaciation such as U-shaped valleys, horns, cirues, knife-edges, hanging valleys, glacial lakes, and waterfalls are depicted. Small-scale events of glaciation are shown by scenes of glacial polish erratic boulders, and glacial moraines (HSC).

"Glaciers" (color, si, 1968). Illustrates three separate glaciers and one iceberg (SRA).

"Grand Canyon—The River" (color, si, 4 min, 1967, p-c). Describes the weathering and erosion that occur as the Colorado River flows through the Grand Canyon (E).

"Ground Water Tables" (color, 4 min, Sup 8, 1970). Natural and perched water tables are shown forming in several experiments using sand and clay (HSC).

"Gullies" (color, si, 1968). Development, types, and sizes of gullies (SRA).

"How Geysers Work" (color, si, 3 min, 1965, i-h). Describes the origin and traces events prior to and following an eruption (BFA).

"How Rivers Receive Water" (color, 4 min, Sup 8, cart, 1970, i-j). Traces the various paths by which water can flow into a river (BFA).

"Infiltration and Runoff" (color, 4 min, Sup 8, 1970). Experiments show how particle size of earth materials determines the amount of infiltration and runoff during a rainstorm (HSC).

"Influence of Rock Structures" (color, 4 min, Sup 8, cart, 1970, i-j). Discusses the effect of rocks on flow of groundwater (BFA).

"Laminar and Turbulent Flow" (color, 4 min, Sup 8, cart, 1970, i-j) (BFA).

"Landforms Produced by Wave Erosion, Part I" (color, 4 min, Sup 8, 1970). The sea is shown invading the land as the coastline sinks. Wave action is shown as the principal erosive force (HSC).

"Landforms Produced by Coastal Deposition, Part II" (color, 4 min, Sup 8, 1970). Beaches of an emerging coastline are shown in the process of formation (HSC).

"Landslide" (color, si, 1 min, 1967, p-c). Traces a landslide from origin to conclusion (E).

"Mass Wasting" (color, si, 3 min, 1967, h-c). Landslides, slump block, talus cone, and their causes (E).

"Mass Wasting: Dry" (color, si, 4 min, 1969). Illustrates a rock slide, temporary damming of a river, and development of talus slopes and cones (HSC).

"Mass Wasting: Moist" (color, si, 4 min, 1969). Shows shoreline stream, and hill or ridge slumping by mudflows and earthflows (HSC).

"Meandering River" (color, si, 2 min, 1967, p-c). Views of a meandering river (E).

"Metamorphism and Coal Formation" (color, 4 min, Sup 8, cart, 1971, i-j). Animated (McGH).

"Mississippi River Bank" (color, si, 1968). Nature and results of flooding of the Des Moines River (SRA).

"Movement of Groundwater" (color, 4 min, Sup 8, 1970, i-j) (BFA).

"Mud Cracks and Jointing" (color, si, 1968). Illustrations of mud cracks and jointed blocks of granite (SRA).

"Mud Pots, Hot Springs, and Geysers" (color, si, 1968). Depicts these features in Yellowstone National Park. Illustrates cause of geysers (SRA).

"Off-Shore Features" (color, si, j-h) (SKI).

"Origin of Moraines" (color, si, 4 min, 1968). Causes, nature, and examples of moraines (EBEC).

"Rising Coastlines: Part I, Natural River Landforms" (color, si, 1970 i-c). Illustrates meanders, ox-bow lakes, terraces, swamps, floodplains, levees, and deltas. (HSC).

"Rising Coastlines: Part II, A City on a Coastal Plain" Depicts the dependence of a coastal plain city on water transportation (HSC).

"River From Youth to Old Age" (color, si, j-h) (SRA).

"River of Ice—Life Cycle of a Glacier" (color, 10 min, (2d ed.), 1964, i-h). Pictures the source, structure, movement, and effects of Alpine glaciers. Discusses the relationship (BFA).

"Rivers" (b/w, 12 min, h-c). Shows resulting topography caused by rivers and the use of a model river bed to investigate current characteristics and topography formations (AEF).

"Rivers: Meanders" (color, si, 1 min, 1966, i-c). Depicts the nature of a meandering river (ICF).

"Rivers and Mountains Streams" (color, si, 1968). Views of various examples (SRA).

"Rivers: Terraces" (color, si, 1965, p-c). Development of terraces and migration of kickpoint after rejuvenation (ICF).

"Sand Dunes" (color, si, 1968). Development and actual views of dunes (SRA).

"Sedimentation" (color, si, 3 min, 1967, h-c). Illustrates river and ocean deposition, changes in bedding, and pinching-out (E).

"Sedimentation" (color, si, 5 min, 1967, j-c). Views of sedimentary strata and re-creation of processes of sedimentation (EBEC).

"Sedimentation and Sedimentary Rocks" (color, 4 min, Sup 8, cart, 1971, i-j). Animated (McGH).

"Sedimentation—Settling Rates" (color, si, 4 min, 1969). Illustrates the effects of size, shape, and density on settling rate with laboratory demonstration (HSC).

"Sedimentation—Turbidity Currents" (color, si, 4 min, 1969). Demonstrates settling rates and characteristics using various flurries in a large flume (HSC).

"Shore Drift" (color, si, 3 min, 1967, j-c). Demonstration of movements and currents, erosion of shoreline, and spit development (EBEC).

"Shorelines" (color, si, 3 min, 1967, j-c). Results of rise and drop of sea level on shoreline (E).

"Sinking Coastlines: Part I, Land Forms Produced by Wave Action" (color, si, 1970, i-c). The sea is shown invading the land as the coastline sinks, producing estuaries and fiords. Wave action is shown as the principal erosive force as it attacks promontories, sea stacks, produces sea caves and an isthmus (HSC).

"Sinking Coastlines: Part II, Land Forms Produced by Coastal Deposition" Broad straight beaches of an emerging coastline are shown in the process of formation. Sand spits and hooks built by waves and off-shore currents are shown by aerial photography. Tidal flats at high and low tide are shown. A cove on the Oregon coast is shown and compared to a model that illustrates how waves refract when they enter the cove (HSC).

"Soil, Parts I & II" (color, 4 min, Sup 8, cart, 1968, i-h). Describes the formation of soil from the action of weathering and erosion on rock (BFA).

"Splash Erosion" (color, 4 min, Sup 8, 1970, i-c). The splatter effect of raindrops on uncovered soil surfaces are studied in slow motion (HSC).

"Springs and Wells" (color, 4 min, Sup 8, 1970, i-c). The concept of water moving through closed aquifer systems is shown in several different demonstrations (HSC).

"Stream Action" (color, 4 min, Sup 8, cart, 1971, i-j). Animated (McGH).

"Stream Cut-Offs" (color, si, 4 min, 1969, i-c). Pictures natural and flood cutoffs in addition to the formation of an oxbow lake (HSC).

"Stream Erosion Cycle" (color, si, 3 min, 1967, h-c). Features of the various stages of the cycle such as meanders, bars, oxbows, and others (E).

"Stream Piracy" (color, si, 4 min, 1969, i-c). Demonstrates stream piracy by four different methods (HSC).

"Surface and Sub-Surface Streams" (color, 4 min, Sup 8, cart, 1970 i-h). Surveys the two basic forms water may be transported by streams (BFA).

"Turbidity Currents on Lakes" (color, 4 min, Sup 8, cart, 1970, i-j) (BFA).

"Type of Shorelines" (color, 4 min, Sup 8, 1970). Shorelines of submergence and varying rock hardness are developed (HSC).

"Water Erosion: Potholes" (color, si, 4 min, 1967, i-j). Photographs and laboratory demonstration concerning the nature and development of potholes (EBEC).

"Waterfalls" (color, si, 4 min, 1969). Traces the causes of waterfalls, their movement, and other characteristics. Pictures several well-known waterfalls in the United States and Canada (HSC).

"Wind Erosion" (color, 4 min, Sup 8, Cart, 1971, i-j). Animated (McGH).

Measurements and Mapping

"Contour Maps" (color, 3 min, Sup 8, cart, 1968, i-h) (SRA).

"Contours" (color, si, 1 min, 1965, p-c). Pictures topographic features shown by contour lines (ICF).

"Earth and Scale" (color, 4 min, Sup 8, 1970). Studies map scale by comparing maps of the same area constructed to different scale (HSC).

"River Sampling" (color, si, 1968). Procedure to sample for sediment and chemical content of river water (SRA).

"Seismic Prospecting" (color, si, 1968). Procedure of a seismic shot and results of such an explosion underground (SRA).

Environmental Geology

"River Sampling" (color, si, 1968). Procedure to sample for sediment and chemical content of river water (SRA).

General Topics and Regional Studies

"Antarctica" (color, si, 3 min, 1967, p-c). Depicts the topography of Antarctica as well as the formation of icebergs from glacial ice (E).

"Death Valley National Monument" (color, sd, 11 min, 1962). Topography, life, history, and resources (BFA).

"Flatland Rivers and Canyons" (color, si, 1968). Describes various features such as sandbars, meandering, goosenecks, and others present in some flatland rivers of the United States (SRA).

"Grand Canyon—River" (color, si, 4 min, 1967, p-c). Describes the weathering and erosion that occur as the Colorado River flows through the Grand Canyon (E).

"Grand Canyon—Geologic Formations" (color, si, 4 min, 1967, p-c). Views of the canyon at different times (E).

"Mountains and Plateaus" (color, si, 5 min, 1967, i-j). Distinguishes between mountains, plateaus, and plains (EBEC).

"Mud Cracks and Jointing" (color, si, 1968). Illustrates mud cracks and jointed blocks of granite (SRA).

"Origin of Rocks, The" (color, sd, 7 min, 1968, i-j). Presents the formation and location of the three major classes of rocks (AL).

"Seismic Prospecting" (color, si, 1968). Procedure of a seismic shot and results of such an explosion underground (SRA).

Overhead Transparencies

Earth Materials and Economic Geology

"Chemical Composition of the Earth's Crust" (UTI)

"Cleavage and Streak" (MMAMC)

"Coal Deposits" (MMAMC)

"Composition of a Common Rock" (EA-V)

"Composition of Igneous Rock" (MMAMC)

"Composition of the Earth's Crust" (MMAMC)

"Crystal Forms of Minerals, No. 1" (MMAMC)

"Crystal Forms of Minerals, No. 2" (MMAMC)

"Crystal Forms of Minerals, No. 3" (MMAMC)

"Crystal Structure of Minerals" (UTI)

"Crystal Systems" (W)

"Drilling Operation" (MMAMC)

"Elements Making Up the Earth" (UTI)

"Faces of Solid Crystals" (WPC)

"Formation of Coal" (N)

"Formation of Sedimentary Rocks" (T)

"Gas Is Found in Gas-Bearing Rock Such As Ls or Ss" (MMAMC)

"Gas Was Formed Millions of Years Ago" (MMAMC)

"Hardness" (MMAMC)

"Identifying Minerals" (MPC)

"Igneous Rock—Granite" (WPC)

"Igneous Rocks" (MPC)

"Key to Rock Types" (MMAMC)

"Key to Rock Types—Earth" (WPC)

"Key to Rock Types—Geology" (MMAMC)

"Main Oil Deposits in U.S." (UTI)

"Metals" (N)

"Metamorphic Rock" (WPC)

"Metamorphic Rock" (MMAMC)

"Metamorphic Rock" (MPC)

"Metamorphosis of Rocks" (EA-V)

"Mineral Uses" (MPC)

"Mineral Veins" (MMAMC)

"Minerals of the Earth" (i-j) (PS)

"Oil-Bearing Sands Under Cap Rock" (UTI)

"Oil Deposits" (MMAMC)

"Petroleum Deposits" (DG)

"Placer Deposit" (MMAMC)

"Production of Lime" (UTI)

"Rock Cycle" (PSC)

"Rock Cycle" (DG)

"Rock Cycle" (N)

"Rock Cycle, The" (HI)

"Rocks" (MPC)

"Rocks—What Are They?" (MMAMC)

"Rocks and Minerals" (A Series) (MMAMC)

"Rocks are Made of Minerals" (N)

"Sedimentary Rock" (WPC)

"Sedimentary Rocks" (PSC)

"Sedimentary Rocks" (MMAMC)
"Sedimentary Rocks" (MPC)
"Specific Gravity" (MMAMC)

"Tests for Minerals Using Heat" (MMAMC)
"U.S. Coal Areas" (UTI)

Igneous Activity

"Cross Sections of Volcanoes" (W)

"Development of Volcanoes, Part I" (W)

"Development of Volcanoes, Part II" (W)

"Development of Volcanoes, Part III" (W)

"Earthquakes And Volcanoes" (N)

"Formation of a Volcano" (HI)

"Formation of Igneous Rock" (MMAMC)

"Geyser Basin, A" (EA-V)

"Geysers" (MMAMC)

"Intrusive, Igneous Formations" (MMAMC)

"Intrusive and Extrusive Igneous Rock Structures" (EA-V)

"Major Types of Volcanic Cones" (EA-V)

"Major Volcanic Belts of the Earth" (EA-V)

"Mountains and Volcanoes" (WPC)

"Shield Volcanoes (Lava Domes)"

"Structure of a Volcanic Cone Mountain" (EA-V)

"Volcanic Activity" (UTI)

"Volcanic Belts" (WPC)

"Volcanic Flows and Their Effect" (T)

"Volcanism" (WPC)

"Volcano" (WPC)

"Volcano" (DG)

"Volcanoes" (PSC)

"Volcanoes" (MPC)

"Volcanoes" (IPC)

"Vulcanism" (WPC)

Crustal Rock Deformation and the Earth's Interior

"Basic Rock Structure of Colorado Plateau Near the Grand Canyon" (EA-V)

"Basic Science—Geology" (A Series) (T)

"Basic Structure of Typical Block Mountains" (EA-V)

"Belts of Greatest Earthquake Activity" (EA-V)

"Bending Earthquake Waves Produce a Shadow Zone" (EA-V)

"Block Mountains" (UTI)

"Deformation of the Earth's Crust" (HI)

"Development of a Synclinal Mountain" (EA-V)

"Development of Block Mountains" (W)

"Development of Dome Mountains" (W)

"Diagram of the Theory of Isostasy" (EA-V)

"Diastrophism May Be the Result of Earth Expansion" (EA-V)

"Dip And Strike" (DG)

"Dip of a Geologic Formation, The" (MMAMC)

"Dome Mountains" (DG)

"Earth Movements" (WPC)

"Earth's Core" (DG)

"Earth's Crust" (MMAMC)

"Earth's Interior, The" (MMAMC)

"Earth's Magnetic Fields, The" (WPC)

"Earthquake Waves" (EA-V)

"Earthquake Waves" (MMAMC)

"Earthquakes" (WPC)

"Earthquakes" (MMAMC)

"Earthquakes" (MPC)

"Earthquakes and Volcanoes" (N)

"Elastic Rebound Theory of Earthquakes, The" (EA-V)

"Extrusion Molding of Thermoplastic Materials" (UTI)

"Fault Mountains" (DG)

"Fault—Block Mountains" (N)

"Faults: Normal and Reverse" (DG)

"Faults: Strike and Slip" (DG)

"Folded Mountains" (DG)

"Folded Mountains" (N)

"Folded Rock Layers" (EA-V)

"Folds and Faults" (PSC)

"Folds and Faults" (T)

"Formation of Anticlines" (MMAMC)

"Formation of Domes" (MMAMC)

"Formation of Fissures" (EA-V)

"Formation of Synclines" (MMAMC)

"Formation of the Salton Sea" (EA-V)

"Half-Life and the Decay Curve" (K&E)

"Isostatic Equilibrium" (UTI)

"Locating the Center of an Earthquake" (EA-V)

"Locating the Focus of an Earthquake with Seismograph" (EA-V)

"Modern Earth Science: Earth Movements" (A Series) (EA-V)

"Modern Earth Science: Earth Formations" (A Series) (EA-V)

"Mountains" (MMAMC)

"Mountain Building" (MMAMC)

"Mountain Building" (MPC)

"Mountain Building" (IPC)

"Mountain Range" (MMAMC)

"Mountains and Volcanoes" (WPC)

"Normal and Reverse Fault" (EA-V)

"Normal Fault" (MMAMC)

"Plunging Folds" (MMAMC)

"Radioactive Decay" (EGH)

"Reverse Fault" (MMAMC)

"Rock Formation" (T)

"Strike and Dip" (EA-V)

"Strike of a Geologic Formation, The" (MMAMC)

"Structure of Folded Mountains" (EA-V)

"Structure of Plains, Plateaus And Mountains" (EA-V)

"Structure of the Earth" (HI)

"Structure of the Earth" (WPC)

"Terraces Caused by Diastrophism" (EA-V)

"Theory of Continental Drift" (N)

"Theory of Mountain Building, A" (EA-V)

"Types of Mountains, No. 1" (MMAMC)

"Types of Mountains, No. 2" (MMAMC)

"Unconformity and Disconformity" (DG)

"Varieties of Faults" (W)

Surficial Geologic Processes

"Age of Topography (MMAMC)
"Alluvial River—Yazoo Type Stream (N)
"Alpine Glaciation" (DG)
"Alpine Glaciation" (N)
"Appearance of Springs" (EA-V)
"Artesian Wells" (UTI)
"Atlantic Coastal Plain, The" (EA-V)
"Canyon" (MMAMC)
"Cavern Development"
"Change in Facies with Advancing and Retreating Sea" (EA-V)
"Channel and Cape" (MMAMC)
"Coastal Plain Development" (W)
"Coastal Plain of the United States" (N)
"Coastlines" (DG)
"Concentrated Flow on a Watershed—Streams" (MMAMC)
"Continental Glaciation" (DG)
"Continental Glaciers During the Last Ice Age" (W)
"Continental U.S.—Physical Features" (i-j) (PS)
"Cycle of Glacier Formation" (EA-V)
"Delta" (MMAMC)
"Depth of Water Table Determines Permanent Bodies of Water" (UTI)
"Development of Caves" (HI)
"Development of Meanders" (EA-V)
"Development of Soil" (HI)
"Drainage Patterns" (DG)
"Earth Science—Evolution of North America" (Projecto-Aid: A Series) (WPC)
"Eroded Folds of Harrisburg, Pa." (W)

"Erosion of Batholith" (W)
"Erosion and Sedimentation" (IPC)
"Erosional Development of Folds" (W)
"Evolution of Landscape" (HI)
"Exfoliation of Granite" (N)
"Factors in Soil Formation" (MMAMC)
"Flat Flood Plain with Natural Levees" (EA-V)
"Formation of an Atoll" (EA-V)
"Formation of Basins" (MMAMC)
"Formation of New Shorelines" (EA-V)
"Formation of a Wind Gap" (EA-V)
"Forms of Intrusive and Extrusive Igneous Rocks" (W)
"From Sediments to Sedimentary Rocks" (N)
"Geyser Basin, A" (EA-V)
"Geysers" (MMAMC)
"Glacial Deposits" (MMAMC)
"Glaciation" (DG)
"Ground Water" (WPC)
"Ground Water" (DG)
"Ground Water Erosion" (N)
"Gulf" (MMAMC)
"Harbor" (MMAMC)
"Headwater Erosion of a Gulley" (N)
"How Soils Are Formed, No. 1" (MMAMC)
"How Soils Are Formed, No. 2" (MMAMC)
"Hydrologic Cycle" (MMAMC)
"Hydrologic Cycle, The" (EA-V)
"Ice Cap of North America" (UTI)
"Karst Topography Showing

Features of Underground Drainage" (EA-V)
"Lake and Island" (MMAMC)
"Last Great Glaciation at Its Peak, The" (EA-V)
"Life Cycle of a River" (WPC)
"Mature Coastline" (N)
"Ocean Floors" (WPC)
"Possible Cause of the Ice Ages, A" (EA-V)
"Refraction of Waves Approaching Shore" (EA-V)
"Reservoir" (MMAMC)
"River Basin" (MMAMC)
"River Bed" (MMAMC)
"River, No. 1" (MMAMC)
"River, No. 2" (MMAMC)
"River, No. 3" (MMAMC)
"Rock Formations That Result in Artesian Wells" (EA-V)
"Sedimentation" (MMAMC)
"Snow Line" (N)
"Soil Composition" (JCA)
"Soil and Its Conservation" (T)
"Soil Particle Size" (MMAMC)
"Soil Profile, A" (MMAMC)
"Soils Differ" (MMAMC)
"Stages in Development of Rivers and Streams" (EA-V)
"Stages in Filling a Lake" (EA-V)
"Stages in Formation of an Ox-

bow Lake" (EA-v)
"Surface of the Earth"
"Surface Water Erosion—Migration of a Waterfall" (N)
"Typical Soil Profile" (MMAMC)
"Typical Watershed, A" (MMAMC)
"Underground Water Storage" (UTI)
"Valley" (MMAMC)
"Valley Development" (N)
"Variation of Water-Flow in a River" (EA-V)
"Water Infiltration and Percolation" (MMAMC)
"Water Movement on a Watershed" (MMAMC)
"Wave Action Along Deep Coastal Water" (N)
"Wave Action Along Shallow Coast Lines" (N)
"Wavestages in the Development of a Breaker" (EA-V)
"Weathering" (MMAMC)
"Weathering and Erosion" (MPC)
"Wells and Springs" (MMAMC)
"Wells and Springs" (N)
"What Is a Watershed" (MMAMC)
"What Is Soil" (MMAMC)
"Young Coastline" (N)

Measurement And Mapping
"Contour Interval" (EA-V)
"Contour Line" (DG)
"Contour Map—Depression" (DG)
"Contour Map—Hill" (DG)
"Contour Map—Valley" (DG)
"Earth Science—Map Reading, 1" (A Series) (DG)
"Earth Science—Map Reading, 2" (A Series) (DG)

"Earthquake Triangulation" (JCA)
"Four U.S. Time Zones" (UTI)
"Hemispheres" (PSC)
"Latitude and Longitude" (PSC)
"Locating a Point by the Township and Range Method" (EA-V)
"Magnetic Pole"
"Special Contour Lines" (EA-V)
"Specific Gravity" (MMAMC)

General Topics And Regional Studies

"Adhesion and Cohesion" (UTI)
"Basic Science: Geology" (A Series) (T)
"Distribution in Time" (W)
"Drilling Operation" (MMAMC)
"Earth Science: Geology and Physical Geography" (A Series) (HI)
"Earth Science: Geology" (A Series) (DG)
"Earth Science: Geology" (A Series) (N)
"Earth Science" (A Series) (IPC)
"Earth Science" (A Series) (HI)
"Earth Science" (A Series) (WPC)
"Earth's Magnetic Fields" (WPC)
"Earth's Shape and Composition" (MPC)
"Earth's Total Relief" (EA-V)
"Elementary Science: Geology" (A Series) (DG)
"Geologic Formations and Pro-

cesses" (A Series) (MMAMC)
"Geology" (A Series) (PSC)
"Geology" (A Series) (EA-V)
"Highland and Lowland" (MMAMC)
"Isthmus" (MMAMC)
"Law of Superposition" (MMAMC)
"Major Land Forms" (N)
"Origin of the Earth" (PSC)
"Penninsula" (MMAMC)
"Physical Geography" (A Series) (MMAMC)
"Physiographic Divisions of North America" (HI)
"Physiographic Provinces of the United States" (MMAMC)
"Some Prehistoric Animals" (MPC)
"Strait" (MMAMC)
"Stream Development" (DG)
"Stream Piracy" (EA-V)
"Terms Used in Geology" (N)

Color Photographs

Curriculum Color Prints (18" x 13")

Key

(1) Earth Materials and Economic Geology
(2) Igneous Activity
(3) Crustal Rock Deformation and the Earth's Interior
(4) Surficial Geologic Processes
(5) Measurement and Mapping
(6) General Topics and Regional Studies

"Earth Movements" (CES), (DG), (IAI), (W)

1. Crustal Folding (3)
2. A Recumbent Anticline (Faulted) (3)
3. Reverse and Thrust Faulting (3)
4. Effects of Faulting (3)
5. Effects of Faulting: Earthquakes (3)
6. Landslides (3)

"Erosion" (CES), (DG), (IAI), (W)

1. What Is Mechanical Weathering? (4)
2. What Is Chemical Weathering? (4)
3. Erosion by Water: How It Takes Place (4)
4. Erosion by Water: Erosion Forms (4)
5. Erosion by Waves (4)
6. Erosion by Wind (4)

"Geological Instruments" (DG), (IAI), (W)

1. The Pocket Transit (5)
2. The Plane Table and Alidade (5)

3. The Microscope and Ultra
Violet Lamp (5)
4. Radiation Detectors (5)
5. The Surveying Altimeter (5)
6. Small Field Instruments (5)

"Glaciers" (CES), (DG), (IAI), (W),

1. What Are Valley Gla-
ciers? (4)
2. What Are Continental Glaciers? (4)
3. How Are Valley and Continental Glaciers Formed? (4)
4. What Are Some of the Features of Glaciers? (4)
5. What Changes Do Glaciers
Make in the Surface of the
Earth? (4)
6. What Are Icebergs? (4)

"Ground Water" (DG), (IAI), (W)

1. Springs in Limestone (6)
2. Springs in Lava (6)
3. Flowing Artesian Well (6)
4. Geysers and Hot Springs (6)
5. Caves (6)
6. Petrified Wood (6)

"Igneous and Metamorphic Rocks" (DG), (IAI), (W)

1. Introduction to Igneous
Rocks (2)
2. Composition of Igneous
Rocks (1)
3. Intrusive Rocks and Their
Forms (2)
4. Extrusive Rocks and Their
Forms (2)
5. What are Metamorphic
Rocks? (1)
6. The Processes of Metamorphism (3)

"Minerals" (DG), (IAI), (W)

1. Crystals (1)
2. Quartz (1)
3. Structures (1)

4. Sulfur (1)
5. Calcite and Aragonite (1)
6. Gems (1)

"Polar Regions—Artic and Antarctic" (DG), (IAI), (W)

1. Polar Ice Caps (6)
2. Polar Seas (6)
3. The Polar Climate (6)
4. The Tundra (6)
5. Tundra "Soils" (6)
6. Polar Animal and Bird Life (6)

"Sedimentary Rocks" (DG), (IAI), (W)

1. The Clastics (1)
2. Water-Deposited Sandstone (1)
3. Wind-Deposited Sandstone (1)
4. Shales (1)
5. Limestones: Part I (1)
6. Limestones: Part II; also special Sedimentary Rocks (1)

"Soils" (DG), (IAI), (W)

1. The Formation of Soil (4)
2. The Soil Profile (6)
3. Soil Color (6)
4. Soil Texture and Structure (6)
5. Soil Classification: Zonal Soils (6)
6. Intrazonal and Azonal Soils (6)

"Volcanoes" (CES), (DG), (IAI), (W)

1. Birth of the Paricutin Volcano (2)
2. Volcanic Activity: Surface Evidence of Internal Unrest (2)
3. A Dormant Volcano in the United States (2)
4. The Shield-Type Volcano (2)
5. Development of a Caldera (2)
6. A Volcanic Neck (2)

Supplementary Reading Materials

The supplementary reading materials listed are not all-inclusive, but they do represent a major portion of the currently available paperback books of interest to both teachers and students. They constitute an economical source that is often overlooked and span all levels of instruction from the junior high school to reference works for the teacher. There has been no attempt to indicate the grade or reading level because many are useful for a wide range of abilities. Prices are subject to fluctuation but most of these publications are reasonably priced. A brief annotation is included for most titles.

Adams, Frank Dawson. *The Birth and Development of the Geological Sciences.* New York: Dover Publications, 1954, 506 pp. Traces the history of the geological sciences, from Greek and Roman times through Middle Ages, Renaissance, and modern era up to the twentieth century. Analyzes ideas of such men as William Smith, Agricola, Geikie, Hutton, Werner, Aristotle, Becher, Cuvier, etc. Recreates birth of modern mineralogy, metals and their ores, mountains and earthquakes, springs and rivers.

Adams, W. M. *Earthquakes—An Introduction to Observational Seismology.* Boston: D. C. Heath and Co., 1964, 128 pp. Observational material on five earthquakes is presented in an inductive manner. Applies principles derived in a deductive manner to observations of earthquakes. Suitable for students in the ninth grade or over.

Ahrens, Louis H. *Distribution of the Elements in Our Planet.* New York: McGraw-Hill Book Co., 1965, 125 pp. Explores the origin of the universe and the evolution of the solar system. Explains how the abundance of elements is determined and analyzes the principal structural components of the planet. Geochemical methods of classifying elements are introduced and actual and theoretical aspects of element distribution are discussed.

American Geological Institute Dictionary of Geological Terms. Garden City, N.Y.: Doubleday & Co., 1962, 545 pp. Abridged glossary, containing approximately 7,500 words for students, teachers, and others interested in the earth sciences. Essential for every earth scientist.

Austin, Mary. *Land of Little Rain.* Garden City, N.Y.: Doubleday & Co., 1961, 171 pp. Description of the semiarid region extending southeast from Yosemite, through Death Valley to the Mojave Desert.

Bates, D. R., ed. *The Earth and Its Atmosphere.* New York: John Wiley & Sons, 1961, 324 pp. Contributions by 15 scientists. Covers knowledge in geophysical science including: composition of interior and deep crust of the earth; circulation of the oceans and atmosphere; causes of auroras and magnetic storms; climatology; meteorology; cosmic radiation; and the geomagnetic field of the earth. Also covers the ice ages and the origin of our planet and its probable end.

Bentley, W. A., and W. J. Humphreys. *Snow Crystals*. New York: Dover Publications, 1962, 226 pp. Contains over 2,000 photographs of snowflakes taken over the course of half a century. Discusses the technique and problems of photographing snow crystals; classification; crystallography; the science of crystal formation; the nature and causes of ice flowers; windowpane frost; and so on.

Blanchard, Duncan C. *From Raindrops to Volcanoes, Adventures with Sea Surface Meteorology*. Garden City, N.Y.: Doubleday & Co., Anchor Books, 1967, 180 pp. Describes how meteorology, oceanography, physics, chemistry, and volcanology merge in the study of the raindrop. Gives descriptions of experiments and observations that can be conducted by the reader.

Bloom, A. L. *The Surface of the Earth*. Foundations of Earth Science Series, Englewood Cliffs, N.J.: Prentice-Hall, 1969, 152 pp. Combines the origin and change of landforms under a central theme of energy flow at the surface of the earth. Summarizes the current research and advances in the field. Both theory and conceptual framework are provided.

Bowen, Norman L. *The Evolution of the Igneous Rocks*. New York: Dover Publications, 1956, 334 pp. Explains igneous rock diversity in terms of chemical composition and fractional crystallization. Discusses liquid immiscibility in silicate magmas, crystal sorting, liquid lines of descent, fractional resorption of complex minerals, petrogenesis, and so on.

Bowen, Oliver, E., Jr. *Rocks and Minerals of the San Francisco Bay Region*. Berkeley: University of California Press, 1962, 71 pp. Describes more than a hundred varieties of minerals and 36 kinds of rocks with an explanation of the processes by which they were formed.

Boyer, Robert E. *Field Guide to Rock Weathering*. ESCP Pamphlet Series PS-1. Boston: Houghton Mifflin Co., 1971, 38 pp.

Bunn, Charles. *Crystals: Their Role in Nature and in Science*. New York: Academic Press, 1964, 286 pp. A nontechnical presentation of crystals—their structure, their manner of growth, the part they have played in the development of our understanding of the nature of light and X rays, and the part they play in revealing the structure of solid substances.

Cailleux, A. *Anatomy of the Earth*. Translated by J. Moody Stuart. New York: McGraw-Hall Book Co., World University Library, 1968, 255 pp. General introduction to geology describing what we know of the earth's external and internal features. Includes chapters on earth origin, movement of continents, and mountain building.

Croneis, C. G., and W. C. Krumbein. *Down to Earth: An Introduction to Geology*. Chicago: University of Chicago Press, 1961, 499 pp. Interesting, lively, and occasionally humorous introduction to geology which explains man's origin, his place in nature, and the interrelationships between geology, physics, biology, and mathematics.

Dana, Edward S. *Mineral and How to Study Them*, 3d ed. Revised by Cornelius S. Hurlbut, Jr. New York: John Wiley & Sons, 1963, 323 pp. A good reference either for field use or for general mineralogic study.

Davis, W. M. *Geographic Essays*. Edited by D. W. Johnson, New York: Dover

Publications, 1954, 777 pp. Collection of essays and monographs by one of the great pioneers of geography and geomorphology. Introduces Davis's concepts of earth processes. (Originally published in 1910.)

Defant, Albert. *Ebb and Flow: The Tides of Earth, Air and Water*. Ann Arbor: University of Michigan Press, 1958, 121 pp. Deals with why tides exist, why they work, and how and what they are.

Dellenbaugh, Frederick S. *A Canyon Voyage*. New Haven, Conn.: Yale University Press, 1962, 277 pp. Account of Powell's second expedition down the Colorado River. Covers journey down the river, over the comparatively unknown high plateaus of Utah, and discovery of the Escalante River and the Henry Mountains.

Dietrich, R. V. *Mineral Tables—Hand Specimen Properties of 1500 Minerals*. Blacksburg, Va.: Virginia Polytechnic Inst., 1966, 220 pp. A fairly complete, concise listing of minerals and their properties, arranged according to luster, color, and hardness. Tables are a useful guide to mineral identification.

Dury, G. *Face of the Earth*. Baltimore: Penguin Books, 1959, 223 pp. A book on geomorphology which discusses problems awaiting solutions and the method whereby geomorphic features do evolve through destructional and constructional affects.

Eddington, Sir Arthur. *The Nature of the Physical World*. Ann Arbor: University of Michigan Press, 1958, 382 pp. Discusses the downfall of classical physics; relativity; time; man's place in the universe; gravitation; the quantum theory; reality; causation; science and mysticism, etc.

Eicher D. L. *Geologic Time*. Foundations of Earth Science Series. Englewood Cliffs, N.J.: Prentice-Hall, 1968, 150 pp. Relates geologic time to rocks. Shows how the concept of geologic time developed, how geologic time is measured, and how events are interpreted within it.

Eklund, Carl R., and Joan Beckman. *Antarctica*. New York: Holt, Rinehart and Winston, 1963, 157 pp. Readable account of current knowledge of the seventh continent at the time of publication. The significance of present and future Antarctic research in relation to the world of science. An insight into the need of information about the Antarctic for all major fields of geophysics.

Ernst, W. G. *Earth Materials*. Foundations of Earth Science Series. Englewood Cliffs, N.J.: Prentice-Hall, 1969, 150 pp. Considers the minerals and rocks which constitute the inorganic portion of the earth. Discusses principles of crystal structure and temperature—pressure, stability, relations of minerals and rocks near the surface, and deep within the earth.

Faul, Henry. *Ages of Rocks, Planets, and Stars*. New York: McGraw-Hill Book Co., 1966, 109 pp. Deals with the measurement of geological and astrophysical time. Emphasizes principles rather than techniques and applications. A clear and concise yet comprehensive book.

Fay, Gordon. *Physical Geography*. Garden City, N.Y.: Doubleday & Co., 1965, 408 pp. An introductory survey of physical geography covering such topics as the size and shape of the earth, map-making, climate, rocks, soil, water, and landforms.

Fenton, Carroll Lane, and Mildred Adams Fenton. *Giants of Geology*. New York: Dolphin Books, 1952, 318 pp. Traces development of earth science from ancient Greece to modern times by means of a series of biographical sketches of history's outstanding geologists.

Fisher, Joseph L., and Neal Potter. *World Prospects for Natural Resources: Some Projections of Demand and Indicators of Supply to the Year 2000*. Baltimore: Johns Hopkins University Press, 1964.

Foster, R. J. *Geology*. 2d ed. Merrill Physical Science Series. Columbus, Ohio: Charles E. Merrill Publishing Co., 1971, 162 pp. An introduction to geology presented in four major sections: Composition of the Earth, The External Processes, Structural Geology, and Principles of Historical Geology.

Foth, Henry, and Hyde S. Jacobs. *Field Guide to Soils*. ESCP Pamphlet Series PS-2. Boston: Houghton Mifflin Co., 1971, 38 pp.

Fox, F. A. *World of Oil*. Elmsford, N.Y.: Pergamon Press, 1965, 221 pp. Introduction to the exploration for and production of oil.

Freeman, Tom. *Field Guide to Layered Rock*. ESCP Pamphlet Series PS-3. Boston: Houghton Mifflin Co., 1971, 46 pp.

Gamow, George. *A Planet Called Earth*. New York: Bantam Books, 1963, 256 pp. Presents theories on the evolution of the solar system and the successive reformations of the earth's surface. Includes origin and evolution of life.

Garland, G. D. *Earth's Shape and Gravity*. Elmsford, N.Y.: Pergamon Press, 1965, 188 pp. Presents knowledge of earth's form and interior that can be obtained from measurements of gravity. Introduction to modern work being carried out in fields of geophysics and geodesy.

Garrett, S. D. *Soil Fungi and Soil Fertility*. Elmsford, N.Y.: Pergamon Press, 1963, 165 pp. Introduction to the science of soil microbiology through the study of soil fungi and their behavior. Introduction to the subject of mycology. Assumes a minimum of previous biological knowledge.

Geike, Archibald. *Founders of Geology*. New York: Dover Publications, 1962, 486 pp. Survey of the work of the major figures of the period in which the main foundations of modern geology were laid—the latter half of the eighteenth century to the first half of the nineteenth century. Covers Palissy, Demarest, Lehmann, Werner, Hutton, Playfair, Hall, Cuvier, Lyell, Darwin, Agassiz, and others.

Goetzmann, W. H. *Army Exploration in the American West, 1803-1865*. New Haven, Conn.: Yale University Press, 1965. Describes and evaluates the role of the U. S. Army in the opening of the American West.

Grabau, Amadeus W. *Principles of Stratigraphy* (2 vols.) New York: Dover Publications, 1960, 1185 pp. Classic work of twentieth-century geology originally published in 1924. Brings together those facts and principles that lie at the foundation of our attempts to interpret the history of the earth from records left in the rocks.

Griffiths, D. H., and R. F. King. *Applied Geophysics for Engineers and Geologists*.

Elmsford, N.Y.: Pergamon Press, 1965, 232 pp. Presents a basic knowledge of the principles of geophysical prospecting and its use in problems of site investigation, geological structure, and mineral prospecting.

Harbaugh, J. W. *Stratigraphy and Geologic Time.* Brown Foundations of Earth Science Series. Dubuque, Iowa: William C. Brown Co., 1968, 113 pp. Introduction to stratigraphy and geologic time. Discusses the methods of dating and correlating the rocks of the earth. Includes chapters on the geologic time scale, sedimentary facies, and radiometric age-dating.

Heath, Monroe. *Great American Rivers.* Menlo Park, Calif.: Pacific Coast Publishers, 1960, 36 pp. The story of the 30 principal rivers of the United States—their economic, geographic, and scenic importance. Illustrated with photographs.

_____ . *Great American Mountains.* Menlo Park, Calif.: Pacific Coast Publishers, 1962, 48 pp. Concise presentation of the mountain areas of the United States and some 30 peaks selected for their geological, topographic, historical, or scenic significance.

_____ . *Our National Parks.* Menlo Park, Calif.: Pacific Coast Publishers, 1963, 36 pp. Significance, history, scenic and geological features of National Parks, plus a chart showing other areas administered by the National Park Service.

Heffernan, Helen, and George Shaftel. *The Energy Story.* Syracuse, N.Y.: L. W. Singer Co., 1963, 128 pp. Covers the sources of energy: petroleum; electricity produced by steam, by running water, and by nuclear reactors; rocket and jet fuels; and solar energy.

_____ . *The Minerals Story.* Syracuse, N.Y.: L. W. Singer Co., 1963, 96 pp. Discusses ways of utilizing available mineral resources to greatest advantage by finding substitute for minerals, locating new ore deposits, developing more efficient ways to mine and mill ores, salvaging waste and scrap for reuse, and determining new uses for some of our more abundant minerals.

_____ . *The Soil Story.* Syracuse, N.Y.: L. W. Singer Co., 1963, 96 pp. Formation of soil, the erosion of soil, and the methods used to save the soil. Includes an account of the transformation of arid land into green fertile land in Israel.

Hodgson, John H. *Earthquakes and Earth Structure.* Englewood Cliffs, N.J.: Prentice-Hall, 1964, 166 pp. Describes great earthquakes of the past and ones of seismological importance, analyzes the information they provide us about the interior of the earth. Reveals the role of seismology in nuclear-test detection, and presents developments in earthquake-resistant construction.

Holden, Alan, and Phylis Singer. *Crystals and Crystal Growing.* Garden City, N.Y.: 1960, 320 pp. For the novice who is interested in methods of growth and experimentation with a few of the basic crystal types.

Howard, A. D. *Evolution of the Landscape of the San Francisco Bay Region.* Berkeley: University of California Press, 1962, 72 pp. Traces the development of the west-central California landscape through the last 28 million years of geological time. Offers explanations for most of the regions scenic features including mountain ranges and peaks, petrified trees, geysers, and sea arches. Discusses development of San Francisco Bay, the Golden Gate, and Monterey Bay.

Hoyt, John H. *Field Guide to Beaches*. ESC Pamphlet Series PA-7. Boston: Houghton Mifflin Co., 1971, 46 pp.

Hurlbut, C. S., Jr. and H. E. Wenden. *Changing Science of Mineralogy*. Boston: D. C. Heath and Co., 1964, 128 pp. Combines some of the quantitative aspects of physics and chemistry with the natural approach of geology. Tells students what mineralogy is and how minerals are studied. Discusses how minerals are built from chemical elements, how the outward forms of crystals are determined by the size and arrangement of the atoms and the forces that hold the atoms together.

Iacopi, Robert. *Earthquake Country*. Menlo Park, Calif.: Sunset Book, Lane Books, 1969, 160 pp. An authoratative and highly readable account of the how why, and where of earthquakes in California.

Jackson, Nora, and Philip Penn. *A Dictionary of Natural Resources and Their Principal Uses*. Elmsford, N.Y.: Pergamon Press, 1966, 138 pp. Alphabetically arranged dictionary of natural resources. Provides the where, why, how, and what, for economically important natural resources.

Jacobs, J. A. *Earth's Core and Geomagnetism*. Elmsford, N.Y.: Pergamon Press, 1963, 201 pp. Technical summation of the state of knowledge and theories of the earth's interior, the origin of the earth, its temperature distribution, its composition, continental drift, and geomagnetism.

Keller, W. D. *Chemistry in Introductory Geology*, 4th ed. Columbia, Mo.: Lucas Brothers Publishers, 1959, 108 pp. Simplified but sound approach to the concepts of chemistry most commonly used in introductory geology. Brings geology and chemistry together with applications of chemical concepts to practical geological examples.

King, Clarence. *Mountaineering in the Sierra Nevada*. Philadelphia: J. B. Lippincott Co., 1963, 292 pp. Unabridged reprint of 1872 edition story of King's adventures from his beginning as a volunteer of the California Survey to his launching of the Fortieth Parallel Survey.

Kirk, Ruth. *Exploring Mount Rainier*. Seattle: University of Washington Press, 1968, 96 pp. Popular presentation of Washington state's most dominant geological features, 14,410-foot Mt. Rainier, and the national park that encompasses it. A beautifully illustrated book with a precise presentation of the mountain's geology, weather, plant life, wildlife, and history.

Kottlowski, Frank E. *Measuring Stratigraphic Sections*. New York: Holt, Rinehart and Winston, 1965, 253 pp. Discusses the chief purpose in measuring sections, then stresses their application to stratigraphy, subsurface correlation, structural geology and sampling problems. Covers the methods and instruments used in section measuring as well as the types of field problems generally encountered.

Krutch, Joseph Wood. *Grand Canyon*. Garden City, N.Y.: Doubleday & Co., 1962, 254 pp. Comprehensive account of one of the most fascinating landmarks on earth.

Kuenen, P. H. *Realms of Water: Some Aspects of Its Cycle in Nature*. New York: John Wiley & Sons, 1963, 327 pp. Discusses the importance of water in determining climate and the landscape. Considers many aspects of physical geography, meteorology, and oceanography, and many natural phenomena from glaciers to the depths of the seas, and from clouds to subterranean grottoes.

Lattman, Laurence, and Richard G. Ray. *Aerial Photographs in Field Geology.* New York: Holt, Rinehart and Winston, 1965, 221 pp. Illustrated guide to field photogrammetric and photointerpretation procedures.

Leet, Don, and Florence Leet, eds. *World of Geology.* New York: McGraw-Hill Book Co., 1961, 262 pp. Group of 20 readings by well-known authors introducing the layman to the earth. Explains the origin of the earth, life, and the atmosphere; describes ocean deeps, interior and exterior of the earth; glaciation; shows how prominent land features are formed; and describes the materials that make up the planet earth.

Lovejoy, Wallace F., and Paul T. Homan. *Methods of Estimating Reserves of Crude Oil, Natural Gas, and Natural Gas Liquids.* Baltimore: Johns Hopkins University Press, 1965, 168 pp. Reviews and analyzes the various approaches used to gauge the nation's supply of crude oil, natural gas, and natural gas liquids. Points out past errors and suggests improvements needed in data collection.

Mann, Wilfred B. and S. B. Garfinkel. *Radioactivity and Its Measurement.* Princeton, N.J.: D. Van Nostrand Co., 1965, 160 pp. Covers the early history of the discovery of radioactivity; briefly reviews the properties of nuclear radiations, and describes methods available for their measurement.

Martin, Lawrence. *The Physical Geography of Wisconsin,* 3rd ed. (Previously published as Wisc. Geographical and Natural History Bulletin No. XXXVI, 1916 and 1932.) Madison: University of Wisconsin Press, 1965, 636 pp. Survey of what was known of the physiography, climatology, and geology of Wisconsin at the time of original publication.

Matthews, William H. *Invitation to Geology: The Earth Through Time.* Garden City, N.Y.: Doubleday & Co., Natural History Press, 1971, 160 pp. Deals with the challenge that faces the earth scientist as with each passing year man's relationship to the earth becomes more strained. Explains modern techniques and tools used to study the earth.

Mears, B. *The Nature of Geology: Contemporary Readings.* New York: Van Nostrand Reinhold Co., 1970, 248 pp. A collection of readings prepared for beginning students of geology, which demonstrate that geology is a dynamic, living science. Includes writings of Hans Cloos, Rachel Carson, John Wesley Powell, John Muir, Samuel Clemens, and others.

Meinzer, O. E., ed. *Hydrology.* New York: Dover Publications, 1957, 723 pp. Symposium on hydrology prepared for the National Research Council. Twenty-four contributing authors. Information on precipitation, evaporation, glaciers, lakes, infiltration, soil moisture, ground water, runoff, drought, physical changes produced by water, hydrology of limestone terrains, and other subjects.

Monkhouse, F. J., and A. V. Hardy. *North American Landscape.* New York: Cambridge University Press, 1965, 96 pp. Regional study of North America, largely based on the detailed interpretation of photographs, including aerial photographs. Physical, human, and economic aspects of geography are covered.

Moore, G. W., and G. Nicholas. *Speleology: The Study of Caves*. Boston: D. C. Heath and Co., 1964, 128 pp. Discusses the origins of caves, characteristics of the underground atmosphere, growth of stalactites and other speleothems, behavior and products of cave microorganisms, habits of cave animals, the evolution of blind cave animals, and man's use of caves.

Morisawa, M. *Streams: Their Dynamics and Morphology*. Earth and Planetary Science Series. New York: McGraw-Hill Book Co., 1968, 175 pp. Explains some of the mysteries of rivers in terms comprehensible to those with little or no previous knowledge of the subject. A nonmathematical treatment of the concepts of fluvial geomorphology and the study of landforms that result from the erosion of running water.

Muir, John. *The Mountains of California*. Garden City, N.Y.: Doubleday & Co., 1961, 300 pp. Gives readers a glimpse of the grandeur of Yosemite, the Sierras, and Mount Shasta as seen by a nineteenth-century American naturalist and leader of the conservation movement.

_____. *Yosemite*. Garden City, N.Y.: Doubleday & Co., 1962, 225 pp. John Muir's portrait of the park he helped establish, presents a guide and description of one of America's most spectacular landscapes.

McDivitt, James F. *Minerals and Men: An Exploration of the World of Minerals and Its Effect on the World We Live In*. Baltimore: Johns Hopkins University Press, 1965, 158 pp.

National Academy of Sciences, Committee on Resources and Man of the Division of Earth Sciences. *Resources and Man*. San Francisco: W. H. Freeman and Co., 1969, 259 pp. Discusses man's ecology, population, food, minerals, and energy.

Osgood, T. H., A. E. Ruark, E. Hutchinson. *Atoms, Radiation, and Nuclei*. New York: John Wiley & Sons, 1964, 503 pp. The atomic nature of matter, the Bohr model of the atom, x-rays, waves, the periodic system, and applications of nuclear physics.

Pearl, Richard M. *Rocks and Minerals*. New York: Barnes & Noble, 1956, 275 pp. Deals with the recognition and identification of minerals, rocks, metals, gems, crystals, meteorites, and radioactive minerals. Also collection and display specimens.

_____. *How to Know the Minerals and Rocks*. New York: New American Library of World Literature, 1965, 192 pp. Practical information for the student, collector, and hobbyist on origin, geographic location, chemical composition and use of rocks and minerals. This illustrated field guide includes gems, ores, native metals, and meteorites.

_____. *Popular Gemology*. New York: John Wiley & Sons, 1965, 312 pp. Covers everything the gem collector and amateur mineralogist need to know about the properties and families of semiprecious and precious stones. Shows how to collect and classify gems.

_____. *Geology*. College Outline Series. New York: Barnes & Noble, 1969, 260 pp. Summary of the material usually presented in an introductory course in geology.

Playfair, John. *Illustrations of the Huttonian Theory of the Earth*. New York: Dover Publications, 1964, 568 pp. Presents ideas of Hutton and Playfair.

Includes commentaries on unconformities, rivers and valleys and their origins, on glaciers erratics, and Playfair's law of concordant stream junction.

Pounder, Elton R. *The Physics of Ice.* Elmsford, N.Y.: Pergamon Press, 1965, 160 pp. General and comprehensive review of the physical properties of ice, with information on its natural occurrence and movement. Emphasizes the scientific side of the subject.

Powell, John Wesley. *Exploration of the Colorado River and Its Canyons—Canyons of the Colorado.* New York: Dover Publications, 1961, 399 pp. Unabridged republication of the work first published in 1895 under the title *Canyons of the Colorado.* Fascinating account of Major Powell's expedition with a party of ten to explore the last great unmapped and unknown part of the U.S.—the Colorado River.

Rapp, George, Jr. *Colors of Minerals.* ESC Pamphlet Series PS-6. Boston: Houghton Mifflin Co., 1971.

Reinfeld, Fred. *Picture Book of Rocks and Minerals.* New York: Sterling Publications, 1963, 64 pp. Survey to introduce mineralogy and petrology to the beginner.

Rice, F. O., and E. Teller. *The Structure of Matter.* New York: John Wiley & Sons, 1961, 374 pp. The properties and behavior of atoms and molecules set forth in a work notable for its clear treatment and its minimal use of mathematics.

Romey, W. D. *Field Guide to Plutonic and Metamorphic Rocks.* ESC Pamphlet Series PS-5. Boston: Houghton Mifflin Co., 1971, 53 pp.

Rummery, G. R. *The Geosystem.* Brown Foundations of Earth Science Series. Dubuque, Iowa: William C. Brown Co., 1970, 135 pp. Presents the earth as a system in which land, sea and air are dynamically integrated in a single system through processes by which energy, matter, and momentum are continually exchanged.

Schultz, Gwen. *Glaciers and the Ice Age.* New York: Holt, Rinehart and Winston, 1963, 128 pp. Combines the findings of geology and anthropology to produce the total glacial picture including landforms, geologic processes, atmosphere, oceans, plants, animals, climate, people, and use of land.

Scientific American, eds. *Planet Earth.* New York: Simon and Schuster, 1957, 164 pp. Collection of 14 articles taken from past issues of *Scientific American.* Discusses the origin of the earth, its core and mantle, its crust, the hydrosphere, the atmosphere, and the edge of space.

Shrager, Arthur. *Elementary Metallurgy and Metallography.* New York: Dover Publications, 1961, 389 pp. Contains information on the structure of metals; slip, plastic deformation, and recrystallization; iron ore, production of pig iron; chemistry involved in the metallurgy of iron and steel; basic processes such as the Bessemer treatment; open-hearth process; the electric arc furnace; annealing, hardening, and tempering of steel; and copper, aluminum, magnesium, and their alloys.

Skinner, B. J. *Earth Resources.* Foundations of Earth Science Series. Englewood Cliffs, N.J.: Prentice-Hall, 1969, 150 pp. Presents information on abundance and availability of earth resources, metals, industrial minerals and rocks, energy, and water.

Sollers, Allen A. *Ours Is the Earth*. New York: Holt, Rinehart and Winston, 1963, 128 pp. Stresses the interdependence of our basic natural resources, and includes discussions of water, soils, forest, rangeland, wildlife, and minerals.

Spar, Jerome. *Earth, Sea, and Air—A Survey of the Geophysical Sciences*, 2d ed. Reading, Mass.: Addison-Wesley Publishing Co., 1965, 152 pp. Gives the student an overview of man's total natural physical environment.

Stegner, Wallace. *Beyond the Hundredth Meridian* Boston: Houghton Mifflin Co., 1962, 438 pp. Biography of John W. Powell, emphasizing the far-reaching and imposing career and ideas of Powell.

Strahler, Arthur N. *A Geologist's View of Cape Cod*. Garden City, N.Y.: Doubleday & Co., Natural History Press, 1966, 115 pp.

Stumpff, Karl. *Planet Earth*. Ann Arbor: University of Michigan Press, 1959, 192 pp. Explains the interaction between the earth and other terrestrial bodies through radiation and gravity, the origin, movements, size, shape, and structure of the earth.

Summer, J. S. *Geophysics, Geologic Structures and Tectonics*, Brown Foundations of Earth Science Series. Dubuque, Iowa: William C. Brown Co., 1969, 115 pp. Presents introductory material in geophysics and structural geology including gravity, magnetism, heat, seismology, and tectonics.

Takeuchi, H., S. Uyeda, and H. Kanamori. *Debate About the Earth: Approach to Geophysics through Analysis of Continental Drift*, rev. ed. San Francisco: Freeman, Cooper and Co., 1970, 281 pp. Discusses continental drift, paleomagnetism, heat in the earth, sea-floor spreading, and global tectonics.

Tuttle, S. D. *Landforms and Landscapes*. Brown Foundation of Earth Science Series. Dubuque, Iowa: William C. Brown Co., 1970, 130 pp. Concise treatment of geomorphology presented at beginning college level.

Turner, D. S. *Applied Earth Science*. Brown Foundations of Earth Science Series. Dubuque, Iowa: William C. Brown Co., 1969, 125 pp. Deals with practical applications of the study of the earth including natural resources, conservation and ecology, military and engineering applications, and applied climatology and meteorology.

Twenhofel, William H. *Treatise on Sedimentation* (2 vols.). New York: Dover Publications, 1961, 926 pp. Originally published in 1932. Discusses the sources and production of sediments, their transportation, deposition, diagenesis, lithification, modification by organisms, and so on. Examines products such as gypsum and saline residues, silica, strontium, and manganese. Environments of sedimentation and field and laboratory techniques are also included.

Verduin, Jacob. *Field Guide to Lakes*. ESCP Pamphlet Series PS-8. Boston: Houghton Mifflin Co., 1971.

Viorst, Judith. *The Changing Earth*. New York: Bantam Books, 1967, 244 pp. Rocks and minerals, the process of erosion, and the geological history of the earth are among topics covered. Many photographs and drawings.

Voskuil, W. H. *A Geography of Minerals*. Brown Foundations of Geography Series. Dubuque, Iowa: William C. Brown Co., 1969, 117 pp. Fairly complete presentation of the distribution of minerals including information on resources, exports, and so on.

Wegener, Alfred. Translated by John Beram. *The Origins of Continents and*

Oceans. New York: Dover Publications, 1966, 246 pp. Wegener's views on continental drift. Covers Wegener's theories on prepleistocene glaciations; on parallel shorelines that are separated by great distances of sea; and on isolated life forms found in widely separated areas.

White, J. F., ed. *Study of the Earth: Readings in Geological Science.* Englewood Cliffs, N.J.: Prentice-Hall, 1962, 408 pp. Articles by well-known authors in the field of geology. Promotes an awareness of the dynamic nature of the earth, the importance of geological science to modern knowledge, and the excitement of research.

Zim, Herbert S. *The American Southeast.* New York: Golden Press, 1959, 160 pp. Guide to the natural features of Florida, and nearby parts of Louisiana, Mississippi, Alabama, Georgia, and South Carolina. Well illustrated.

————. *The Rocky Mountains.* New York: Golden Press, 1964, 160 pp. Covers the major portion of the Rocky Mountains, including parts of Colorado, Wyoming, Montana, Idaho, Utah, British Columbia, and Alberta. Gives facts on the minerals and rocks, fossils, birds, mammals, fish, flowers, trees, and places to go. Well illustrated.

————, and Paul R. Shaffer. *Rocks and Minerals.* New York: Golden Press, 1957, 157 pp. Guide to the identification of rocks and minerals for beginners. Covers most of the common minerals, igneous, metamorphic and sedimentary rocks, and also gems. Discusses locations and methods of collecting specimens.

Free and Inexpensive Materials

Earth Materials and Economic Geology

"About Ohio Rocks and Minerals" (Educational Leaflet No. 5) (ODLS).

"Advanced Experiment with Gas" (Pub. Ed-4). Twenty-two laboratory investigations that can be done with fuel gas. Equipment, procedures, conclusions, and uses are included (AGA), free.

"Anthracite" (Bulletin #585, 18 pp.). Follows all aspects of the mining of anthracite coal (USBM).

"Areas Producing Dimension Stone in Indiana" Map (1 " = 30 mi). (IGS)

"Areas Producing Oil in Indiana" Map (1 " = 30 mi). (IGS).

"Areas Producing Sand and Gravel in Indiana" Map (1 " = 30 mi). (IGS).

"Beginning of Coal, The" *Scientific American* reprint discussing the development of coal with illustrations of plant fossils (NCA), free.

"Boxed Collection of 25 Rocks and Minerals from Idaho" Accompanied by description of the mineral resources (IBMG), free.

"Class Report: Coal" (22 pp.). Traces the development, history, processing, and uses of bituminous coal. Includes a quiz and list of activities (NCA), free.

"Coal Products Tree" (1 p.). Diagram illustrating some of the products of coal through present-day processing methods (USBM), free.

"Coal Wall Charts" (Set of two 18 " x 24 "). The two charts contain photographs and text material that describes the mining and transportation of coal (NCA), free.

"Cobalt" (12 pp.). Discusses the cobalt industry with the aid of statistical tables (USBM), free.

"Collecting Rocks" (10 pp.). Major rock types, their formation, location, identification, and collection of specimens (USGS), free.

"Collection of Chips of Rocks and Minerals from Idaho" (IBMG), free.

"Common Rocks and Minerals of Georgia" (6 pp.). Characteristics and types of the state's rocks and minerals (CDMMG), free.

"Common Rocks and Minerals of Pennsylvania" (27 pp.). Characteristics and occurrence of the state's rocks and minerals (PTGS).

"Conquest of the Land Through 7,000 Years" (30 pp.). Traces the history of man's utilization of the soil (USDA), free.

"Copper—The Cornerstone of Civilization" (24 pp.). Origin, types, production methods, world production, and consumption of copper. Bibliography included (CBA), free.

"Copper—The Oldest and Newest Metal" (16 pp.). Traces the history of copper and includes present-day mining and processing (CBA), free.

"Dealers in Rocks and Minerals of Alaska" (Information Circular #9). List of commercial sources (ADNR), free.

"Dimension Limestone" (1 p.). Discusses the formation, composition, location, and use of the limestone (IGS), free.

"Engineering Geology" Discusses the relationship between geology and urban development. Also reviews disasters that rise when the geology of an area is ignored (USGS), free.

"Experiments with Gas" (Pub. Ed-e); Twenty-nine laboratory investigations using fuel gas, complete with necessary materials, procedures, conclusions, uses for businesses, and ways for student participation (AGA), free.

"Facts About Salt" History, production, uses of the mineral (TSI), free.

"Flint, Ohio's Official Gem Stone" (Educational Leaflet No. 6) (ODLS).

"Gem Stones of the United States" (51 pp., Cat. #I-19.3; 1042—6, 1957). (USGPO), 25¢.

"Geography of Iron and Steel in the United States" (4 pp.). Map and description showing the location of raw materials and steel manufacturing centers in the United States (AISI), free.

"Going Places in Oil" (24 pp., career booklet; one set of four posters 11 " x 14 " (API), free.

"Gold" (16 pp.). History of gold's use, geologic environments, and origins. Discusses types of deposits, mining, production and study of gold (USGS), free.

"Graphite: A Mineral Which Has Many Uses" (4 pp.). Characteristics and value of the mineral (DCC), free.

"Guide to Rocks and Minerals of Illinois" (40 pp., Educational Series 5). Properties, characteristics, identification tables, and collecting hints of the state's rocks and minerals. Includes a geologic map and time scale (ISGS), free.

"Gypsum" (1 p.). Origin, composition, uses of the mineral and its location in Indiana (IGS), free.

"History of Granite" (18 pp.). Pictorial explanation of the origin, mining, and finishing of Barre Granite (BGA), free.

"History of Natural Gas" (Pub. Ed-18; comic book form). (AGA), free.

"How an Oil Field Grows" (18 pp.). Exploration, land acquisition, and movement of crude oil to refinery (SOC), free.

"How Coal Chemicals Are Made" (1 p.). Black-and-white chart showing the various operations involved in the production of steel (USSC), free.

"How Steel Is Made" (1 p.). Black-and-white chart showing the various operations involved in the production of steel (USSC), free.

"Idaho's Mineral Industry—The First Hundred Years" (71 pp., Bull. #18). (IBMG), free.

"Indiana Rock, Mineral and Fossil Set" (IGS), free.

"Industrial Limestone in Indiana" (7 pp.). Occurrence, use, and origin of the state's industrial limestone (IGS), free.

"Inside Illinois Mineral Resources" (27 pp.). Describes the economic minerals of Illinois (ISGS), free.

"Iowa Rocks and Minerals Set" (IGS), free.

"Iron Ore Today" (20 pp.). Use, location, mining, and improvement processes of iron ore (AIDA), free.

"Kansas Rocks and Minerals" (64 pp.). Characteristics, occurrence, and use of the state's rocks and minerals (SGSK), free.

"Lignite in North Dakota" (5 pp.). Surveys the state's lignite resources (NDGS).

"List of Collecting Localities for Rocks, Minerals and Fossils in Missouri" (MDGSWR).

"Maine Mineral Collecting" (24 pp.). Nature, occurrence, and collection of certain minerals found in the state (MAGS), free.

"Making of Iron and Steel" (set of 24 pictures complete with captions). Illustrates various aspects of steel production; includes a teacher's guide (USCC), free.

"Map of Coal Areas in the USA" Illustrates the deposits of the various types of coal in the U.S. On the reverse side of the map coal reserves and levels of production are listed for each state (NCA), free.

"Mesa Miracle" (34 pp.). Describes the exploration, mining, and processing of uranium ores (UCC), free.

"Michigan's Oil and Gas Fields" Statistical summary of production (MGSD).

"Mineral Industry of—, The" Each state survey puts out a reprint from the U.S. Bureau of Mines, *Minerals Yearbook*. Reprints describe the mineral resources and related industries of that particular state. (Published annually), free.

"Mineral Resources and Industries of Florida" (map, complete with symbols). Illustrates resource areas and various mineral industries of the state (FGS).

"Mineral Resources of Wisconsin" (13 pp.). Resources, production, and future of the state's mineral industry (WGNHS), free.

"Minerals Yearbook. Reprint" Each state survey puts out a reprint from the U.S. Bureau of Mines, describing the mineral resources and related industries of that particular state. (Published annually), free.

"Mineral Wealth of Kansas" Surveys the mineral industry of state. (Published annually) (SGSK), free.

"Mining and Mineral Resources" (132 pp.). Nature, exploration, and utilization of the economic minerals of Florida (FGS), free.

"Natural Gas—Science Behind Your Burner" (Pub. Ed–1). Complete instructional unit including slides, charts, teacher guide, and student sheets (AGA), free.

"Nickel" (15 pp.). Characteristics of the United States nickel mining industry (USBM), free.

"Nickel Deposits of North America" (62 pp., Cat. #I–19.3; 1223, 1966). (USGPO), 25¢.

"North Dakota Rock, Mineral and Fossil Collection" (NDGS).

"Oil" (49 pp.). Illustrations depicting the total range of activities of the oil industry (SOCC), free.

"Oil for Today and for Tomorrow" (84 pp.). Origin, history, production, conservation, and distribution of oil (IOCC), free.

"Oil Pictures" (26 pp.). Illustrate aspects of the industry (SOCC), free.

"Oil Producing Industry in Your State" (110 pp.). Statistical information about the oil industry of each state (IPPA), free.

"Oregon Minerals, Fossils and Rocks and Where to Find Them" (12 pp.). (OSHD), free.

"Oregon Rock and Mineral Lending Set" (OSHD), on loan.

"Oregon Rock and Mineral Set" (ODMMR), free.

"Our Indiana Coal" (10 pp.). Discusses the formation, location, and relation of Indiana coal to Pennsylvanian rocks. Shows plant fossils associated with coal deposits (ICS), free.

"Outline of Geology and Mineral Resources in Oregon, An" (ODMMR). Traces geologic history, features, and mineral resources of the state.

"Pennsylvania Student Rock and Mineral Set" (PTGS).

"Pennsylvania Teacher's Rock and Mineral Set" (PTGS).

"Petrified River, The" (25 pp.). Film, includes origin, location, mining, processing, and use of uranium (UCC), free.

"Petroleum Tree, The" (1 p.). Chart of the products derived from crude oil (USBM), free.

"Phosphate—Florida's Hidden Blessing" (28 pp.). Origin, mining, and uses and importance of the state's phosphate deposits (FPC), free.

"Phosphate Specimens" (FPC), free.

"Placer Gold in Maine" (1 p.). Location and extent of placer deposits in Maine (MAGS), free.

"Potomac—Its Water Resources" (23 pp., 1966). Description of the river basin, climate, river, water bank, history, and problems of the Potomac (USGS), free.

"Prospecting for Gold in the United States" Present-day prospecting methods, locations, history and varieties of gold deposits. Lists state agencies where prospecting and mining information can be obtained (USGS), free.

"Reading List of Publications and Catalogs of Visual Aids on Steel" (9 pp.). (USSC), free.

"Reference and Audio-visual Materials on Iron and Steel" (84 pp.). (AISI), free.

"Rock and Mineral Collecting Areas in Iowa" (2 pp.). List of locations and mineral types (IOGS), free.

"Rock and Mineral Collection of New York" (NYSMSS), on loan.

"Rocks and Minerals of Florida" (40 pp., Special Pub. 8). Discusses rocks and minerals of Florida including their identification, occurrence, and importance (FGS), $1.50.

"Rocks and Minerals of Florida" (41 pp.). Descriptive text to accompany a Florida mineral and rock collection (FPC), free.

"Rocks and Minerals of Iowa" (4 pp.). Characteristics and locations of rocks, minerals, and fossils in the state (IOGS), free.

"Rocks and Minerals of New York" (20 pp.). Complete description of many of the rocks and minerals found in the state, their physical properties, identification, and selected references. Includes a geologic map of the state (NYSMSS), free.

"Salt" (26 pp.). History, mining, and research connected with salt industry (MSC), free.

"Science in Its Search for Oil" (wall chart 34 " x 44 "). Illustrates geologic areas, the index fossils and the various roles that earth science plays in the search for oil (API), one per class, free.

"Scientists at Work in the Gas Industry" (Pub. Ed-1; B/w, 48 fr., 35mm filmstrip with guide). Describes the nature of the work of career scientists in the gas industry (AGA), free.

"Skin Diving for Gold in Alaska" (2 pp., Information Circular #10). One method used in prospecting for gold (ADNR), free.

"Sources of Nuclear Fuel" (67 pp., 1968). Historical development, exploration, mining, processing, and uses of uranium (USAEC), free.

"Steel Materials Sample Kit" (Pub. #103). Bottled samples of raw materials used in steel manufacturing (USSC), free.

"Story of Gas, The" (48 pp., Pub. Ed-22). Traces the source, origin, exploration, resources, uses, and by-products of natural gas (AGA), free.

"Story of Oil, The" (24 pp.). History and value of the petroleum industry (SOCC), free.

"Story of Oil and Gas, The" (16 pp.). Formation, history, production, and marketing of petroleum products (PPC), free.

"Story of Petroleum" (32 pp.). Formation, location, production, processing, and marketing of petroleum products (PPC), free.

"Story of Petroleum" (32 pp.). Formation, location, production, processing, and marketing of oil (SOC), free.

"Study of Florida Minerals" (Complete instructional unit on phosphate (FPC), free.

"Sulphur—Mining (5 pp.). Describes the Frasch process of sulphur mining (TGSC), free.

"Teaching Collection of Rocks and Minerals of Missouri" (MDGSWR).

"Tennessee Rock and Mineral Samples" (TDG).

"Twenty Rocks and Minerals of Kansas" (SGSK), free.

"Twenty Rocks, Minerals and Fossils Common in Oklahoma" (OGS).

"What Is Water?" (8 pp.). Occurrence and properties of water (USGS), free.

"World of Steel, The" (31 pp.). Discusses various aspects of the steel and iron industry including careers, history, and achievements (USSC), free.

Igneous Activity

"Volcanoes" (10 pp.). Describes the nature, distribution, and types of volcanic activity. Information on famous volcanoes (USGS), free.

"Volcanoes of the United States" (20 pp., 1967). Considers volcanic activity, eruptions, and related phenomena in the U.S. (USGS), free.

"Batholiths" (30 pp., Cat. #I-19.16; 554-c, 1967). (USGPO), 30¢.

"Hawaii Volcanoes National Park, Hawaii" (Cat. #I-29.6; H31/2). (USGPO), 15¢.

Crustal Rock Deformation and the Earth's Interior

"Active Faults of California" (USGS), free.

"Alaska's Good Friday Earthquake, March 27, 1964—A Preliminary Report" (35 pp.). Discusses the total effect of the quake and the geologic influences on the resultant damage (USGS), free.

"Earthquakes" (24 pp.). Nature, detection, recording, measurement, and prediction of earthquakes (USGS), free.

"Great Alaska Earthquake, March 27, 1964, The" (35 pp., Circular 491, 1964). Discusses nature and effects and damage from the earthquake with the aid of maps and other illustrations (USGS), free.

"Interior of the Earth, The" (4 pp.). Describes how the earth's crust and interior are studied by scientists (USGS), free.

"Madison River Canyon Earthquake Area" (20 pp.). Account of the 1959 earthquake and landslide in Montana; includes many maps and photos of the area (USFS), free.

"Our Changing Continent" (15 pp., 1967). Describes the paleogeography of North America and procedures used to reconstruct the geologic past (USGS), free.

"San Andreas Fault, The" (10 pp., 1967). Describes the origin, placement, nature, and behavior of the fault (USGS), free.

Surficial Geologic Processes

"Caves of Illinois" (87 pp., Report of Investigation 15). Deals with the development, characteristics, and locations of caves in Illinois (ISCS).

"Conquest of the Land Through 7,000 Years" (30 pp.). Traces the history of man's utilization of the soil (USDA), free.

"Facts About Wind Erosion Dust Storms" (8 pp., Leaflet #394). Nature of such storms and the related conservation efforts used to prevent them (USDA), free.

"From the Dust of the Earth" (16 pp.). Importance of soil in man's life (USDA), free.

"How to Recognize Erosion in the Northeast" (16 pp., Bull. #27). (USDA), free.

"Glacial Lakes Surrounding Michigan, The" (19 pp.). Outlines the glacial origin of the Great Lakes (MGSD).

"Glaciers—A Water Resource" Provides information regarding the nature of glaciers and their potential use as sources of water (USGS), free.

"Great Ice Age, The" (16 pp., 1967). Origin, nature, and effects of the Ice Age (USGS), free.

"Ground Water" (11 pp., Educational Series #3). Characteristics, locations, and importance of ground water (PTGS), free.

"Landforms of the United States" (24 pp.). Surveys how the various landforms of the United States were formed (USGS), free.

"Let's Stop Soil Erosion" (15 pp., Circular #613). Discusses erosion, its effect on the land surface, and methods to control it (UW), free.

"Marine Geology—Research Beneath the Sea" The booklet provides a survey of such topics as the ocean floor's topography, sediments, rocks underlying sea bottom, and processes at work on the floor's surface (USGS), free.

"Michigan's Sand Dunes" Origin and location of dunes in the state (MGSD).

"Mountains and Plains—Denver's Geologic Setting" Provides the reader with a field trip westward from Denver across older and older rocks illustrating the geologic events of the past (USGS), free.

"Pennsylvania and the Ice Age" (33 pp., Educational Series #174). Discusses the origin and effects of sediments and the control of runoff (USDA), free.

"Sediment Is Your Problem" (16 pp., Booklet AIB #174). Discusses the origin and effects of sediments and the control of runoff (USDA), free.

"Soil and Its Conservation" Origin and nature of soil and its conservation in Ohio (ODLS), free.

"Soil Conditions That Influence Wind Erosion" (40 pp., Technical Bull. 1185). Booklet uses a wide variety of visual techniques in the discussion of the topic (USDA), free.

"Soil Erosion—The Work of Uncontrolled Water" (16 pp., Bull. #260). Discusses the effects of erosion and methods by which it can be minimized (USDA), free.

"Soil—Know What It Needs" (8 pp.). Reasons for soil testing, method of testing, value of its various constituents, and methods of its management (OSU), free.

"Some Features of Karst Topography in Indiana" (20 pp.). Guide book complete with background information, diagrams, illustrations, and bibliography dealing with Karst topography with an emphasis on the features of south-central Indiana (IGS).

"Something About Caves in Michigan" (8 pp.). Describes the origin, features, and locations of caves in Michigan (MGS).

"Springs of Florida" (198 pp.). Locations and nature of the state's springs (FGS), free.

"Water Intake by Soil" (10 pp., Pub. #295). Presents three different experiments that can be run to study the water intake of soil accompanied by a description of the conditions that contribute to a flood (USDA), free.

"Wind Erosion in Oklahoma" (16 pp., Circular E–667). Factors that cause such erosion, and procedures by which it can be controlled and prevented (OSU), free.

"Wisconsin Glacial Deposits" (Colored map). Illustrates location of such deposits in the state complete with a brief survey of the Ice Age in Wisconsin (WGNHS).

"You Never Miss the Water—A Few Pointers on Ground Water Supplies" (44 pp.). Deals with the water cycle, its importance, and its relationship to geologic conditions (MGSD), free.

"Your Soil: Crumbly or Cloddy?" (8 pp., Leaflet #328). Conditions affecting soils (USDA), free.

Measurements and Mapping

"Amazon—Measuring a Mighty River, The" (16 pp.). Reports findings of cooperative Geological Survey—Brazilian hydrologic investigations on the river; also includes facts on the climate, population and other features of the basin (USGS), free.

"Around the World—Alaska, Soviet Union, South America" Series of articles describing the use of gloves and maps in studying geographic relationships (NSC), free.

"Fundamentals of Modern Geography" (4 pp.). A look at physical geography and its relationship to other academic fields of physical and social sciences (DG), free.

"Geological Survey: Photographic Library" (2 pp.). Nature and services offered by the library (USGS), free.

"Geographic Center of the United States" (1 p.). The change in geographic center brought about by the admission of Hawaii into the United States (USC & GS), free.

"How Soil Surveys Help" (8 pp., Circular #612). Benefits of soil surveys (UW), free.

"How to Take a Soil Sample" (6 pp., Leaflet #L-55). Procedures involved in such a test and where the samples may be tested.

"Index to Topographic Mapping" Status of topographic mapping in a particular state, The listing also includes a wide variety of special sheets, location of a map reference library, U.S. Geological Survey office, and other locations where topographic maps may be obtained (USGS).

"Key to Soils of Kentucky, A" (35 pp.). Origin, classification, and location of soils in Kentucky (UK), free.

"Map Projections for Modern Charting" (4 pp.). Discusses the types of projections and their use in modern charting (USC & GS).

"Practical Uses of Magnetism" (22 pp., Serial #618). Describes the nature, changes, measurements, and uses of magnetism (USC & GS).

"Soil Tests" (Extension Folder #278). Needs and values and methods of soil testing (MSU), free.

"Topographic Maps" (24 pp.). Surveys all aspects of topographic maps from their preparation to uses and characteristics (USCS), free.

"Topographic Maps—Silent Guides for Outdoorsmen" (8 pp., 1967). Benefit of using topographic maps (USGS), free.

"What's in That Soil Map" (16 pp.). Nature of soil and the construction and interpretation of soil maps (UW), free.

Environmental Geology

"Concepts of Conservation" (64 pp.). Discusses the relationship between resources and conservation (CF), free.

"Conservation" (60 pp.). Discusses the problems associated with the conservation of a wide range of resources (NYSMSS), free.

"Conservation" (A picture discussion kit). Set of seven full-color plates (11 " x 14 ") complete with descriptive material. Titles included in the kit: (1) Nature's Way; (2) Soil and Water Resources; (3) Forest and Wildlife Resources; (4) Oilmen Play Their Part; (5) Conservation in Petroleum Production and Recovery (6) Mineral Resources; (7) Conserving Our Waters. (One kit per classroom) (API), free.

"Conserving Our Waters and Clearing the Air" (Kit). Kit contains 16-pp. booklet for each student; an 18 " x 23 " poster, a 28-pp. research materials booklet, and a 28-pp. teacher's guide (API), free.

"Early American Soil Conservation" (62 pp., Pub. #449). Discusses the contributions of the early conservationists (USDA), free.

"Engineering Career for You in the Soil Conservation Service, An" (Miscellaneous Pub. #175). (USDA), free.

"Engineering Geology" (16 pp., 1967). General discussion of how geologic environments affect location, design, and construction of engineering works. Compares certain disasters to illustrate close line between engineering works and their geologic environments (USGS), free.

"Geologic Contributions to Michigan Conservation" (12 pp.). (MGSD), free.

"Our Resources" (24 pp.). Discusses the state's resources and the methods of their conservation (USU), free.

"Outline for Teaching Conservation in High Schools, An" (21 pp., Pub. #PA-201). Includes units, objectives, topics for study, and suggested activities for use in presenting conservation in a number of subjects (USDA), free.

"Principles of Petroleum Conservation" (10 pp.). (IOCC), free.

"Radioactive Wastes" (46 pp., 1969). Nature, management, research, and development of radioactive wastes (USAEC), free.

"Scientific Experiments in Environmental Pollution" (40 pp.). Edited by E. C. Weaver, 1968 (HRWI).

"Soil and Water Conservation Activities for Boy Scouts" (30 pp., Pub. #PA-348). Activities to do in studying the various aspects of conservation (USDA), free.

"Soil and Water Conservation Demonstrations" (Pub. #MP-397). (TAES), free.

"Soil and Water Conservation Projects and Activities: A Guide for 4-H Leaders" (30 pp., Pub. #PA-377). (USDA), free.

"Soil Conservation at Home" (27 pp., Bull. #244). Describes conservation practices for both the urban and dweller (USDA), free.

"Soil and Water Conservation for Oklahoma" (16 pp., Circular #E-658). Causes and control of erosion in the state (OSU), free.

"Soil Erosion and Some Means of Its Control" (Special Report Bulletin #29). (ISU), free.

"Teaching Conservation in Indiana High Schools" (50 pp.). Complete and comprehensive teacher's guide including films, references, materials, and personnel (IGS), free.

"Teaching Soil and Water Conservation—A Classroom and Field Guide" (30 pp., Pub. #PA-341). Includes classroom activities and field problems in soil and water conservation (USDA), free.

"Water and Industry" (12 pp.). Industrial uses, problems, and effects of industry on water quality (USGS), free.

"Water for Thirsty Industry" (9 pp., Leaflet #2). Outlines the needs of Florida in relation to water for industry (FGS), free.

"World Around You—Our Natural Resources Educational Packet, The" Includes material on the National Parks, soil and soil erosion, and a study guide on natural resources (GCA), free.

"Your Water Resources" (35 pp., Leaflet #1). Surveys the resources and conservation problems of the state's water supply (FGS), free.

General Topics and Regional Studies

"Advanced Experiments with Gas" (Pub. EC-4). Twenty-two laboratory investigations that can be done with fuel gas. Equipment, procedures, conclusions, and uses are included (AGA), free.

"Agate Fossil Beds National Monument, Nebraska" (Cat. #I-29.21:AG 1). (USGPO), 15¢.

"Amazon, The—Measuring A Mighty River" (16 pp.). Reports findings of cooperative Geological Survey—Brazilian hydrologic investigations on the river; also includes facts on the climate, population, and other features of the basin (USGS), free.

"Antarctic and Its Geology, The" (16 pp., 1968). History of exploration, geological and climatological characteristics of the continent (USGS), free.

"Astrogeology" Surveys the nature and activities of the Geological Survey in lunar mapping, water investigations, lunar explorations, and astronaut training (USGS), free.

"Bedrock Surface Of Illinois" (Map, b/w, 1 ″/8 mi.). (ISGS), free.

"Bibliography of Earth Science Materials" (1969). (MFMGS), $1.00.

"Bibliography of Geology of Michigan, 1956-60" (66 pp.). (MGSD), free.

"Bibliography of Minnesota Geology" (Bull. #34, supplement). (MGS).

"Bureau of Mines, The" (4 pp.). Presents the activities of the bureau (USBM), free.

"California School Library Kit" Publications dealing with geologic aspects of areas in which schools are located (CDMG), free.

"Careers in Atomic Energy" (29 pp., 1969). Outlines the nature of college programs, work of an atomic scientist, and location benefits of such a position (USAEC), free.

"Careers in Conservation" (TSCS), free.

"Conquest of the Land Through 7,000 Years" (30 pp.). Traces the history of man's utilization of the soil (USDA), free.

"Devil's Tower National Monument, Wyoming" (Cat. #I-29.21:D #4914). (USGPO), 10¢.

"Dinosaur National Monument, Colorado, Utah" (Cat. #I-29.21:D 61). (USGPO), 10¢.

"Dinosaur Quarry, Dinosaur National Monument, Colorado—Utah" (Cat. #1-29.21:DC 1/2). The story of the quarry from which a large quantity of dinosaur remains have been recovered (OUSGPO), 25¢.

"Earth Science and Energy" (24 pp., Booklet). 1 per student (API), free.

"Experiments with Gas" (Pub. Ed-e). Twenty-nine laboratory investigations using fuel gas; complete with necessary materials, procedures, conclusions, uses for businesses, and ways for student participation (AGA), free.

"Film Catalog—U.S. Bureau of Mines" (29 pp.). Annotated listing of all films distributed by the bureau (USBM), free.

"From the Dust of the Earth" (16 pp.). Importance of soil in man's life (USDA), free.

"Fundamentals of Modern Geography" (4 pp.). A look at physical geography and its relationship to other academic fields of physical and social sciences (DG), free.

"General Mineral Information of Alaska" (9 pp., Information Circular #5). (ADNR), free.

"Generalized Bedrock of Indiana" (Map, 1″/30 mi.), (IGS).

"Generalized Geologic Time Chart for Oregon" (ODMMR), free.

"Generalized Section of Rocks in Ohio" (Chart of geologic formations in Ohio, Information Circular #4). (ODLS), free.

"Geology—Science and Profession" Describes the science of geology, examples of some geological problems, and practical views of geology as a career (AGI), free.

"Geology: Reprints of Books and Journals" (Cat. Published yearly). (JRC), free.

"Geology" List of paleontology, seismology, volcanology, and geology papers available from the Smithsonian Institution (SI), free.

"Geology" Annual price list of publications dealing with geology that are available from the Superintendent of Documents. (USGPO), 15¢.

"Geology and the Gettysburg Campaign" (15 pp., Educational Series #5). The effects of geology and topography on the outcome of the Battle of Gettysburg (PTGS), free.

"Geologic Map of Illinois" (Color, 1″/16 mi). (ISGS), free.

"Geologic Map of Idaho" (IBMG), free.

"Geologic Map of Wisconsin" (Colored map). Complete with cross section and brief geologic history of Wisconsin (WGNHS), free.

"Georgia Mineral Newsletter" (Quarterly publication describing various aspects of Georgia's mineral resources (GDMMG).

"Glacier National Park, Montana" (Cat. #I-29.6:G 45/8). United States section of Waterton-Glacier International Peace Park (USGPO), 15¢.

"Glacier National Park" (39 pp., two maps, Cat. #I-19.16:29 K, 1959). Story of the origin and history of the rocks and fossils found within the park (USGPO), $1.25.

"Grand Teton National Park, Wyoming" (Cat. #I-29.6:G 76/20). (USGPO), 15¢.

"Guide to Geologic Map of Illinois" (24 pp., Educational Series 7). Description of geological features of Illinois accompanied by a colored geological map (ISGS), free.

"Guide to Rocks and Minerals of Illinois" (40 pp., Educational Series 5). Properties, characteristics, identification tables, and collecting hints on the state's rocks, and minerals. Geologic map and time scale included (ISGS), free.

"Handbook for Field Trips" (18 pp.). Discusses the organization of a field trip and recommends additional references and audiovisual aids (IGS), free.

"Hawaii Volcanoes National Park, Hawaii" (Cat. #I-29.6:H 31/2). (USGPO), 15¢.

"Idaho's Mineral Industry—The First Hundred Years" (71 pp. Bull. 18). (IBMG), free.

"Illinois Field Trip Guides" Wide variety of field trip guides (each containing geologic information, diagrams, photos, and maps) are available from Survey (refer to publications listing from the State Survey) (ISGS), free.

"Indiana Rock Chart and Geologic Time Scale" (1 p.). (IGS), free.

"Information Sources and Services" (2 pp.). Annotated listing of the various information sources and services available through the USGS (USGS), free.

"Introduction to the Topography, Geology, and Mineral Resources of North Carolina" (17 pp., Educational Series 2). Overview of geology of the state with geological map and cross section included (NCDMR).

"Kansas Field Conference Guidebooks" (Refer to publication listing from the State Survey as to nature and areas covered by these publications) (SGSK).

"Kansas Rock Chart and Geologic Time Table." (SGSK), free.

"Kansas Scene" (48 pp.). Scenery of state as it is related to its geology and physiography (SGSK).

"Key to the Soils of Kentucky, A" (35 pp.). Origin, classification, and location of soils in Kentucky; includes physiographic and geologic maps of Kentucky (UK), free.

"Know Your Soil" (16 pp.). Nature of soil, soil tests and surveys, and uses of data from such surveys (USDA), free.

"Land Judging Guide for Michigan" (Extension Bull. #326). (MSU), free.

"Land Judging in New York State" (Extension Bull. #904). (CU), free.

"Land Judging in North Carolina" (Extension Bull. #393). (NCSU), free.

"Lists of Collecting Localities for Rocks, Minerals, and Fossils in Missouri" (MDGSWR).

"Looking at Ohio Rocks" (5 pp.). Nature and distribution of Ohio rocks (ODLS), free.

"Madison River Canyon Earthquake Area" (20 pp.). An account of the 1959 earthquakes and landslide in Montana; includes many maps and photos of the area (USFS).

"Maine Mineral Collecting" (24 pp.). Nature, occurrence, and collection of certain minerals found in Maine (AGS), free.

"Major Soils of Kansas" (Experimental Station #336). Nature and distribution of soil types in Kansas (KSU), free.

"Michigan Beach Stones" (4 pp.). Description and photos (MGSD), free.

"Michigan Geological Sourcebook" (15 pp., Circular #1). Provides sources of information on the geological aspects of Michigan. Also includes the facilities, services, and publications of the state (MGSD).

"Michigan's Rock Column and Time Scale" (1 p.). (MGSD).

"Michigan Sand Dunes." Origin and location of dunes in Michigan (MGSD).

"Mineral Industry of (state), The" Each state survey puts out a reprint from the U.S. Bureau of Mines, *Minerals Yearbook* Reprints describe the mineral resources and related industries of the particular state. (Published annually), free.

"Mineral Resources and Industries of Florida" (Map, complete with symbols). Illustrates resource areas and various mineral industries of Florida (FPC), free.

"Mineral Resources of Wisconsin" (13 pp.). Resources, production, and future of Wisconsin's mineral industry (WGNHS), free.

"Mineral Wealth in Kansas" Surveys the mineral industry of Kansas. (Annual publication) (SGSK), free.

"Minnesota's Water Resources" (32 pp.). Discusses the various aspects of the Minnesota's subsurface and surface water supplies (MIA).

"Mining and Mineral Resources" (132 pp.). Nature, exploration, and utilization of the economic minerals of Florida (FGS), free.

"Mountains and Plains—Denver's Geologic Setting" (23 pp. 1967). Discusses the valley, foothills, mountains, rocks and their formation, found near Denver, Colo. (USGS), free.

"Oregon Minerals, Fossils and Rocks and Where to Find Them" (12 pp.). (OSHD), free.

"Our Indiana Coal" (10 pp.). Discusses the formation, location, and relation of Indiana coal to Pennsylvanian rocks. Shows plant fossils associated with the coal deposits (IGS), free.

"Outline of Geology and Mineral Resources in Oregon, An" (ODMMR).

"Outline of Geology of Idaho" (74 pp.). Surveys the geology of the state (IBMG).

"Pennsylvania and the Ice Age" (33 pp., Educational Series 6). Describes the effect of glaciers on the geology of Pennsylvania (PTGS), free.

"Pennsylvania Field Trip Guides" Refer to the publication list of the State Survey for the nature of the field trip guides (PTGS), free.

"Pennsylvania Geology Summarized" (17 pp., Educational Series 4). Fundamental principles of geology as applied to Pennsylvania along with a colored geologic map (PTGS), free.

"Phosphate—Florida's Hidden Blessing" (28 pp.). Origin, mining uses, and importance of phosphate deposits (FPC), free.

"Physical Geography of Wisconsin" (7 pp). (WGNHS), free.

"Physiography of Iowa" (1 p.). Surveys the geology, history, and formation of the present landforms of Iowa (IOGS), free.

"Physiography of Iowa" (48 pp.). History and formation of the landforms of Iowa (IOGS), free.

"Popular Publications of the Geological Survey" (2 pp.). An annotated bibliography of the popular publications available from the Survey (USGS), free.

"Potomac, The—Its Water Resources" (23 pp., 1966). Description of the river basin, climate, river water, history, and problems of the Potomac (USGS), free.

"Practical Uses of Magnetism" (22 pp., Serial #618). Describes the nature, changes, measurement, and uses of magnetism (USCCS).

"Prospecting in Washington" (26 pp.). Describes the opportunities for prospecting in the state (WDMG), free.

"Public Inquiries Office" (2 pp.). Description of the nature and location of the respective offices (USGS), free.

"Rock and Mineral Collecting Areas in Iowa" (2 pp.). List of locations and mineral types (IOGS), free.

"Rocks and Minerals of Florida" (40 pp., Special Publication 8). Discusses rocks and minerals of Florida, including their identification, occurrence, and importance (FGS), $1.50.

"Rocks and Minerals of Iowa" (4 pp.). Characteristics and locations of rocks, minerals, and fossils in Iowa (IOGS), free.

"Rocks and Minerals of New York" (20 pp.). Complete description of many rocks and minerals found in New York State, their physical properties and identification plus selected references. Includes a geologic map of the state (NYSMSS), free.

"Rocks and Reservoirs Along the Wabash" (19 pp., 1963). Guidebook complete with road log, map, section diagrams, and bibliography (IGS).

"Scenery of Florida As Interpreted by a Geologist" (118 pp.). Compares the scenery of Florida to its geology (FGS), free.

"Science Clubs of America Sponsor Handbook" Describes the operation, benefits, and uses of science clubs (SCA), free.

"Soil—Know What It needs" (8 pp.) Reasons for soil testing, methods of testing, value of its various constituents, and methods of its management (OSU), free.

"Soil Map of Wisconsin" Map complete with text describing soils of the state (WGNHS), free.

"Soil Science Career for You in SCS, A" (Pub. 716). Discusses the activities of a soil scientist and the Soil Conservation Service (USDA), free.

"Soil and Fertilizers" Price list of government publications on soils, erosion, soil surveys and conservation. (Published annually) (USFPO), free.

"Soils and Soil Associations of New York" (Extension Bull. #930). (CU), free.

"Soils of Michigan" (Special Bull. #402). (MSU), free.

"Some Features of Karst Topography in Indiana" (20 pp.). Guide book complete with background information, diagrams, illustrations, and bibliography dealing with Karst topography with an emphasis on the features of south-central Indiana (IGS).

"Something About Caves in Michigan" (8 pp.). Describes the origin, features, and locations of caves in Michigan (MGS).

"Springs of Florida" (198 pp.). Locations and nature of Florida's springs (FGS), free.

"Stories of Resource-Full Kansas: Featuring the Kansas Landscape" (42 pp.). Resources of Kansas and related geology (SGSK), free.

"Study of Florida Minerals" Complete instructional unit on phosphate (FPC), free.

"Surface Occurrences of Geologic Formations in Florida" (Color). Geologic map with formation names, stage, and age illustrated (FPC), free.

"Teacher Resource Reference" Listing of free materials available from the API (API), free.

"Teaching Aids Available from the American Iron and Steel Institute" (4 pp.). (AISI), free.

"Texas Through 250 Million Years" (32 pp.). Illustrates geological history of Texas and the use of fossils as clues to the past (HORC), free.

"That Land Down There" (16 pp., Bull. 255). Deals with the different views of the land and its usage (USDA), free.

"United States Geological Survey Library" (2 pp., 1969). Describes functions, organization, and activities of the USGS (USGS), free.

"Understanding Vermont Soils" (12 pp.). Origin, naming, description, and identification of state's soils (UVSAC), free.

"Water Intake by Soil" (10 pp., Pub. #295). Presents three different experiments that can be run to study the water intake of soil accompanied by a description of the conditions that contribute to a flood (USDA), free.

"Water Resources of Wisconsin, The" (21 pp.). Surveys Wisconsin's surface and subsurface water resources (WGNHS), free.

"Water Witching" (10 pp.). History, validity, and accuracy of water witching. How hydrologists locate ground water today (USGS), free.

"What Is Water?" (8 pp.). Occurrence and properties of water (USGS), free.

"What Is a Watershed?" (Pub. PA–420). Function and importance of a watershed (USDA), free.

"Wind Erosion in Oklahoma" (16 pp., Circ. E–667). Factors that cause such erosion, and procedures by which it can be controlled and prevented (OSU), free.

"Wisconsin Glacial Deposits" (Map color). Illustrates location of glacial deposits in the state complete with a brief survey of the ice age in Wisconsin (WGNHS).

"You Never Miss the Water"—A Few Pointers on Ground Water Supplies (44 pp.). Deals with the water cycle: its importance and its relationship to geologic conditions (MGSD), free.

"Your Soil: Crumbly or Cloddy?" (8 pp., Leaflet #328). Conditions affecting soils (USDA), free.

APPENDIX

Survey of Textbooks and Supplementary Reading Materials

Earth and Space Science Textbooks

There are many earth and space science textbooks available for use at the junior high school and senior high school levels. Many of these are fairly recent publications, whereas others have enjoyed repeated revisions and republication. We have attempted to include most of the textbooks that were available at the time of publication of this Sourcebook. No attempt has been made to determine grade or reading level for the listed books.

Bishop, M. S., Lewis, P. B., and R. L. Bronaugh. *Focus on Earth Science*. Columbus, Ohio: Charles E. Merrill Publishing Co., 1969, 534 pp. (Test booklet available to accompany this textbook.).

Blanc, S., A. Fischler, and O. Gardner. *Modern Science: Earth, Life, and Man*. New York: Holt, Rinehart and Winston, 1971, 450 pp.

Brown, F. M., G. H. Kemper, and J. H. Lewis. *Earth Science*. Morristown, N.J.: Silver Burdett Co., 1970. (Laboratory manual is available to accompany this textbook.)

Earth Science Curriculum Project. *Investigating the Earth*. Boston: Houghton Mifflin Co., 1967, 594 pp. (Complete text and laboratory investigations contained in one volume. An accompanying Teacher's Guide to text laboratory investigations is available, as well as a Laboratory Supplement book. (Revision is scheduled for 1972.)

Hibbs, A., and A. Eiss. *The Earth-Space Sciences*. River Forest, Ill.: Laidlaw Brothers, 1971, 576 pp. (A laboratory manual is available to accompany this textbook.)

Jacobson, et al. *Earth and Space Science*. New York: American Book Co., 1969.

Marean, J., et al. *Earth Science—A Laboratory Approach*. Reading, Mass.: Addison-Wesley Publishing Co., 1970.

McCracken, H. R., D. G. Decker, J. G. Read, and A. Yarian. *Basic Earth Science*. Syracuse, N.Y.: L. W. Singer Co., 1968.

Namowitz S. N., and D. B. Stone. *Earth Science: The World We Live In*. 4th ed. New York: American Book Co., 1969, 675 pp. (*Activities in Earth Science* and *Earth Science Transparencies* accompany this textbook.)

Oxenhorn, J. M., and M. N. Idelson. *Pathways in Science—The Earth We Live On*, 1968, 182 pp.; *Pathways in Science—Oceans of Air and Water*, 1969, 180 pp.; *Pathways in Science—Man and Energy in Space*, 1970, 184 pp. (Three separate paperback volumes designed for slow-learning junior and senior high school students at a fifth grade reading level.)

Ramsey, Wm. L., R. A. Burckley, C. R. Phillips, and F. M. Watenpaugh. *Modern Earth Science*. New York: Holt, Rinehart and Winston, 1969, 550 pp. (Available accompanying materials include: *Laboratory Experiments for Modern Earth Science*; *Activities for Modern Earth Science*; and *Tests for Modern Earth Science*.)

Scott, B. A., and J. E. Ayres. *Natural Science—Earth I* (1969); *Natural Science—Earth II*. Wellesley Hills, Mass.: Independent School Press, 1970.

Secondary School Science Project (SSSP, Princeton Project). *Time, Space and Matter*. New York: McGraw-Hill Book Co., 1966.

Strahler, V., and J. Navarra. *Our Planet in Space—The Earth Sciences*. New York: Harper & Row, 1967.

Suchman, J. R., and L. McCombs. Inquiry Development Program in Earth Science. Chicago, Ill.: Science Research Associates, 1968. (*Problem Book* and *Idea Book* are available to supplement the textbook.)

Thurber, W. A., and R. E. Kilburn. *Exploring Earth Science*. Boston: Allyn and Bacon, 1970.

Wolfe, C. W., L. W. McCombs, H. Skornik, L. J. Battan, R. H. Fleming, and G. S. Hawkins. *Earth and Space Science* 2d ed. Boston: D. C. Heath and Co., 1971, 630 pp. (A laboratory manual is available to accompany this textbook.)

Supplementary Reading Materials for Environmental Earth Science

This environmental earth science section contains publications that are appropriate for environmental studies that are closely related to the earth sciences. Many of the publications listed with units 2, 3, 4, 5, and 6 are also appropriately listed with this section.

American Chemical Society, eds. *Cleaning Our Environment—A Chemical Basis for Action*. Washington, D.C.: American Chemical Society, 1969, 249 pp.

Anderson, David D. *Sunshine and Smoke: American Writers and the American Environment*. Philadelphia: J. B. Lippincott Co., 1971, 535 pp.

Anderson, Paul K. *Omega: Murder of the Ecosystem and the Suicide of Man*. Dubuque, Iowa: William C. Brown Co., 1971, 446 pp. Contains approximately 50 writings on various aspects of ecology and man's environment including articles on population, types of pollution, natural resources, and alternatives for the future.

Bascom, Willard. *Waves and Beaches: The Dynamics of the Ocean*. Science Study Series. Garden City, N.Y.: Doubleday & Co., 1964, 267 pp. Readable and authoritative account of the interaction between sea and land. A section is devoted to man's attempts to defend the shoreline against the relentless onslaught of the sea. Illustrated throughout with excellent line drawings and photographs.

Battan, Louis J. *The Unclean Sky—A Meteorologist Looks at Air Pollution*. Science Study Series. Garden City, N.Y.: Doubleday & Co., Anchor Books, 1966, 141 pp. Describes how the atmosphere has become a dumping ground, how this has affected the world of man and nature, and what can still be done to improve this worsening situation.

Behrman, A. S. *Water Is Everybody's Business: The Chemistry of Water Purification*. Chemistry in Action Series. Garden City, N.Y.: Doubleday & Co., Anchor Books, 1968, 229 pp. Presents a broad and useful picture of water supply and water purification. Discusses basic principles in sufficient detail to give the reader a good, working knowledge of the subject. Includes chapters on water supply, fluoridation of water, desalting the ocean, and the future.

Benarde, Melvin. *Our Precarious Habitat*. New York: W. W. Norton & Co., 1970, 362 pp. Discusses complex interactions in the environment.

Bresler, Jack B. *Environments of Man*. Reading Mass.: Addison-Wesley, 1968, 289 pp. Anthology of 24 articles on a broad variety of topics concerned with man, his environment, and his society. Discussion of problems such as air pollution, population, diseases, and so on.

Brown, Harrison. *The Challenge of Man's Future*. New York: Viking Press, 1954, 290 pp. The physical potential for man on this planet is discussed.

Brown, Harrison, James Bonner and John Weir. *The Next Hundred Years, Man's Natural and Technological Resources*. New York: Viking Press, 1963, 192 pp. The future of the earth's resources; based on discussions between scientists and leaders of American industry.

Brown, T. L. *Energy and the Environment*. Columbus, Ohio: Charles E. Merrill Publishing Co., 1971, 141 pp. Provides information on the atmosphere, influence of CO_2 and particulate matter on climate, effects of energy production, and climatic change.

Carson, Rachel. *The Edge of the Sea*. New York: New American Library of World Literature, 1959, 238 pp. Describes inhabitants of three typical tidal environments: rocky shore, sand beach, and coral coast. Relates tides, waves, and currents with ecology.

_____. *The Sea Around Us*. New York: New American Library of World Litarature, 1950, 169 pp. History of the sea from its earliest beginnings to later discoveries, including geography, life forms, man's heritage of the sea, ocean currents, tides, winds, oceanographic mapping, and origin of the oceans.

_____. *Silent Spring*. Greenwich, Conn.: Fawcett Publications, 1962, 304 pp. Exposé of disastrous consequences of chemical mass-warfare against insects, weeds, and fungi. Presents thesis that man is well on the road to destroying or altering life as we know it on this planet.

Chorley, Richard J., ed. *Water, Earth, and Man: A Synthesis of Hydrology, Geomorphology, and Socio-Economic Geography*. London: Methuen, and New York: Barnes and Noble, 1969, 58 pp.

Clarke, Arthur C. *Profiles of the Future*. New York: Bantam Books, 1965, 156 pp. Forecast of the probable world of tomorrow; based on scientific data and technology.

Coker, R. E. *This Great and Wide Sea: An Introduction to Oceanography and Marine Biology*. New York: Harper & Row, 1962, 325 pp. Comprehensive introduction to the science of the sea including discussion of conversion of salt water to fresh water and the use of the sea as a source of food.

Commoner, Barry. *Science and Survival*. New York: Viking Press, 1967, 150 pp. An indictment of the failure to consider the effect of new technologies on the environment.

Cootner, Paul H., and O. G. George. *Water Demand for Steam Electric Generation: An Economic Projection Model*. Baltimore: Johns Hopkins, 1965, 168 pp. The identification of the technological opportunities, costs of water recirculation, water quality, and adjustment in thermal plants.

Daniel, Hawthorne, and Francis Minot. *Inexhaustable Sea*. New York: Collier Books, 1961, 192 pp. Forecasts the continuing growth of the world's population and the resulting insufficiency of food produced from the soil. Explains how this need may be filled from the resources of ocean life.

Darling, F. F., and J. P. Milton, eds. *Future Environments of North America*. Garden City, N.Y.: Doubleday & Co., Natural History Press, 1966, 792 pp. This classic work brings together 34 ecologists, regional planners, economists, jurists, and conservationists to probe the nature of pressures on the North American continent and explore the possibilities for solution. Contributors explore the limits of the strained balance between man and nature. This volume is the product of the Conference on the Future Environments of North America, which was sponsored by the Conservation Foundation.

DeBell, Garrett, ed. *The Environmental Handbook.* New York: Ballantine Books, 1970, 360 pp. Readings for the first national environmental teach-in, April 22, 1970.

Detwyler, Thomas R., ed. *Man's Impact on Environment.* New York: McGraw-Hill, 1971, 731 pp.

Dubos, René. *Man, Medicine, and Environment.* New York: Frederick A. Praeger, 1968. The interrelationships that govern man's life today and the environmental factors that relate to health.

Esposito, John C. *Vanishing Air: The Ralph Nader Study Group Report on Air Pollution.* New York: Grossman Publishers, 1970, 328 pp. Startling report which shows that ecological disaster within our lifetime is not beyond the realm of possibility—and yet industry and government show relatively little concern about air pollution.

Ewald, William, Jr., ed. *Environment and Change: The Next Fifty Years.* Bloomington: Indiana University Press, 1968.

_____ , ed. *Environment and Policy: The Next Fifty Years.* Bloomington: Indiana University Press, 1968, 459 pp.

_____ , ed. *Environment for Man: The Next Fifty Years.* Bloomington: Indiana University Press, 1967, 308 pp.

Fisher, Joseph L., and Neal Potter. *World Prospects for Natural Resources: Some Projections of Demand and Indicators of Supply to the Year 2000.* Baltimore: Johns Hopkins Press, 1964, 73 pp.

Fortune Magazine, ed. *The Environment: A National Mission for the Seventies.* New York: Harper & Row, 1970, 220 pp. Contains thirteen chapters which originally appeared in the October 1969 and February 1970 issues of *Fortune Magazine.*

Friedmann, Wolfgang. *The Future of the Oceans.* New York: George Braziller, 1971, 128 pp. Presents the ocean as a great source of wealth. Discusses our potential to exploit the abundant minerals contained in the oceans as well as the fish—one of the world's most important foods—in the waters above. Technology also reveals ways of using the seas and the sea floors for military and strategic purposes. The question of who controls the oceans is raised as one of the most complicated international legal problems.

Giles, Donald C. *Chemicals from the Atmosphere.* Chemistry in Action Series. Garden City, N.Y.: Doubleday & Co., 1969. Deals with technology and chemistry of the earth's atmosphere.

Griffiths D. H., and R. F. King. *Applied Geophysics for Engineers and Geologists.* Elmsford, N.Y.: Pergamon Press, 1965, 232 pp. Presents a basic knowledge of the principles of geophysical prospecting and its use in problems of site investigation, geological structure, and mineral prospecting.

Hawkins, Mary E., ed. *Vital Views of the Environment,* Washington, D.C.: National Science Teachers Association, 1970, 32 pp. Collection of 26 brief articles which are presented to emphasize major ideas and concepts relative to the environment which should be of interest to science teachers.

Hay, John. *In Defense of Nature*. New York: Viking Press, 1969, 210 pp.

Heffernan, Helen, and George Shaftel. *The Minerals Story.* Syracuse, N.Y.: L. W. Singer Co., 1963, 96 pp. Discusses ways of utilizing available mineral resources to greatest advantage by finding substitutes for minerals, locating new ore deposits, developing more efficient ways to mine and mill ores, salvaging waste and scrap for reuse, and determining new uses for some of our more abundant minerals.

_____ . *The Energy Story*. Syracuse, N.Y.: L. W. Singer Co., 1963, 128 pp. Covers the sources of energy: petroleum; electricity produced by steam, by running water, and by nuclear reactors; rocket and jet fuels; and solar energy.

_____ . *The Soil Story*. Syracuse, N.Y.: L. W. Singer Co., 1963, 96 pp. Formation of soil, the erosion of soil, and the methods used to save the soil. Includes an account of the transformation of arid land into green fertile land in Israel.

Hodgson, John H. *Earthquakes and Earth Structure*. Englewood Cliffs, N.J.: Prentice-Hall, 1964, 166 pp. Describes great earthquakes of the past and ones of seismological importance, analyzes the information they provide us about the interior of the earth. Reveals the role of seismology in nuclear-test detection, and presents developments in earthquake-resistant construction.

Iacopi, Robert. *Earthquake Country*. Menlo Park, Calif.: Sunset Book, Lane Books, 1969, 160 pp. Authoratative and highly readable account of the how, why, and where of earthquakes in California.

Jackson, Wes. *Man and the Environment*. Dubuque, Iowa: William C. Brown & Co., 1971, 322 pp. Compilation of nearly 100 writings which cover a wide group of environmental topics centered around the population-food problem and environmental destruction.

Landsberg, Helmut E. *Weather and Health—An Introduction to Biometeorology*. Garden City, N.Y.: Doubleday Co., 1969, 168 pp.

Long, John L. *New Worlds of Oceanography*. New York: Pyramid Publications, 1965, 221 pp. Account of the scientific assault on the sea; its history, creatures, resources, and, particularly, its future.

Love, Sam. *Earth Tool Kit, A Field Manual for Citizen Activists*. New York: Pocket Books, 1971, 369 pp.

Lovejoy, Wallace F., and Paul T. Homan. *Methods of Estimating Reserves of Crude Oil, Natural Gas, and Natural Gas Liquids*. Baltimore: Johns Hopkins Press, 1965, 168 pp. Reviews and analyzes the various approaches used to gauge the nation's supply of crude oil, natural gas, and natural gas liquids. Points out past errors and suggests improvements needed in data collection.

Marx, Wesley. *The Frail Ocean*. New York: Ballantine Books, 1967, 248.

_____ . *Man and His Environment: Waste*. New York: Harper & Row, 1971, 179 pp.

Matthews, William H. *Invitation to Geology: The Earth Through Time*. Garden City, N.Y.: Natural History Press, Doubleday & Co., 1971, 160 pp. Deals with the challenge that faces the earth scientist as with each passing year man's relationship to the earth becomes more strained. Explains modern techniques and tools used to study the earth.

Mayda, Jaro. *Environment and Resources: From Conservation to Ecomanagement.* Rio Piedres: University of Puerto Rico, School of Law, 1967, 254 pp.

Mears, B. *The Nature of Geology: Contemporary Readings.* New York: Van Nostrand Reinhold Co., 1970, 248 pp. A collection of readings prepared for beginning students of geology, which demonstrates that geology is a dynamic, living science. Includes writings of Hans Cloos, Rachel Carson, John Wesley Powell, John Muir, Samuel Clemens, and others.

Mitchell, J. G., and D. L. Stallings, eds. *Ecotactics: The Sierra Club Handbook for Environment Activists.* New York: Simon and Schuster, 1970, 288 pp.

Muir, John. *The Mountains of California.* Garden City, N.Y.: Doubleday & Co., 1961, 300 pp. Gives readers a glimpse of the grandeur of Yosemite, the Sierras, and Mount Shasta as seen by a nineteenth-century American naturalist and leader of the conservation movement.

Murdoch, William W., ed. *Environment: Resources, Pollution and Society.* Stamford, Conn.: Sinauer Associates, 1971, 440 pp. Compilation of 20 chapters, each an original writing, covering major environmental topics. Chapters are grouped under three major headings: Population and Resources, Environmental Degradation, and Environment and Society. Includes chapters on mineral resources, energy resources, water resources, air pollution, ocean pollution, fresh water pollution, and so on.

Murphy, Earl Finbar. *Man and His Environment: Law.* New York: Harper & Row, 1971, 168 pp.

McDivitt, James F. *Minerals and Men: An Exploration of the World of Minerals and Its Effect on the World We Live In.* Baltimore: Johns Hopkins Press, 1965, 158 pp.

National Academy of Sciences. Committee on Resources and Man of the Division of Earth Sciences. *Resources and Man.* San Francisco: W. H. Freeman and Co., 1969. Discusses man's ecology—population, food, minerals, and energy.

Olson, Ralph E. *A Geography of Water.* Brown Foundations of Geography Series. Dubuque, Iowa: William C. Brown Co., 1970, 132 pp. Contains chapters on water in the oceans, rivers, lakes in the atmosphere, ground water, and the management of water.

Overman, Michael. *Water: Solutions to a Problem of Supply and Demand.* Garden City, N.Y.: Doubleday & Co., 1969. Discusses the problem of supply and demands of water and solutions.

Rienow, Robert, and Leona Rienow. *Moment in the Sun: A Report on the Deteriorating Quality of the American Environment.* New York Ballantine Books, 1969, 286 pp.

Rockefeller, Nelson A. *Our Environment Can Be Saved.* Garden City, N.Y.: Doubleday & Co., 1970, 176 pp. The author speaks out on the dominant issue of the hour, emphasizing how we can and must save the air, water, and land around us from the pollution that daily threatens to destroy them. Contains lists of organizations active in working toward solutions to environmental problems.

Rudd, Robert L. *Pesiticides and the Living Landscape*. Madison: University of Wisconsin Press, 1966, 320 pp.

Schwartz, William, ed. *Voices for the Wilderness*. New York: Ballantine Books, 1969, 366 pp.

Shuttlesworth, Dorothy E. *Clean Air—Sparkling Water*. Garden City, N.Y.: Doubleday & Do., 1968;

Skinner, B. J. *Earth Resources*. Foundations of Earth Science Series. Englewood Cliffs, N.J.: Prentice-Hall, 1969, 150 pp. Presents information on abundance and availability of earth resources, metals, industrial minerals and rocks, energy, and water.

Storer, John H. *Man in the Web of Life*. New York: New American Library of World Literature, 1968. Discusses ecological problems.

Soller, Allen A. *Ours Is the Earth*. New York: Holt, Rinehart and Winston, 1963, 128 pp. Stresses the interdependence of our basic natural resources, and includes discussions of water, soils, forest, rangeland, wildlife, and minerals.

Udall, Stewart. *The Quiet Crisis*. New York: Avon Books, 1963. Introductory materials on environmental problems.

_____. *1976: Agenda for Tomorrow*. New York: Holt, Rinehart and Winston, 1969, 173 pp.

Turner, D. S. *Applied Earth Science*. Brown Foundations of Earth Science Series. Dubuque, Iowa: William C. Brown Co., 1969, 125 pp. Deals with practical applications of the study of the earth including natural resources, conservation, and ecology, military and engineering applications, and applied climatology and meteorology.

U.S. Department of the Interior *Man . . . An Endangered Species?* Washington, D.C.: Government Printing Office, 1968.

_____. *The Population Challenge*. Washington, D.C.: 1966, 80 pp.

_____. *Quest for Quality*. Washington, D.C.: Government Printing Office, 1965, 96 pp. Urges us to look at our handling of natural resources with a view to tomorrow's demands and needs.

_____. *The Third Wave* Washington D.C.: Government Printing Office, 1967. Concerned with preserving the quality of the nation's air, water, land, minerals, recreation, and fish and wildlife.

Voskuil, W. H. *A Geography of Minerals*. Brown Foundations of Geography Series. Dubuque, Iowa: William C. Brown Co., 1969, 117 pp. Fairly complete presentation of the distribution of minerals including information on resources, exports, and so on.

Yasso, Warren E. *Oceanography: A Study of Inner Space*. New York: Holt, Rinehart and Winston, 1965, 176 pp. Emphasizes the significance of the oceans to weather and climate, food production, mineral resources, and waste disposal, in addition to presenting information on oceanography in general.